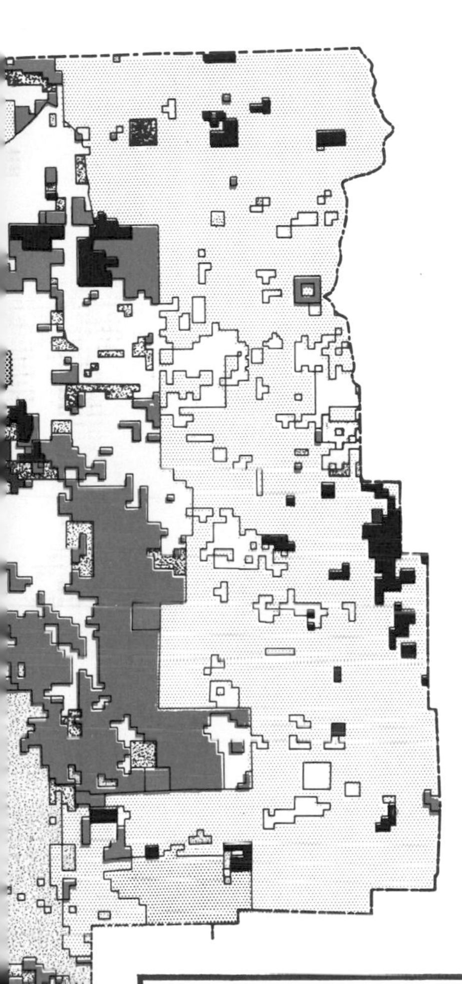
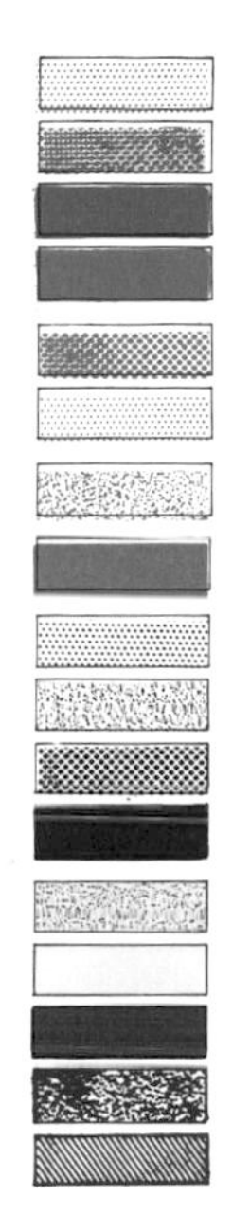

OWNERSHIP CLASSES

- NATIONAL FOREST
- NATIONAL PARK
- INDIAN RESERVATION
- PUBLIC DOMAIN
- STATE PARK
- OTHER STATE
- OTHER PUBLIC
- TAX DEEDED
- TIMBER OPERATING COMPANY
- TIMBER HOLDING COMPANY
- TIMBER OPERATING INDIVIDUAL
- TIMBER HOLDING INDIVIDUAL
- RANGE LIVESTOCK FARMING COMPANY
- RANGE LIVESTOCK FARMING INDIVIDUAL
- OTHER FARMERS
- OTHER NONFARMERS
- STATE FORESTS

UNCOLORED PORTIONS ARE FARM, RESIDENTIAL, AND OTHER STRICTLY NONFOREST AREAS

TYPES OF

LAND OWNERSHIP

NORTHERN MENDOCINO COUNTY, CALIFORNIA

1944

(JACKSON STATE FOREST IN 1953)

A Help or a Hindrance to Best Land Use and Management?

California Lands

OWNERSHIP, USE, AND MANAGEMENT

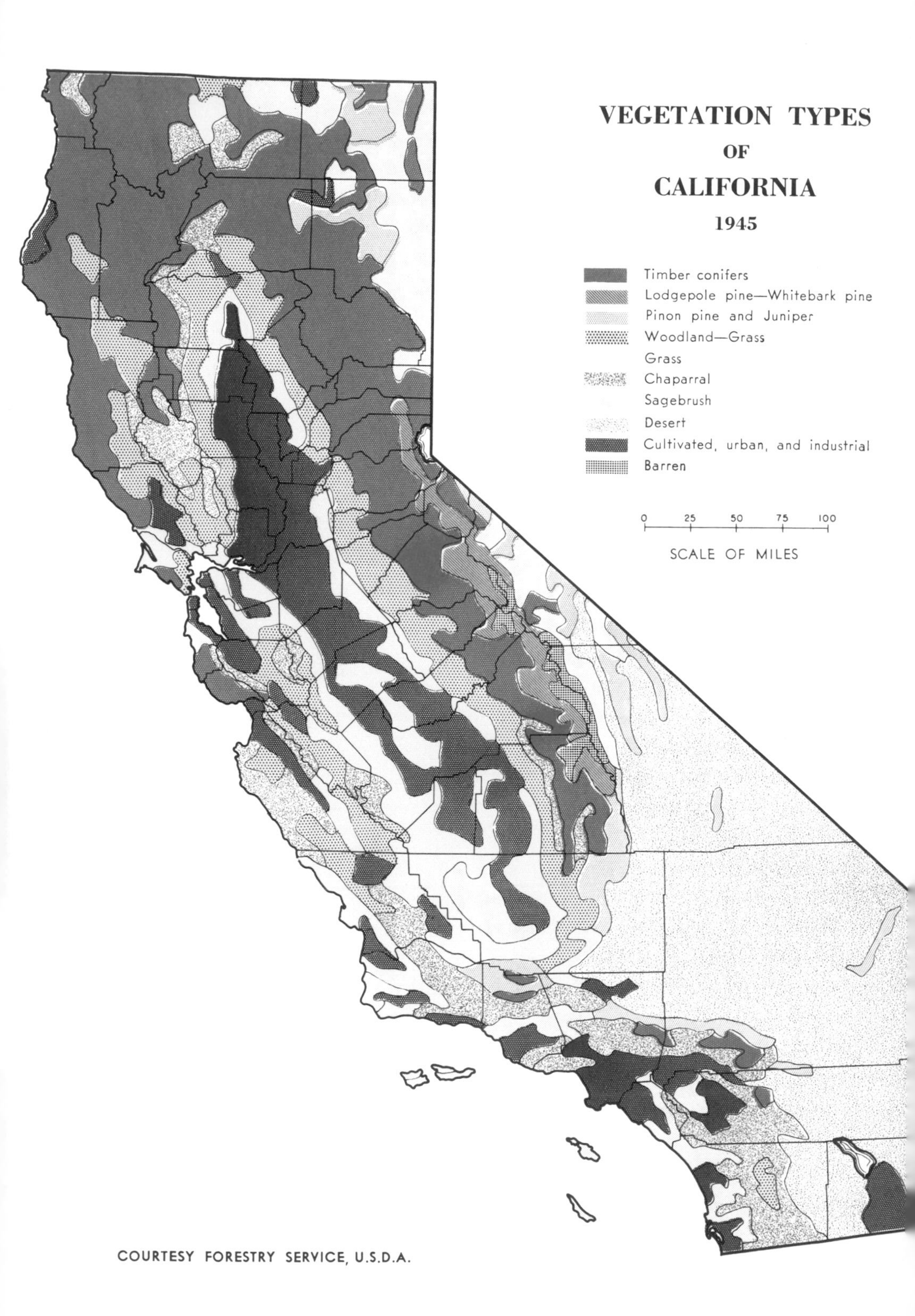
VEGETATION TYPES
OF
CALIFORNIA
1945
Timber conifers
Lodgepole pine—Whitebark pine
Pinon pine and Juniper
Woodland—Grass
Grass
Chaparral
Sagebrush
Desert
Cultivated, urban, and industrial
Barren
0
25
50
75
100
SCALE OF MILES
COURTESY FORESTRY SERVICE, U.S.D.A.

California Lands

OWNERSHIP, USE, AND MANAGEMENT

SAMUEL TRASK DANA
Dean Emeritus, SCHOOL OF NATURAL RESOURCES
UNIVERSITY OF MICHIGAN

MYRON KRUEGER
Professor Emeritus, SCHOOL OF FORESTRY
UNIVERSITY OF CALIFORNIA

THE AMERICAN FORESTRY ASSOCIATION
919 17th Street, N. W.
Washington 6, D. C.

1958

CALIFORNIA LANDS

Library of Congress Catalog Card No. 58-8789

PRINTED BY THE LIVINGSTON PUBLISHING COMPANY
NARBERTH, PENNSYLVANIA

California's zooming population will soon top that of any other state—with no end in sight.

To meet the needs of its people for living room, food, water, raw materials, and recreation it has 100 million acres of land—a fifth barren and desert, only a sixth suitable for cultivation.

Since the area is fixed, production can be increased only by more intensive management.

Full use of information already available, continuous study to find still more effective methods of management, and widespread application of the findings are urgent needs.

Progress will be facilitated by adjustments in the present, often illogical, pattern of ownership.

Combined and coordinated efforts by state and federal agencies, private landowners, and the general public are essential for the development of sound policies, the conduct of effective programs of study, and the translation of knowledge into practice.

The most promising device for obtaining unified action is a Natural Resources Council, created by the legislature, and consisting of representatives of public agencies, various classes of landowners, and the citizenry of the state.

Prompt action is imperative if production is to keep pace with population—if future Californians are not only to live, but to live well.

California's mounting population will soon top that of any other state—with no end in sight.

[illegible] food [illegible] at least [illegible] and [illegible]

[illegible]

[illegible] management should [illegible] continuous study to find still more effective methods [illegible] and widespread application of the findings [illegible]

Progress will be facilitated by adjustments in the present, often illogical, pattern of ownership.

Combined and coordinated efforts by state and federal agencies, private landowners, and the general public are essential for the development of sound policies, the conduct of effective programs of study, and the translation of knowledge into practice.

The most promising device for obtaining unified action is a Natural Resources Council, created by the Legislature and consisting of representatives of public agencies, various classes of landowners, and the citizenry of the state.

Prompt action is imperative if production is to keep pace with population—if future Californians are not only to live, but to live well.

FOREWORD

Today's world is one of rapid and constant change. More and more people want more and more of the good things of life. Scientists and inventors are steadily increasing our power both to create and to destroy.

The optimists view the situation with confidence, the pessimists with alarm. On one thing they agree: for better or for worse, man's future depends largely on how he handles the basic resources of land and water. These resources can provide a transient prosperity or they can contribute permanently to the kind of life Americans wish to lead.

The present study and report, initiated by The American Forestry Association, and financed as a public service by the Nutrilite Foundation and the Foundation for American Resource Management, deal with one aspect of the problem – land ownership and its influence on land management. The aim is to provide a sound foundation for further, statewide studies, and to indicate some of the directions which such studies might profitably take.

The Association hopes that the findings will prove of value both to the State of California, in which this pilot study was made, and to other states in which similar projects may be undertaken.

Don P. Johnston

President, The American Forestry Association

PREFACE

Ownership of the timber, range, watershed, and recreational lands of the United States is one of the most crucial factors in determining the effectiveness of their contribution to the economic and social well-being of the nation and its constituent states.[1] The kind and pattern of ownership affect such vital matters as purpose, stability, and intensity of land management; feasibility of multiple-use management; establishment and stability of wood-using and other industries; and community support in the form of taxes or contributions in lieu of taxes.

The land-disposal, and later the land-reservation and land-acquisition, policies of both the federal and the state governments have led to a confused and often illogical pattern of ownership. The situation is complicated by the wide variety of agencies to which the administration of publicly owned lands has been assigned, and by the division of ownership among large and small private owners. What amounts and what kinds of timber, range, watershed, and recreational lands should be in federal, state, community, corporate, farm, and other ownership, and what pattern these ownerships should form, are examples of questions to which no clear answers

[1] In California and elsewhere, these lands are often referred to collectively as "wildlands" to distinguish them from urban land and tilled land. For ease of expression the term is occasionally used in the present report to include non-urban land not devoted to residences, roads, or cultivated crops. It conveys no implication as to the value of the land or the intensity of its management.

are at present available. Study and improvement of the existing situation is essential to assure effective land management and the development of the economy on a sound and permanent basis.

In recognition of these facts, "The Program for American Forestry" adopted by The American Forestry Association in 1954 contained these recommendations:

"1 — Early action by the Congress to establish a joint Congressional Committee, consisting of members of the Senate and House Committees on Interior and Insular Affairs, the Senate Committee on Agriculture and Forestry and the House Committee on Agriculture whose objectives would be:

"a) To consider a desirable pattern of ownership for federal, state and private forest, range and other conservation lands.

"b) To formulate policies to guide action of public agencies towards achieving this pattern.

"c) To recommend to the Congress legislation needed to enable Federal agencies to implement these policies.

"2 — Early action by the governor of each state to appoint a representative committee to report on the conditions in his state as they may relate to items a), b), and c) above, and render a report which will be made available to the Joint Congressional Committee."

In the belief that a few exploratory studies would help to facilitate and to coordinate the more intensive investigations proposed by the Association, the directors made known their willingness to undertake such studies. At the suggestion of several responsible state officials, and with the financial support of the Nutrilite Foundation, the first of these exploratory studies was conducted in California during the past year. The present report is the result of that study, which was handled by Samuel T. Dana, Dean Emeritus of the School of Natural Resources, University of Michigan, and Myron Krueger, Professor Emeritus of the School of Forestry, University of California, under the supervision of a national committee appointed by the directors.

This committee held two meetings covering respectively three and four days, with 100 per cent attendance, at which it approved plans for the study, reviewed in detail the results obtained, and arranged for their publication. The chairman was in intimate personal contact with the work throughout its progress. The project was also discussed at a public meeting in San Francisco on July 26, 1956, and the first draft of the report was reviewed at a second public meeting in San Francisco on September 18, 1957. In addition, both the outline for the report and the preliminary draft were widely circulated for review and criticism, with decidedly helpful results.

Emphasis should be placed on the exploratory nature of the study, which involved review of pertinent literature, collection and analysis of a large amount of published and unpublished data, and consultation with many individuals with a wide variety of interests and experience, both in and out of governmental service. Its purpose was not to solve California's land ownership problems, but rather to lay a sound foundation for more thorough subsequent investigations of the subject. To this end, it analyzed the character and importance of California's wildland resources; the increasing pressure being placed on them by an exploding population; the history and present pattern of land ownership in the state; the great variety of problems faced by both public and private owners; and the next steps that should be taken in their solution. It unearthed no facts and discovered no problems with which some one was not already familiar. The present report does, however, bring together for the first time much basic information that has hitherto been widely scattered and largely unavailable; it throws new light on many of the problems; and it relates the various parts of the land ownership picture, with their accompanying problems, to the situation as a whole.

Two conclusions are of major importance. First, California does not have *a* land problem which can be studied and solved by a governor's committee or any other group or agency. It has rather many closely related problems which will require continuing research as long as people are dependent on natural resources. Second, machinery is needed to assure continuity and coordination in the consideration of these problems; to direct research along the most productive lines by the best qualified agencies; and to foster practical application of the results of research. Prompt action is needed, since population pressure is giving natural resource problems a rapidly increasing urgency.

The committee and the authors wish to acknowledge their indebtedness and to extend their thanks to the many individuals and organizations whose cooperation in supplying information, in expressing their views, and in offering constructive criticism has been invaluable. Special recognition is due to the Nutrilite Foundation and to the Foundation for American Resource Management for their generosity in financing, respectively, the conduct of the study and the publication of this report.

GEORGE L. DRAKE
Forest Consultant
Tacoma, Washington

J. WALTER MYERS, JR.
Executive Director
Forest Farmers Association
Atlanta, Georgia

LLOYD E. PARTAIN
Manager
Trade and Industry Relations
The Curtis Publishing Company
Philadelphia, Pennsylvania

JAY H. PRICE
Regional Forester Retired
U. S. Forest Service
Phoenix, Arizona

CARL D. SHOEMAKER
Conservation Consultant
National Wildlife Federation
Washington, D. C.

HAROLD G. WILM
Associate Dean, College of Forestry
State University of New York
Syracuse, New York

OTTO J. WOLFF
Rancher and President
Black Hills
Livestock Protective Association
Rapid City, South Dakota

DEWITT NELSON, *Chairman*
Director
State Department of Natural Resources
Sacramento, California

COMMITTEE ON LAND OWNERSHIP STUDY

CONTENTS

LIST OF TABLES AND FIGURES

Tables

Figures

HIGHLIGHTS

People

In a century, California has become the second most populous state in the Union. In a few years it will be at the top. Today, birth and immigration bring it a new resident every 55 seconds. No limit to the increase is yet in sight.

California's people are not only numerous — they are industrious and productive. Among the states in the nation California is first in cash farm income — second in the production of lumber — third (and most diversified) in value of mineral production. In the eight years from mid-1947 to mid-1955 its gain in number of employees engaged in manufacturing was 8 per cent greater than that in New York, Pennsylvania, Ohio, Indiana, Michigan, and Illinois combined.

Land

Wherever people live, whatever they do, they are inescapably dependent on natural resources — land, water, and their products. California's size (100,314,000 acres) is second only to Texas. This is a vast area. It is also a fixed area. Within limits, however, its yield of food and services can be increased or decreased.

These 100 million acres vary widely in character. The chief value of more than one-third is for forest and watershed purposes. About a fifth is barren and desert land. Only a sixth is suitable for cultivation. Scenic and recreational resources — beaches, forests, lakes, mountains, and wildlife — are outstanding. Water is abundant — its distribution, seasonally and geographically, constitutes the problem. The solution requires engineering, economic, and political adjustments of major magnitude.

Ownership

When California entered the Union, title to its entire land area was vested in the United States with the exception of some 8,850,000 acres in Spanish and Mexican grants. Congress has since disposed of 47,700,000 acres in grants to the state and to railroad corporations, and by sales and grants to individuals. The state and railroads in turn disposed of much of the area granted them.

Since 1890, when three national parks were established in California, reservation and withdrawal of public lands from entry have become increasingly characteristic of federal land policy. The state still owns nearly a million acres of school-grant lands. Both federal and state governments have acquired limited amounts of land by purchase and exchange.

Today, California lands are almost equally divided between public and private ownership. Some 47 million acres are in federal ownership, some 3 million acres in state and local ownership, and some 50 million acres in private ownership. Unreserved public domain (including grazing districts), national forests, and military installations comprise the bulk of the area in federal ownership. State beaches and parks, school-grant lands, and tax-deeded lands are the major forms of state ownership. Of the privately owned land, nearly 38 million acres are in farm and ranch ownership and about 6.5 million acres in commercial forest land not in farms.

The prevalent pattern of "scrambled" land ownership, with many small holdings, increases the difficulties of administration and management.

Management

Exploitation characterized the early use of California lands. Natural resources — soil, water, timber, forage, wildlife, and minerals were thought inexhaustible. So, why be thrifty in their use?

Changes in attitude and practice first appeared in agriculture. Production of irrigated crops led to more intensive management. The upsurge of the conservation movement in the early 1900's resulted in the planned, although at first not intensive, management of the resources in national forests. Improved management of the resources in national parks, wildlife refuges, and grazing districts followed.

State acquisition of parks, wildlife areas, and state forests resulted in placing them under management. The state also enacted legislation aimed at promoting the conservation of oil and gas resources in private ownership and the improved management of private timberlands.

A conspicuous recent change in the situation has been the new attitude toward management evidenced by many private owners (particularly the larger owners) of forest and range resources. The growing demand for these resources, increased values, and improved technologies of production and utilization have made management profitable.

Problems

California faces an inescapable problem which is rapidly becoming more acute. How can its limited natural resources meet the needs of a skyrocketing population? This one central problem involves innumerable interrelated problems.

Lands outside of farms yield a wide variety of products and services. Of these, water is universally given top priority. But ample timber, forage, wildlife, and opportunities for recreation, including the preservation of some unspoiled wilderness, are indispensable elements in modern civilization. "Multiple use" is commonly regarded as a cornucopia from which will flow unlimited supplies of everything we need, with little appreciation of its limitations. Not all uses are compatible. Even with compatible uses, as we increase the yield of one product or service, we often decrease the yield of others. In some places, if we want more water, we may have to grow less timber.

Ownership of land resources controls their management. It is therefore essential to know what results may be expected from different forms of public and private ownership. But results can be evaluated only by comparing costs and returns — direct and indirect, tangible and intangible. Such comparisons pose problems for the study of which we do not yet have reliable techniques. A simpler but highly important task is to determine the influence of intermingled ownerships on the intensity of management, and to effect the blocking up of ownerships where this seems desirable. Public ownership raises difficult questions as to financial responsibility of the public owner to the local community.

WHAT NEXT?

The first step in solving the many problems of natural-resource management is for all owners to make more effective use of the information already available. In general, knowledge is far ahead of practice. The next step is to conduct the studies necessary to expand existing knowledge as to the ownership patterns, management techniques, and public policies that will give the most satisfactory results from the standpoint both of the owners and the general public.

Three things are certain — (1) That far more intensive resource management by all classes of owners will be essential to close the prospective gap between needs and supplies, (2) that such management is dependent on increased and continuous study, and (3) that the results must find practical application.

The fact that all resource problems are interrelated points to the need for some device by which the combined efforts of the landowners and managers (both public and private) and of the general public can be mobilized to seek their solution. The most promising approach to this goal is the creation by the legislature of a Natural Resources Council consisting of qualified representatives of the state and federal agencies, the private interests, and the citizenry of the state. The duties of such a council should be:

1. To identify, stimulate, and coordinate studies of current problems connected with the ownership and management of natural resources;
2. To advise the legislature, the Governor, and the various agencies and interests represented in its membership with respect to natural-resource problems, administration, and management; and
3. To facilitate contacts and promote cooperation among the groups and interests represented in its membership.

The need for prompt action is urgent. California now has five more residents than when you started to read this statement. It has no more land.

PART I

CALIFORNIA'S PEOPLE AND RESOURCES

California's land problems stem from the mounting pressure of a vigorous and rapidly expanding population on rich and varied, but limited, natural resources. They have developed since the state's admission to the Union in 1850, and have become acute only in the last few decades.

"Astonishing People"

In 1846 Pío Pico, the last Mexican Governor of California, lamented: "We find ourselves suddenly threatened by hordes of Yankee emigrants, who have already begun to flock into our country, and whose progress we cannot arrest. Already have the wagons of that perfidious people scaled the almost inaccessible summits of the Sierra Nevada, crossed the entire continent, and penetrated the fruitful valley of the Sacramento. What that astonishing people will next undertake, I cannot say; but in whatever enterprise they embark they will be sure to prove successful."

The wonders which that "astonishing people" have wrought in a single century would undoubtedly amaze even the author of this prophecy. They may be illustrated by a few excerpts from a report to the Commonwealth Club of California by its Section on Business Economics on October 23, 1956:

"California has been the fastest growing state in the United States and this trend may be expected to continue in the foreseeable future. From comparative obscurity in 1850, California has become the second largest state in population and may soon pass New York . . .

"California is the nation's foremost state in cash farm income; it has more passenger car registration than any other; is third and most diversified of all states in value of mineral production; it leads the states in value of new construction; is second in personal income . . .

"The Census of Manufactures shows that California has raised its relative position in industrial output from eighth place in 1939, to seventh in 1947, and to sixth place in 1954 . . .

"California's irrigated land is approximately one-fourth of all irrigated acreage in the nation. Total crop land in California is small compared to that in other agricultural states, and is only a little more than 2 per cent of the national total. Yet this intensive type of cultivation causes nearly 12 per cent of the nation's cash income from crops to go to California farmers . . .

"Water resource development appears to be California's most serious economic problem. We do not have enough developed water to meet the domestic needs of our people, as well as their agricultural and industrial water demands. Assuming we are able to retain our present Colorado River water rights, there is no over-all shortage of water in the state. The problem is rather one of inadequate development, conservation and maldistribution . . .

"Since the end of World War I, the surge of population toward this great state has encouraged the development of small manufacturing enterprises, the location of assembly plants of large eastern industries, and more recently the establishment of basic manufacturing enterprises such as those engaged in the production of aluminum, steel and chemical products . . .

"The major fields in which industrial expansion is taking place are in fabricated metals, electronics, building materials and food products. Other industries which are growing and appear to have an excellent future in this state include textiles, lumber, paper, chemicals, apparel, furniture, petroleum by-products, leather, primary metals, machinery and transportation equipment . . .

"California is second only to Oregon as a lumber producer and uses more lumber than any other state . . .

"Usage of utility service has increased more rapidly than population. In the ten years since the end of World War II (1946 - 1955) population mushroomed over fifty per cent. In this same decade electric customers increased nearly two million, or 73 per cent; gas customers increased a million and a half, or 70 per cent; telephone customers increased over two million, or 129 per cent. As the number of customers grew, so did usage per customer . . .

"As a result of their continued large construction programs, the plant investment of utilities in California has nearly tripled since the end of World War II. Literally, decades of growth at earlier rates were telescoped into this one ten-year period . . ."

Facts such as these testify to the attractiveness of the California environment and to the ability of its citizens. They also raise the question as to whether the response to the exhortation "Bring me men to match my mountains" is not being overdone.

"Bring Me Men . . ."

Permanent occupation of California by white men began in 1769 with the establishment by Father Junípero Serra of the mission at San Diego. The population of Mexicans increased slowly and of other nationals still more so. Hubert Howe Bancroft, California's eminent historian, estimates that in 1820 there were 3,720 "gente de razon" (people of quality, persons of Spanish blood) and 13 "foreigners" — 3 Americans, 2 Scotchmen, 2 Englishmen, 1 Irishman, 1 Russian, 1 Portuguese, and 3 Negroes. No accurate information is available concerning the population of Indians, but estimates indicate that their numbers decreased from possibly 200,000 in 1769 to about 100,000 in 1840.

Overland migration from the East to the province of Alta California began in earnest in 1841. Although the total number of immigrants from the United States during the next few years remained small, their influence increased sufficiently to make possible the "Bear Flag" episode of 1846 and the annexation of California to the Union in 1848 following the Mexican war. These events and the discovery of gold in 1848 brought a veritable influx of settlers and miners from the United States and resulted in California's admission to the Union in 1850 as the thirty-first state.

The first fairly complete census of population was made by the

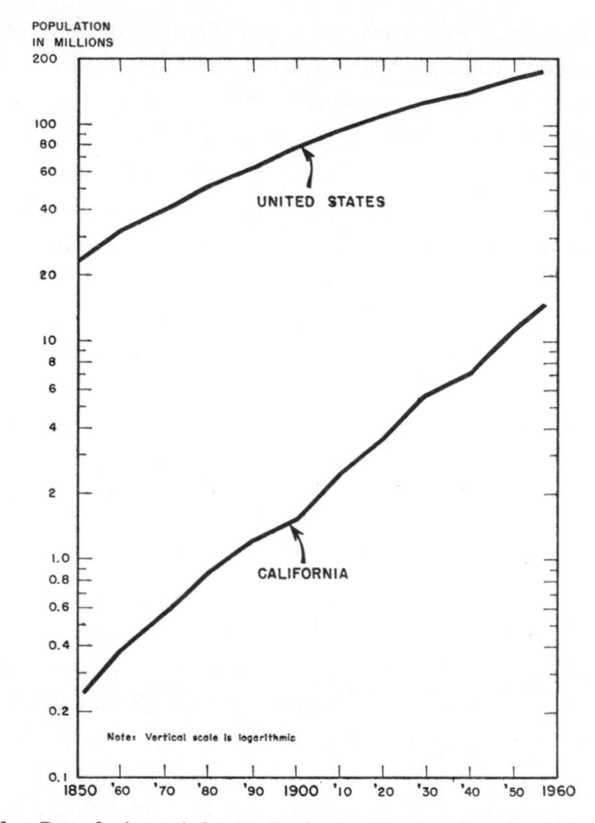

Figure 1. Population of the United States and of California, 1850-1957.

state in 1852. Interpretation of the results by the Census Office and the state, respectively, showed a population of 255,122 and 264,135. Census figures divide the total population into 171,841 whites, 2,206 blacks and mulattoes, 9,809 Chinese, and 31,266 domesticated Indians, excluding El Dorado County's estimated but unenumerated population of 40,000. The influence of mining on the distribution of population is shown by the fact that, with the exception of San Francisco County (36,154), the only counties with a population of more than 10,000 were El Dorado, Nevada, Calaveras, Yuba, Tuolumne, Sacramento, and Placer.

The Seventh Census of the United States, for 1850, gave California a population of only 92,597, but the figures are not comparable with those for 1852 and later years since they included only whites (91,632) and free colored persons (965). Furthermore, they omitted Contra Costa County and Santa Clara County, the returns for which were lost, and San Francisco County, the returns for which were destroyed by fire. Of the 77,631 individuals who indicated their occupation, 74 per cent were miners, and this ratio probably increased during the next decade.

"Population explosions" are nothing new in California (Table 1, Figs. 1-2). During the 30 years following its admission to the Union its population increased approximately 50 per cent every ten years. Increases of 60 and 66 per cent were recorded for the decades 1900 – 1910 and 1930 – 1940. From 1940 to 1950 the increase of 3,678,836 persons was the highest in the country in both numbers and per cent (53.3), with only five other states (Arizona, Florida, Nevada, Oregon, and Washington) having increases of more than 30 per cent. Three counties – Contra Costa, Solano, and San Mateo – more than doubled their population during this period. Since 1950 the state has ranked next to New York in number of inhabitants.

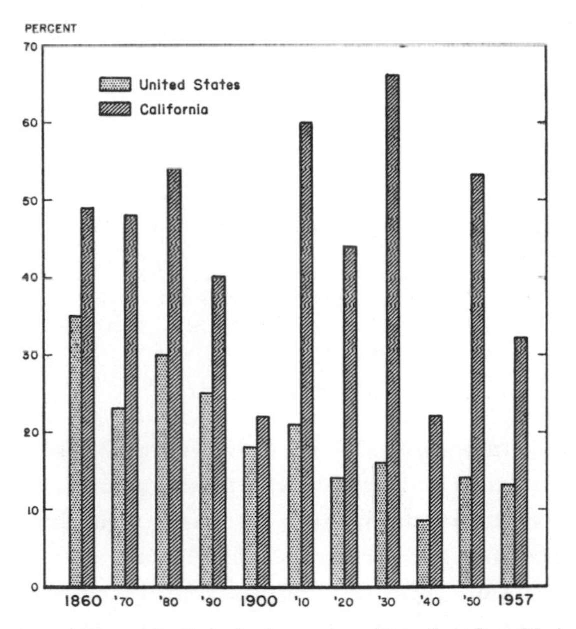

Figure 2. Increase in population during preceding decades, United States and California, 1850-1957.

Early in 1957 Carl Frisen of the State Department of Finance estimated that California's population had passed the 14,000,000 mark and that by 1965 it would exceed that of New York. With an average daily migration to the state of 1,000 persons and a daily excess of births over deaths of 600, California is gaining a new resident every 55 seconds. Today it has no dearth of men.

Table 1. Growth of Population in California and the United States, 1850-1957.

	California		United States	
Year	Population	Per cent of increase during preceding decade	Population	Per cent of increase during preceding decade
1850	92,597[1]	—	23,191,876	—
1860	379,994	49[2]	31,443,321	36
1870	560,247	47	38,558,371	23
1880	864,694	54	50,155,783	30
1890	1,213,398	40	62,622,250	25
1900	1,485,053	22	76,303,387	22
1910	2,377,549	60	91,972,266	21
1920	3,426,861	44	105,710,620	15
1930	5,677,251	66	122,775,046	16
1940	6,907,387	22	131,669,275	7
1950	10,586,223	53	150,697,361	14
1957	14,160,000	34[3]	172,000,000	14[3]

[1] Census incomplete.
[2] Based on census estimate of population of 255,122 in 1852.
[3] Seven-year period.

Source: Bureau of the Census, except for the 1957 estimate for California (as of July 1), which is by Carl M. Frisen, California Department of Finance.

". . . To Match My Mountains"

California's "mountains," the most conspicuous of its physiographic features, may be regarded as symbolic of its natural resources. These resources are of the utmost diversity. The Encyclopedia Britannica characterizes the state as physically one of the most remarkable in the Union. "The physiography of the state is simple, its main features are few and bold; a mountain fringe along the ocean, another mountain system along the east border, between them —

closed in at both ends by their junction — a splendid valley of imperial extent, and outside all this a great area of barren, arid lands, belonging partly to the great basin and partly to the open basin region . . . There is the widest and most startling variety of climates." Different parts of the state have vivid contrasts of sunshine and fog, heat and cold, heavy precipitation and perpetual drought.

Land resources include some of the best and some of the poorest in the nation, from agricultural soils of outstanding fertility to sterile deserts and barren mountain tops. Lands suitable for the production of harvested crops, livestock, and wood play a prominent part in the economic life of the state. There are rich deposits of metals, petroleum, and other minerals. Water resources are abundant but for the most part originate at considerable distances from centers of population. Fish, waterfowl, upland game, and big game still occur in wide variety and considerable abundance. Recreational assets along the shore, in the forests, and in the mountains are among the finest in the United States.

The wide variations in climate, physiography, and soil are responsible for a large number of natural vegetative types with strikingly different characteristics. The approximate distribution of the major types is shown in the frontispiece.

Land Capability Classes

The Soil Conservation Service of the U. S. Department of Agriculture has devised a land capability classification for the purpose of showing the uses for which particular pieces of land are best suited on the basis of their soil properties and their environment. Classes I through IV are suited for cultivation; Classes V through VII are not suited for cultivation but are suited for grazing or forestry; and Class VIII is not suited for cultivation, grazing, or forestry but may be used for wildlife, recreation, or protection of water supplies. In 1948 and 1949 the Soil Conservation Service, in cooperation with other agencies, made a rapid reconnaissance of the land capability classes of the state, by counties, and of the uses to which they were then being put. The results are shown in Tables 2 and 3 and Figures 3 and 4.

Table 2. Land Capability Classes in California by Land Uses, 1948 - 1949.

Land Capability Class	Land in crops, fallow, hay, and pasture		Dominantly grazing use		Dominantly forest		Miscellaneous and barren		All land uses		
	M acres	Per cent of class	M acres	Per cent of class	M acres	Per cent of class	M acres	Per cent of class	M acres	Per cent of class	Per cent of state
I	1,581	97	53	3	*	*	—	—	1,633	100	1.5
II	3,955	78	1,111	22	10	*	—	—	5,077	100	5
III	3,560	63	1,992	35	95	2	—	—	5,647	100	6
IV	1,271	30	2,753	65	216	5	—	—	4,241	100	4
I - IV	10,367	62	5,909	36	322	2	—	—	16,598	100	16.5
V	9	4	241	96	—		—	—	251	100	*
VI	199	1	10,631	65	5,524	34	—	—	16,353	100	16.5
VII	4	*	11,718	38	18,828	62	—	—	30,550	100	30.5
VIII	—	—	57	*	11,467	35	21,382	65	32,906	100	33
V - VIII	212	*	22,647	28	35,819	45	21,382	27	80,060	100	80
Unclassified	—	—	—	—		—	3,696	100	3,696	100	3.5
Total	10,579	11	28,556	28	36,141	36	25,078	25	100,354[2]	100	100

* Less than 1,000 acres or 0.5 per cent.

[1] Unclassified lands include cities and towns — 1,332,790 acres; roads and railroads — 1,354,650 acres; and other — 1,008,100 acres.

[2] Minor discrepancies often occur in area figures from different sources. The official Bureau of the Census figures are 100,314,000 acres for the land area of California, and 1,250,000 acres for the inland water area.

Source: Leonard R. Wohletz and Edward F. Dolder: "Know California's Land," California Department of Natural Resources and Soil Conservation Service, 1952.

Table 3. Land Uses by Land Capability Classes in California, 1948 - 1949.

Land Uses	Classes I - IV		Classes V - VIII		Unclassified		All Classes	
	M acres	Per cent of use	M acres	Per cent of use	M acres	Per cent of use	M acres	Per cent of use
Crops, etc.	10,367	98	212	2	—	—	10,579	100
Grazing	5,909	21	22,647	79	—	—	28,556	100
Forest and watershed	322	1	35,819	99	—	—	36,141	100
Barren, desert, etc.	—	—	21,382	85	3,696	15	25,078	100
Total	16,598	16.5	80,060	80	3,696	3.5	100,354	100

Source: Same as Table 2.

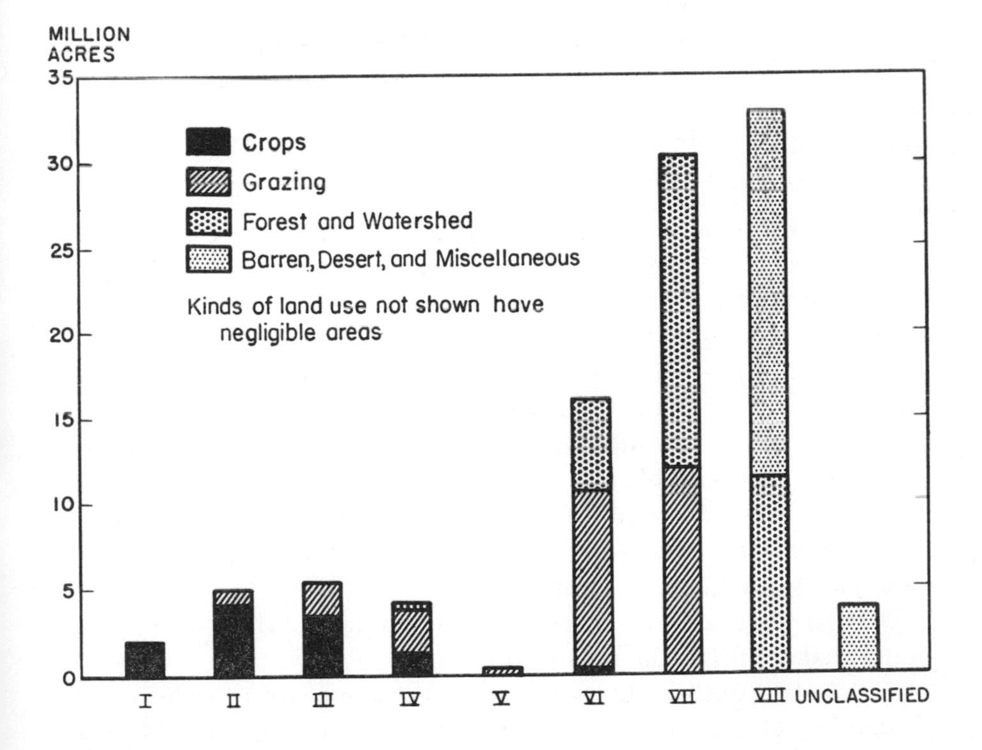

Figure 3. Land capability classes in California by land uses.

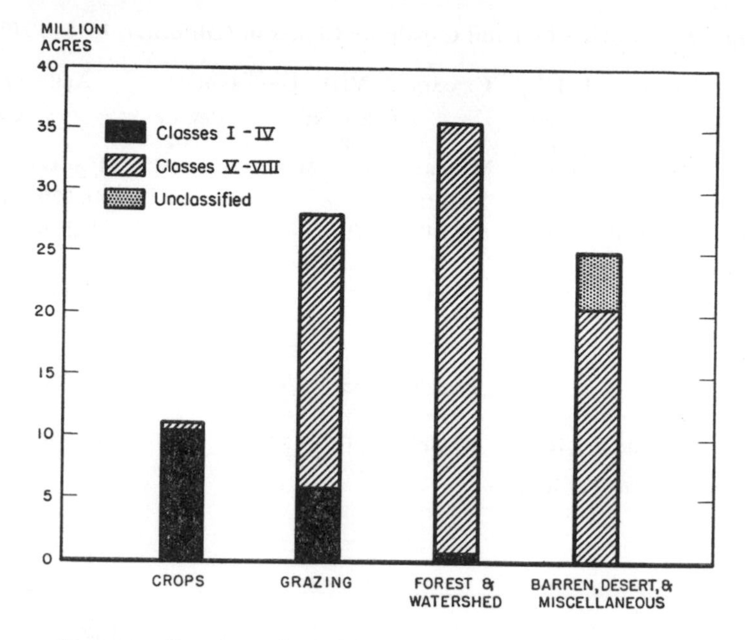

Figure 4. Land uses in California by land capability classes.

Some of the more striking facts brought out by these figures are as follows:

1. The relatively small area of land suited for cultivation – only one-sixth of the total land area of the state.

2. The much smaller area of very good cultivable land (Class I) – only 1.5 per cent of the land area of the state.

3. The use for grazing (in addition to pasture) of nearly 36 per cent of the land suitable for cultivation, mostly in Classes III and IV.

4. The large area used for forest and watershed purposes (36 per cent of the state), practically all on land not suitable for cultivation and mostly on Classes VII and VIII.

5. The large area of barren and desert land, which constitutes more than a fifth of the area of the state.

6. Land capability classes are intended primarily to indicate the suitability of land for the production of harvested crops, forage, and wood, and do not show clearly the state's assets in the form of wildlife, recreational opportunities, water, and minerals.

Forest and Range Lands

Forest Service estimates, made in connection with its Timber Resource Review, give a picture of the land-use situation that is similar in its broad outlines but that differs somewhat in details (Table 4 and Fig. 5). Particularly worthy of note are the large area of noncommercial forest land (59 per cent of the total) and the large area of pasture and range land in farms (65 per cent of the total).

Table 4. Land Area of California by Major Classes of Land, 1953.

	M acres		Per cent of land area	
Forest land				
Commercial	17,317		18	
Noncommercial	25,224		25	
Total		42,541		43
Pasture and range land				
In farms	17,074		17	
Not in farms	9,226		9	
Total		26,300		26
Crop land in farms[1]		10,235		10
Other[2]		21,238		21
Total		100,314		100

[1] 1950 Census of Agriculture.

[2] Farmsteads, roads, power lines, urban, desert, barren, etc.

Source: "Timber Resource Review," Forest Service, 1955.

A breakdown of the commercial forest area is given in Table 5. The figures show California to have the largest percentage of its total commercial forest area in old-growth sawtimber stands of any state in the Union – 65 per cent as compared with 45 per cent in Oregon and 30 per cent in Washington. Moreover, in absolute amounts, California's area of old-growth timber is practically the same as that of Oregon and nearly twice that of Washington. In other words, California's old-growth stands have been depleted relatively less than those of its neighbors to the north in spite of the fact that since 1948 it has been second only to Oregon in its production of lumber.

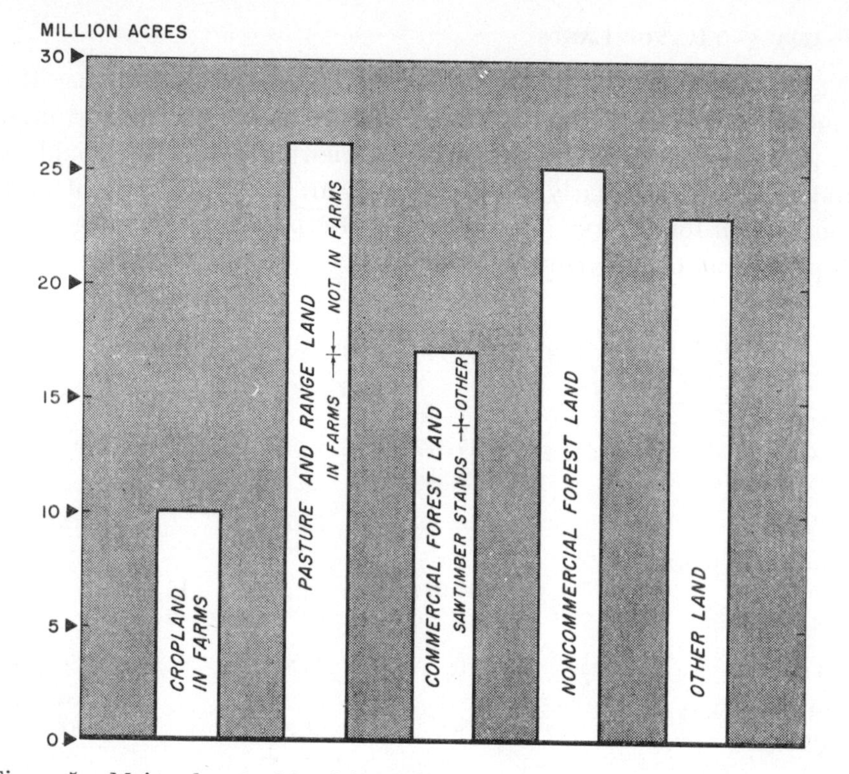

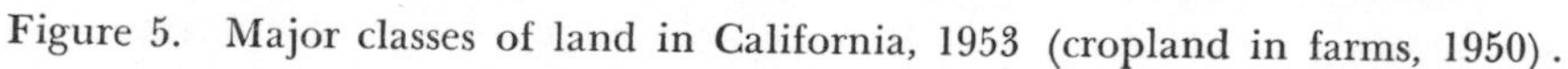
Figure 5. Major classes of land in California, 1953 (cropland in farms, 1950).

At the same time, California has less than 0.5 per cent of its commercial forest area in seedling and sapling stands, as compared with 10 per cent in Oregon and 15 per cent in Washington. This comparison may be lacking in significance because of the difference in cutting practice between the Douglas fir stands of Oregon and Washington and the pine stands of California. In the former, clear cutting predominates; in the latter, partial cutting. Therefore in California very little of the seedling and sapling growth can be identified as "stands."

An item of much greater concern is the large "nonstocked and other areas" — 12 per cent of the total as compared with approximately 6 per cent each in Oregon and Washington. The California area is considerably greater not only relatively but in actual acreage than that in the other two states.

Table 5. Commercial Forest Area in California by Stand-Size Classes, 1953.

	M ACRES		PER CENT OF TOTAL	
Sawtimber stands				
Old growth	11,240		65	
Young growth	2,798		16	
Total		14,038		81
Poletimber stands		1,122		7
Seedling and sapling stands		44		*
Nonstocked and other areas		2,113		12
Total		17,317		100

* Less than 0.5 per cent.

Source: "Timber Resource Review," Forest Service, 1955.

Table 6. Net Volume of Live Sawtimber and Growing Stock on Commercial Forest Land in California, 1953.

	SAWTIMBER		GROWING STOCK	
	MILLION BOARD FEET	PER CENT	MILLION CUBIC FEET	PER CENT
Softwoods				
Douglas fir	116,912	32	20,758	31
True firs	88,717	25	16,099	24
Ponderosa and Jeffrey pine	66,741	19	11,935	18
Redwood	36,124	10	6,360	9
Sugar pine	29,515	8	*	*
Other	16,015	4	8,512	13
Total	354,024	98	63,664	95
Hardwoods	5,977	2	3,047	5
Grand total	360,001	100	66,711	100

* Included with "other."

Source: "Timber Resource Review," Forest Service, 1955.

Table 6 emphasizes the fact that Douglas fir and the true firs comprise 57 per cent of the sawtimber volume in the state, with ponderosa pine, Jeffrey pine, and redwood adding another 29 per cent. That Douglas fir and the true firs will play an increasingly important part in the lumber cut seems clear. Hardwoods, although important locally, play an insignificant part in the picture for the state as a whole.

Table 7 shows by ownership classes the commercial forest area and the live sawtimber stand in California. The percentages for federal ownership are about the same as those for Oregon and Washington, but the percentages for state ownership are appreciably smaller and those for private ownership appreciably greater than in those states.

Table 7. Ownership of Commercial Forest Area and Sawtimber Stand in California, 1953.

	Forest area		Sawtimber stand	
	M acres	Per cent	Million board feet	Per cent
Federal	9,070	52	189,069	53
State	186	1	4,547	1
County and municipal	8	*	195	*
Private	8,053	47	166,190	46
	17,317	100	360,001	100

* Less than 1.0 per cent.

Source: "Timber Resource Review," Forest Service, 1955.

The low ratio of growth to cut of softwoods shown in Table 8 is not surprising in view of the prevalence of old-growth stands in California forests. It does, however, emphasize the importance of conducting future logging operations so as to obtain well-stocked stands of thrifty reproduction. In no other way is sustained yield at a level approaching the productive capacity of the forest lands of the state attainable.

Outside of pastures, open grassland and grass-woodland provide the best opportunities for the grazing of livestock. In the large area occupied by chaparral and brush, pasturage is usually poor because the brush is of low palatability and the understory vegetation is sparse and largely inaccessible. The still more extensive coniferous forest zone is of relatively minor importance from a state-wide viewpoint but constitutes a locally important grazing resource, particularly since green forage is available when feed is dry over most of the lower ranges. This situation makes the forage resources of the national forests, which lie largely in this zone, a more valuable asset than might be inferred from the fact that they provide scarcely 3 per cent of California's total range requirements.

Table 8. Comparison of Net Annual Growth with Annual Cut of Sawtimber and of Growing Stock in California, 1952.

	Sawtimber			Growing stock		
	Growth	Cut	Ratio of growth to cut	Growth	Cut	Ratio of growth to cut
Species	Million board feet		Per cent	Million cubic feet		Per cent
Softwoods						
Douglas fir	787	2,333	34	144	371	39
Ponderosa and Jeffrey pine	553	1,274	43	99	206	48
Redwood	396	987	40	77	163	47
Sugar pine	207	324	64	32	51	63
Other	952	786	121	187	130	144
Total	2,895	5,704	51	539	921	59
Hardwoods	44	20	220	56	11	509
Grand total	2,939	5,724	51	595	932	64

California's range resources have been reduced greatly in both quantity and quality. Farms, cities, brush, and trees have taken over extensive areas once available for grazing; overuse has changed the stocking and the character of the vegetation. Particularly striking has been the replacement of native vegetation, largely perennials, by less desirable introduced species, mostly annuals. Although the situation is improving as a result of the development of improved and irrigated pastures and the adoption of improved methods of handling the open range, California continues to be an importer of red meat.

Rich as California's natural resources are, it is clear that they are neither unlimited nor inexhaustible. It is also clear that competition for the use of land for different purposes will become more and more intense as population pressure increases. To better understand the nature of that competition and the problems which it raises, it will be helpful to trace briefly the development and present status of some of the major land uses.

". . . . With Empires in Their Purpose"

The success of the "astonishing people" who so impressed Governor Pico in 1846 has been far greater than he could have anticipated. In every field of activity the results of their enterprise have been spectacular.

Farming

Agriculture in California began with the introduction by the missionaries of cattle from Mexico in 1769 and with the sowing of wheat the following year. Attention centered largely on beef and grain, the basic food requirements, but hides and tallow soon became important staples of trade. Large areas were given over to grazing, but the area of cultivated fields probably never exceeded 5,000 to 10,000 acres for all of the missions.

Following secularization of the missions in 1833, came the pastoral era when agriculture was dominated by the great cattle ranches. The rapid growth in population that followed the gold rush and California's admission to the Union resulted in an impressive expansion of the livestock industry. During the ten years following 1850 cattle increased to about 1,000,000 head and sheep to perhaps twice that number. Both cattle and sheep were hard hit by the great drought of 1862, but sheep made the better recovery and by 1876 reached their all-time high, with an estimated 7,700,000 head.

Meanwhile field crops were coming into their own. Barley was the first grain to be grown extensively, but by 1860 wheat had passed it with a yield of nearly 6,000,000 bushels. Early in the present century the position of the two crops was again reversed. Census figures for 1949 show 1,500,426 acres planted to barley and 620,884 acres planted to wheat. Hay production jumped from a mere nothing in 1860 to 1,135,000 tons in 1880 and to 3,000,000 tons in 1890. Alfalfa became a major crop in the 1870's and today is the leading forage crop in the state.

Grapes were the first fruit to be grown extensively. Then came apples, peaches, and plums, and still later the citrus fruits. With the development of irrigation, fruits and vegetables were planted in such bewildering variety as to earn for California the reputation of having both the most diverse and the most specialized agriculture in the world. One feature of this specialization is that many farms in the state, unlike those in most other parts of the country, do not keep livestock or poultry.

California's commanding position in the field of agriculture is shown in Table 9. In 1956 it contributed 9.3 per cent of the total value of all farm products sold in the United States. It was particularly strong in the production of crops, of which it contributed 13.0 per cent of the total value. On the other hand, it was relatively weak in the production of livestock and livestock products.

During the five years from 1949 to 1954 the value of all farm products sold in California increased by 30 per cent. This increase made it the leading state in value of agricultural production, with Iowa, Texas, and Illinois next in order of importance. These four states together accounted for 29.4 per cent of the value of all farm products sold, and were the only states in which this value exceeded a billion dollars.

Table 9. Value of Farm Products Sold in the United States and California, 1956.

	United States		California		
	Value M dollars	Per cent of total	Value M dollars	Per cent of total	Per cent of United States
Crops, including forest products	14,122,190	46.5	1,829,774	64.9	13.0
Livestock and livestock products	16,250,307	53.5	989,921	35.1	6.1
Total	30,372,497	100.0	2,819,695	100.0	9.3

Source: Agricultural Marketing Service.

Fresno County, in 1956, was the leading county in the United States in value of farm products sold. Eleven counties – Fresno, Kern, Tulare, Los Angeles, Imperial, San Joaquin, Riverside, Stanislaus, San Bernardino, Orange, and Monterey – each sold farm products valued at more than $100,000,000 (Fig. 5). Together they accounted for well over half of the value of all farm products sold in California, and more than 5 per cent in the United States. Los Angeles County, which led the state (and the nation) in 1949,

Figure 6. Counties selling farm products valued at more than $100,000,000, 1956.

dropped to fourth place in 1956, probably as a result of urban encroachment on farm lands. In spite of this encroachment and of the metropolitan character of the county, it still led the state in value of dairy products sold and was third in value of poultry products.

California's preeminence in agriculture is due in considerable part to its extensive use of irrigation. Although irrigation dates back to early mission days, its development on a large scale has taken place chiefly during the present century. The 1,445,872 acres which were irrigated in 1900 had grown by 1954 to 7,048,049 acres. Here again California holds a national record, with 24 per cent of the total irrigated land in the United States. Texas comes next with 16 per cent, while Idaho and Colorado each have 8 per cent. Within the state, the irrigated area constitutes 19 per cent of the land in farms and 53 per cent of the cropland.

Table 10. Area of Pastured Land and Woodland on Farms in California, 1954.

	Acres		Per cent of farm area	
Pastured land				
Cropland used only for pasture	3,018,010		8	
Woodland pastured	5,142,261		13	
Other pasture (not cropland or woodland)	16,871,060		45	
		25,031,331		66
Woodland				
Woodland not pastured	712,517		2	
Woodland pastured	5,142,261		13	
		5,854,778		15
Pastured land and woodland[1]		25,713,848		68

[1] "Woodland pastured," which appears under both "pastured land" and "woodland," is included only once in this total.

Source: Bureau of the Census.

Table 10 shows the area of pastured land and of woodland in farms in 1954. The large area pastured, 66 per cent of the farm area of the state, indicates the growing tendency to shift from the open range to pasture in the production of livestock. Irrigated pasture (1,099,981 acres) comprised 16 per cent of the total area of irrigated land within the state and 36 per cent of the cropland used only for pasture.

Figure 7. Counties in which the value of forest products sold from farms in 1954 exceeded $100,000.

Woodland plays a relatively small part in the farm picture. Although it comprises 15 per cent of the farm area, the value of forest products sold amounts to only 0.2 per cent of the value of all farm products. In only six counties (Humboldt, Mendocino, Sonoma, Tulare, Siskiyou, and Butte) did the value of forest products sold in 1954 exceed $100,000 (Fig. 7). Of the state total of slightly more than $4,000,000, 57 per cent came from Humboldt and Mendocino Counties alone.

Mining

California's early history as a state was greatly influenced by Marshall's discovery of gold in 1848. Fabulous riches were to be had for the taking; population soared; the production of cattle, sheep, wheat, and other crops increased amazingly; land suddenly became valuable. Developments that might otherwise have taken place far more slowly were compressed into a few short decades. The feverish pace which the state adopted in the middle of the last century has never slackened.

Although the gold "rush" subsided about 1860, production of the precious metal on a large scale has never ceased. California is still the "Golden State." In 1940 its production of gold was some 50 per cent greater than the combined production of South Dakota and Utah, its nearest competitors with the exception of Alaska; but in recent years these two states have generally been in the lead.

Today "black gold" far exceeds yellow gold in value. Production of petroleum increased from an estimated 2,677,875 barrels in 1899 to 355,779,000 barrels in 1954, with a value of more than $900,000,000. Next in value come natural gas and natural gas liquids, construction materials (cement, sand, gravel, and stone), and boron minerals.

In comparison with other states, California ranks below Texas in the value of its mineral production and alternates with Pennsylvania in second place. In 1954 mineral production was valued at $1,420,859,399, which was about 63 per cent of the value of all farm products sold in that year. From the standpoint of diversity of resources, the State Division of Mines estimates that California has a greater variety of valuable mineral deposits in workable form than any other area of equal size in the world.

MANUFACTURING

California's rise as a manufacturing state has been even more spectacular than its development in most other fields, particularly during and after World War II. Between 1947 and 1954, Census figures show a rise in factory employment of 55 per cent as compared with 10 per cent for the United States as a whole. Value added by manufacture in the latter year increased to over $8 billion, which was more than double the figure for 1947 and about 7 per cent of that for the United States. Another measure of California's rapid industrial growth is furnished by figures from the Bureau of Labor Statistics which show that between mid-1947 and mid-1955 its gain in number of employees engaged in manufacturing was 8 per cent more than that in New York, Pennsylvania, Ohio, Indiana, Michigan, and Illinois combined.

For the purposes of this report, particular interest attaches to the manufacturing industries using wood as their principal raw material — lumber and wood products, pulp and paper, and furniture. These industries gave employment in 1956 to nearly 100,000 workers — a number exceeded by only two other groups of manufacturing industries. In that same year the wood-using industries were responsible for value added in manufacturing of nearly $800,000,000.

LUMBER INDUSTRY. The lumber industry started early and for many years was one of the state's leading manufacturing industries. Prior to the gold rush only small quantities of lumber and timbers had been produced in California. With the discovery of gold, however, many power sawmills were established in the Sierra Nevada foothills, and in 1851 the first sawmills made their appearance in Humboldt and Mendocino Counties. By 1869, the year of the first lumber-volume census in the state, production had increased to 354 million board feet — a figure that was exceeded by only nine other states.

Table 11 and Figure 8 compare the lumber production of California and Nevada (the latter usually negligible) with that of the

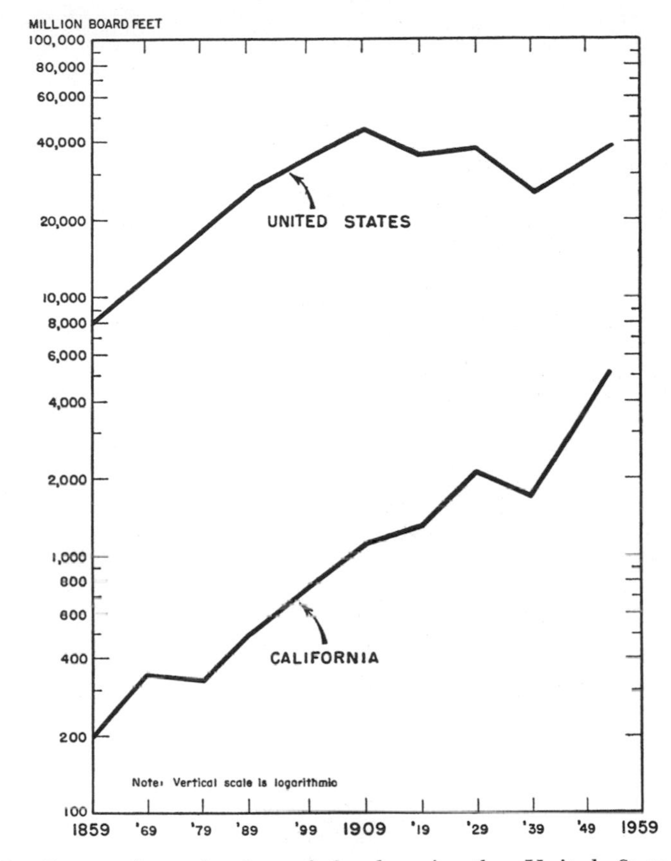

Figure 8. Reported production of lumber in the United States and in California, 1859-1953.

United States between 1859 and 1956. Until 1909 its production averaged about one-fiftieth of that for the entire country. Since then the ratio has increased rather steadily until in 1956 the state accounted for nearly one-sixth of the country's total production of lumber.

The gold rush and the accompanying increase in population enabled the lumber industry to get off to an earlier start than in Washington and Oregon, but these states soon took the lead. By 1889 Washington was producing more than twice as much lumber as California, but in 1948 California again outstripped it. Since then it has ranked second only to Oregon in its lumber cut. It differs

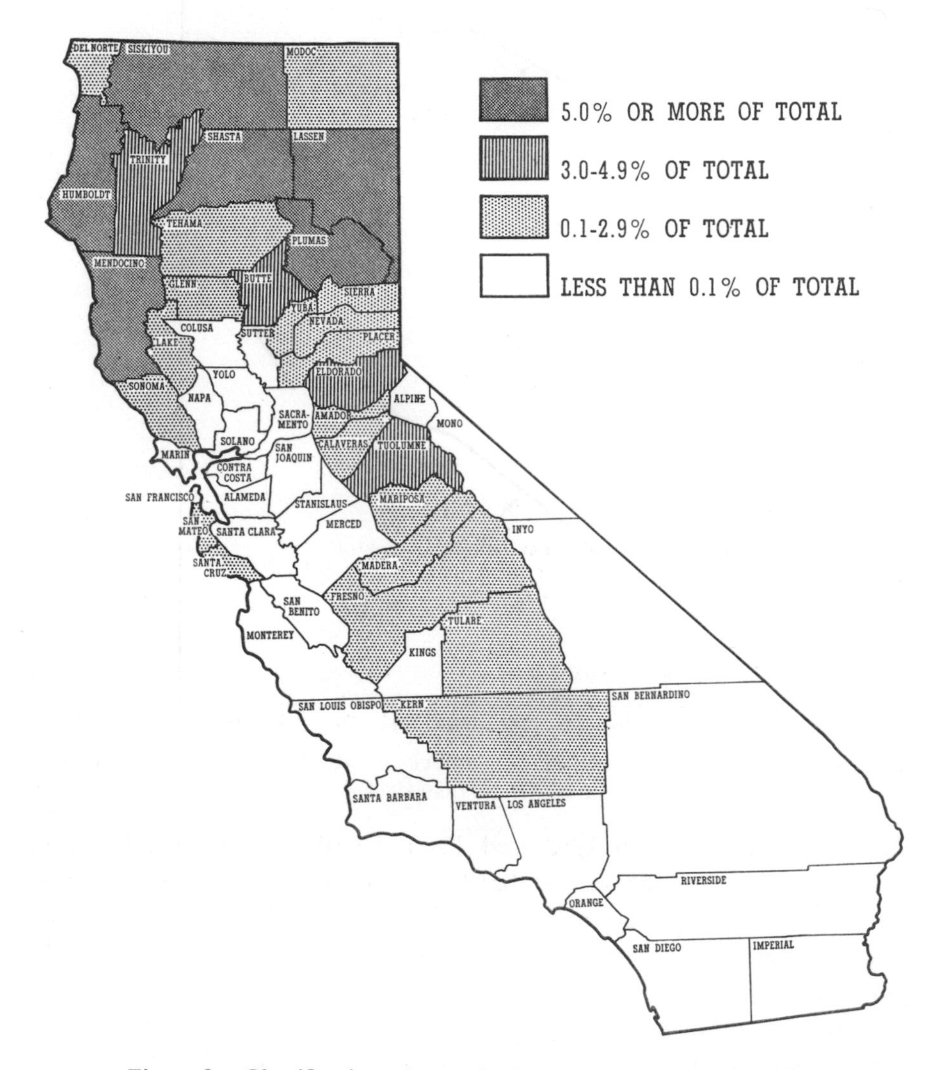

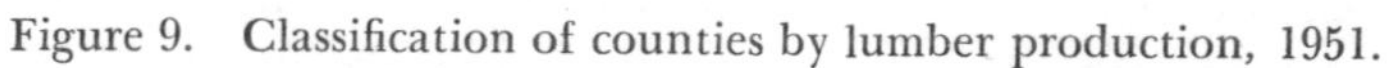

Figure 9. Classification of counties by lumber production, 1951.

Table 11. Reported Lumber Production in California and Nevada, 1859 - 1956.

Year	Volume M board feet	Per cent of U. S.	Rank in U. S.
1859	196,000	—	—
1869	353,842	2.8	10
1879	326,340	1.8	17
1889	528,554	2.0	16
1899	737,760	2.1	22
1909	1,154,007	2.6	18
1919	1,279,698	3.7	9
1929	2,063,229	5.6	5
1939	1,684,694	6.7	3
1944	2,468,943	7.5	3
1949	3,811,642	11.8	2
1953	5,109,000	13.9	2
1956	5,881,465	15.9	2

Note. The figures for volume of production include Nevada in order to avoid revealing the production of individual mills except for 1889 and 1956, when they are for California alone. Rank in 1869 and 1879 is also based on figures for California alone. The volume of production shown for 1859 is not a census figure but an estimate by Richard H. May of the California Forest and Range Experiment Station.

Source: Bureau of the Census and Forest Service.

markedly from its two neighbors to the north in that for many years its lumber imports have exceeded its lumber exports. As a result of this situation Mr. May estimates that California's annual consumption of lumber is greater than that of any other state in the Union.

Lumber production has always been centered in the northern part of the state, but with a tendency in recent years toward a somewhat wider distribution of the cut. During the 30 years from 1920 to 1951 (1949 and 1950 are excluded because of lack of data) Humboldt County led in lumber production in 19 years and Siskiyou County in 11 years. Other high-ranking counties have been Lassen, Mendocino, Plumas, El Dorado, Butte, and Tuolumne (Fig. 9).

Either ponderosa pine or redwood held the lead in lumber production until 1951, when Douglas fir went to the top, with a spectacular gain in cut of 332 per cent in 6 years. Of the 1951 production, 57 per cent came from the pine region and 43 per cent from the redwood region.

Table 12. Distribution of Lumber Cut in California by Species, 1956.

Species	Per cent
Douglas fir	41
Redwoods	18
Ponderosa pine	18
True firs	14
Sugar pine	6
Cedar	2
Others	*
	100

* Less than 0.5 per cent.

Source: California Forest and Range Experiment Station.

In 1956, Douglas fir assumed a still more leading position, with 41 per cent of the total lumber cut of the state. Redwoods (including giant sequoia) and ponderosa pine were second and third, each with 18.4 per cent (Table 12). The pine region dropped to 48 per cent of the total production, while the redwood region rose to 52 per cent. Humboldt County (26 per cent) and Mendocino County (15 per cent) accounted for two-fifths of all lumber cut in the state.

Plywood and Veneer. Consumption of logs and bolts for the manufacture of plywood, green veneer, container veneer, and special veneer has increased greatly in recent years, as is shown in Table 13. For the state as a whole, consumption in 1956 was more than 10 times what it was in 1946, and for the redwood region more than 27

Table 13. Consumption of Logs and Bolts for Plywood and Veneer in California, 1946 - 1956.

	Consumption, M board feet		
Year	Redwood Region	Pine Region	Total
1946	15,730	32,537	48,267
1948	50,440	46,730	97,170
1950	107,625	52,765	160,390
1952	193,075	57,680	250,755
1956	425,600	70,400	496,000

Note. Consumption is assumed to equal mill receipts except for 1948 and 1952, when certain adjustments were required.

Source: California Forest and Range Experiment Station.

times as much. Even in the four years between 1952 and 1956, consumption increased 98 per cent in the state, 120 per cent in the redwood region, and 22 per cent in the pine region. In addition to the peeler logs and bolts manufactured in California in 1956, some 6 million board feet were exported to Oregon.

CONTAINERS AND FURNITURE. The use of lumber for boxes is decreasing because of the competition of fibre board, but is on the upgrade for furniture and fixtures. In the latter industry, the value added by manufacture increased by 68 per cent between 1947 and 1954 to a total of $153,651,000.

PAPER AND ALLIED PRODUCTS. The industries grouped by the Bureau of the Census under the heading "paper and allied products" have shown remarkable growth in California in recent years. Between 1947 and 1954 value added by manufacture increased by 126 per cent to a total of $182,701,000. Pulp and paper mills have multiplied and are steadily increasing their consumption of wood.

Table 14 gives the production of pulpwood for selected years from 1944 to 1956. Particularly noteworthy is the growing use of chips from sawmill residues and veneer clippings. The use of chips from mill ends from box factories and other remanufacturing plants, and from the manufacture of wood flour is apparently declining. The decreased drain on the forest resulting from advances in technology is striking. Imports of veneer cores and wood flour brought California's consumption of pulpwood in 1956 to about 5,000 cords more than its production.

Table 14. Production of Pulpwood in California, 1944 - 1956

YEAR	LOGS AND BOLTS[1]	CHIPS	MILL ENDS AND WOOD FLOUR	TOTAL
	EQUIVALENT IN CORDS			
1944	11,000	—	—	11,000
1946	4,482	—	—	4,482
1948	31,854	—	—	31,854
1950	97,680	—[2]	—[2]	191,000
1952	200,000	27,000	74,000	301,000
1956	132,000	250,000	67,000	449,000

[1] Converted to cords on basis of 2 cords per M board feet gross log scale.
[2] Figures not available in detail.
Source: California Forest and Range Experiment Station.

Recreation

Tourism has become big business in California, as in many other parts of the United States. In 1953 some 4,334,000 tourists spent $771,800,000 in the state. These figures represent increases of 132 per cent and 216 per cent over 1940.

Most tourists come by automobile (78 per cent in 1952), and many of them use national parks, national forests, state parks, and other wildland areas for recreational purposes. In addition, these facilities were used to a far greater extent by residents of California than by tourists from outside of the state. Yosemite National Park claims about 25 per cent of the total number of visitor-days at all national parks, of whom some 85 per cent come from California. Visits to national forests in California in 1955 numbered 7,715,000, or more than in any other Forest Service region; and the precentage of visitors who were Californians was even larger than in the case of the Yosemite National Park. This figure represents an increase of nearly 100 per cent over 1946, with a further increase of 57 per cent, to a total of 12,100,000 visits, anticipated by 1962. State-administered parks, exclusive of state-owned beaches operated by local communities, welcomed 11,000,000 visitors in 1954.

While the chief value of recreation lies in its effects on the recreationist as a human being and as a citizen, the large expenditures which it involves for many kinds of goods and services give it an important place in the economic life of the state. Since the tourist by definition spends his money in a different place from that in which he earned it, his business constitutes a sort of export trade for the locality visited. As Morris E. Garnsey has expressed it in "America's New Frontier, the Mountain West": "On the export side, the Mountain West is a major supplier of recreational resources to the rest of the nation. Expenditures in the region by tourists for food, lodging, transportation, licenses, and equipment are very significant in the regional economy. A net balance in this sector of the economy provides the region with large sums which can be used to purchase the manufactures and services which the inhabitants of the region buy abroad." This is also true of a state and of places within the state which persons from elsewhere visit for recreational purposes.

Urbanization

California, like the rest of the United States, is becoming increasingly urbanized, but at a faster rate (Fig. 10). In 1950, 81 per cent of the state's population was classified as urban under the new Census definition which includes in that category the fringe settlements near cities and unincorporated places with more than 2,500 inhabitants. Well over half the people of the state resided in four counties (San Francisco, Los Angeles, Alameda, and San Mateo), in

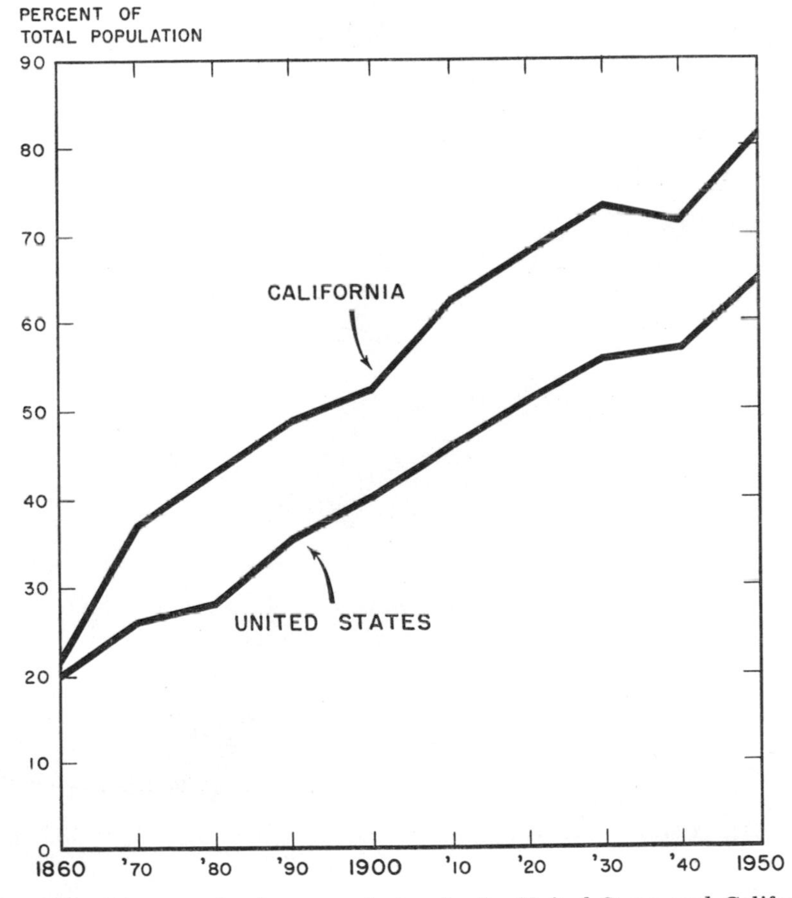

Figure 10. Per cent of urban population in the United States and California, 1860-1950.

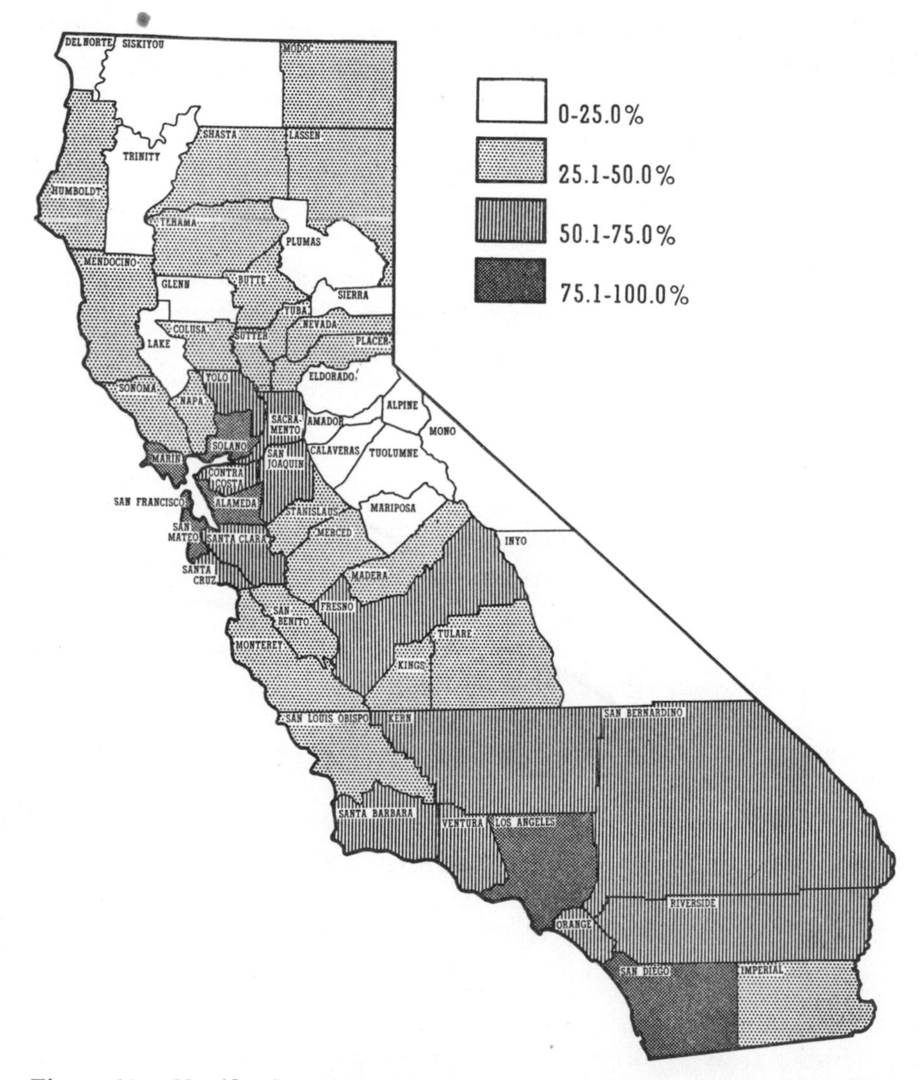

Figure 11. Classification of counties by per cent of urban population, 1950.

each of which more than 90 per cent of the population was urban (Fig. 11). Eleven counties had no urban population whatever. Eight of the 26 "standard metropolitan areas" in the United States which showed a gain in population of 50 per cent or more between 1940 and 1950 were located in California.

Even the rural population is for the most part semi-urban. Only 617,367 persons, or 5.8 per cent of the total population, were listed in 1950 as living on farms, as compared with 15.5 per cent for the entire United States. It is interesting that the state which leads all others in the value of its agricultural products is also one of the most highly urbanized and has one of the smallest percentages of its population on farms. Los Angeles County, with 97.5 of its population classed as urban, is exceeded only by Fresno, Kern, and Tulare Counties in the value of its agricultural products, and tops all other counties in the state in the value of its dairy products.

Urbanization is, however, inevitably encroaching on the land available for agriculture. In the four years from 1950 to 1954, for example, the area devoted to the production of oranges decreased by 48 per cent in Los Angeles County, by 33 per cent in San Diego County, by 29 per cent in San Bernardino County, and by 25 per cent in Orange County. Santa Clara County is struggling to retain a reasonable amount of its more fertile land in agriculture under the "greenbelt law" of 1955. San Mateo County is disturbed because its "bedroom communities," made up of San Francisco commuters, require expensive schools and other facilities, to the support of which they contribute less than would industrial communities. "The automobile is not only one result of land eaters; it also eats up land by developing great strung-out subdivisions along the highway." How to prevent the "hop, skip, and jump" type of urbanization by a more orderly development is a problem in many parts of the state.

Urban, and still more suburban, development is also taking considerable areas of forest land out of production. Even the desert is being increasingly occupied not only by individuals but by new communities. Practically all of California's 100 million acres appear to be on their way to acquiring a value as space, irrespective of their productive capacity.

WATER DEVELOPMENT

Conservation of water is generally regarded as California's most urgent need. The growth of the state in every direction is dependent on adequate supplies of water. As the State Water Resources Board has pointed out, "Even without the recent disastrous flood example [of December, 1955], the problems of water in California have never before assumed such large proportions nor been of such vital significance as they are today. Their critical nature largely stems from the unprecedented recent growth of population, industry, and agriculture in our semiarid state, coupled with an extended period in which the construction of both water conservation and flood control works has lagged far behind the increasing needs . . . It is apparent to most that the continued growth and prosperity of California is dependent upon prompt and substantial efforts by the responsible local, State, and Federal governments to provide physical solutions to the problems of water, commensurate with the needs."

Engineers and economists estimate that California has enough water to meet its anticipated "ultimate requirements," but only through the construction of extensive and expensive engineering works. The problem is complicated by the seasonal distribution of precipitation, its concentration in the northern part of the state, and the periodic occurrence of dry cycles. Again quoting the State Water Resources Board: "Well over 70 per cent of the stream flow occurs north of a line drawn roughly through Sacramento. In contrast, an estimated 77 per cent of the present consumptive water requirements and 80 per cent of the forecast ultimate are found south of the same line."

Solution of California's water problem requires control of the estimated mean surface runoff of all streams of about 71,000,000 acre-feet and maintenance of the underground reservoir, which is estimated to have a storage capacity of over 130,000,000 acre-feet within 200 feet of the ground surface in the Central Valley alone. Two items illustrate the difficulties to be overcome: (1) The North Coastal Area provides 41 per cent of the state's natural water supply but should ultimately require only about 4 per cent of the water consumptively used throughout California. (2) The ground water level has been falling throughout the state, particularly in the more fertile agricultural districts, and in some instances the continued overdraft is of such magnitude as to threaten irreparable damage to the underground storage reservoir. "The California Water Plan" to meet the situation envisions an eventual capital expenditure of between $12 billion and $13 billion.

SUMMARY

California is now one of the leading states of the Union in population, production, and wealth, and is rapidly forging ahead in every field of activity. Increasing strains are being placed on its agricultural, forest, range, recreational, and mineral lands, and even more on its limited and unevenly distributed water supply. Conflicting demands for the use of land and water already exist and will become more acute as population expands and standards of living rise. California's future depends in large measure on the intelligence and the vision with which its natural resources are handled. Ownership of these resources inevitably influences strongly the way in which they are managed and administered, and the problems which ownership poses are therefore worthy of careful study.

PART II

EVOLUTION OF LAND OWNERSHIP

Today's complex pattern of land ownership and management in California is the outgrowth of two centuries of evolution under the ever-changing policies of colonial, federal, state, and local governments and of corporations and individuals.

Spanish and Mexican Grants

With the permanent occupation of Alta California by Spain in 1769, ownership of all land in the province was assumed by the Crown. The Laws of the Indies recognized the rights of the Indians to the use of as much land as they needed for homes, tillage, and pasturage, but did not recognize any right of actual ownership. In practice, the white man gave as little heed to the Indians' right of occupancy "as the Indians themselves had given to the occupation by animals of the lands that interfered with their wishes or needs."

No title to the lands which they occupied was acquired by the missions. Their tenure was regarded as a temporary one, to be terminated with the completion of their task of Christianizing the Indians. At least 30 "grants" of land for use as ranches were made by military commanders and governors during the Spanish regime, but none by the King, in whom absolute title vested. These grants actually amounted to little more than cattle-grazing permits. They did not at the time result in private ownership, although such ownership was in some cases later affirmed by the American Government.

Following 1822 when Mexico became an empire, and later a republic, the situation changed materially. In 1824 a colonization law was passed by the Mexican Congress, and regulations for its administration were issued in 1828. Under the new system private ownership of land became a reality, although boundaries were usually vague, and few persons took the steps necessary to acquire perfect title. Grants were made in increasing number, with many of them running up to 11 square leagues (about 47,700 acres) in size. Some of the recipients were Americans, most of whom had become naturalized Mexican citizens in order to qualify for a grant.

American Annexation

The treaty of Guadalupe Hidalgo of February 2, 1848, which ended the war with Mexico, promised to respect the property rights of Mexican landowners in the territory ceded to the United States, whether or not they were actually established on the lands. All other land became the property of the United States. Over this land Congress had, and still has, complete control under the provision of the Constitution giving it "Power to dispose of and make all needful Rules and Regulations respecting the Territory or other Property belonging to the United States."

Two years later the act of September 9, 1850, admitted California to the Union "on an equal footing with the original states in all respects whatever." Section 3 was more specific with regard to the public lands in the state: ". . .That the said State of California is admitted into the Union upon the express condition that the people of the said State, through their legislature or otherwise, shall never interfere with the primary disposal of public lands within its limits, and shall pass no law and do no act whereby the title of the United States to, and right to dispose of, the same shall be impaired or questioned; and that they shall never lay any tax or assessment of any description whatsoever upon the public domain of the United States, and in no case shall non-resident proprietors, who are citizens of the United States, be taxed higher than residents; and that all the navigable waters within the said State shall be common highways, and forever free, as well to the inhabitants of said State as to the citizens of the United States, without any tax, impost, or duty therefor . . ."

One of the first concerns of Congress was to determine just what were public lands. The act of March 3, 1851, established a Claims

Commission of three members which was charged with the responsibility of passing upon the validity of the claims to Spanish and Mexican land grants. Review of the commission's decisions by the courts was at first permitted on appeal and was later made automatic. All lands to which claims were rejected by the commission or held invalid by the courts, and all lands to which no claim was presented to the commission within two years, were to be considered part of the public domain. Under a ruling by the Supreme Court all grants made after July 7, 1846, when Commodore Sloat took possession of Monterey in the name of the United States, were held to be invalid.

The commission's activities continued from January, 1852, to March, 1856. Commonly, however, final action was not taken by the courts and the General Land Office until much later. Robinson ("Land in California") states that 17 years was the average time a successful claimant had to wait for his patent. The commission on the whole adopted a liberal attitude and was less interested in technicalities than in proof of possession and use of the land. Out of 813 cases acted on by the commission, 553 grants involving some 8,850,000 acres were eventually confirmed. The location of the confirmed grants is shown in Figure 12.

The entire procedure adopted by Congress has been severely criticized on the ground that it involved ruinous costs and delays for many holders of valid claims, without being necessary to protect the interests of the government. It has been defended as the only method by which the confirmation of many invalid claims could have been prevented. There is, however, general agreement that the lawyers and land speculators were the chief beneficiaries, and the honest claimants and the squatters the chief victims, of the long-drawn-out adjudication of titles. To the victims should be added the Indians, who were quite unaware of what was happening and who therefore did nothing about the lands they were occupying prior to the expiration of the two years within which claims had to be filed.

Grants to the State

Upon California's admission to the Union in 1850, the State became entitled to a grant of 500,000 acres, to be used for purposes of

Figure 12. Spanish and Mexican land grants confirmed by the United States. From *Land in California* by William W. Robinson, University of California Press, Berkeley and Los Angeles, 1948.

internal improvement. This grant had been made by Congress in 1841 to the nine public-land states already in existence (Ohio, Louisiana, Indiana, Mississippi, Illinois, Alabama, Missouri, Arkansas, and Michigan) and to such new states as might later be admitted. Title to the land passed to the state, without the issuance of patent, upon its selection by the state and certification by the Secretary of the Interior.

The next grant came within less than three weeks after California became a state, when the act of September 28, 1850, granted to California and to eleven other states all of the swamp and overflowed land within their borders, with the proviso that the proceeds from their sale should be used exclusively, as far as necessary, for the construction of levees and drains. Under this act the state obtained patent to 2,192,875 acres. Much of the land was overflowed only during the rainy season, and at two places irrigation works were found on land claimed as swamp. A liberal interpretation of what constituted swamp and overflowed lands was common in other states as well as in California.

An act passed on March 3, 1853, granted to California Sections 16 and 36 in each township, the proceeds from which were to be used for the support of common schools. In 1866 the state was permitted to select "lieu lands" of equal acreage in the unreserved public domain whenever any of the granted sections were settled upon prior to survey, were reserved for public uses, or were coverd by Spanish or Mexican grants or other private claims. The act made no specific exception of mineral lands, but the U. S. Supreme Court ruled that the intention was to convey agricultural lands and that lands known to be mineral did not pass to the state. In 1927, however, Congress granted to the states all mineralized school sections which were not then in controversy, with the restriction that the state should reserve the coal and other minerals in disposing of any of these sections.

The total area granted to California for common-school purposes was about 5,534,000 acres, but the state has not yet acquired title to some 266,700 acres which are still unsurveyed or have been withdrawn for some federal purpose such as military reservations. The same act which gave Sections 16 and 36 to the state also granted 46,080 acres for the use of a "seminary of learning," which proved to be the University of California. A third educational grant, of 150,000 acres, was made by the Morrill Act of July 2, 1862, for the support of a college of agriculture and the mechanic arts. This action brought the total grants for educational purposes to about 5,730,000 acres.

Other grants included 6,400 acres for public buildings and 394,368 acres for parks (Anza Desert State Park and Borrego State Park). Total grants to the state aggregated 8,824,000 acres — a figure that approximates the area included in confirmed Spanish and Mexican land grants.

Disposal of Public Lands to Individuals and Corporations

Agricultural Lands

In 1853 Congress extended to California the provisions of the Preemption Act of 1841, which permitted settlers to "squat" on public land prior to its being offered for sale and later to purchase it at the minimum price of $1.25 per acre. A still more liberal policy was adopted in 1862 with the passage of the Homestead Act, which gave land to settlers after five years of residence and cultivation. The great bulk of the land which passed directly from the federal government to individuals was acquired under these two acts. In 1912 the length of residence necessary to obtain patent under the Homestead Act was reduced to three years, and the provisions of the Enlarged Homestead Act of 1909, which raised the maximum area obtainable under the original Homestead Act from 160 to 320 acres, were extended to California.

The Forest Homestead Act of June 11, 1906, authorized the Secretary of Agriculture to open for entry lands in national forests chiefly valuable for agriculture which are not needed for public purposes and which in his judgment might be occupied without injury to the forest. Under this act some 344,000 acres were opened to entry.

That the Secretary of Agriculture was liberal in his classification of land as agricultural is indicated by the fact that many of the patented lands have subsequently been abandoned. For example, L. A. Barrett of the Forest Service reported on January 8, 1919, that "not to exceed 25% of the lands listed on the Sierra [National Forest] are now being occupied," and on August 2, 1921, that "we know from actual experience that 50% of the homesteads that have been listed under the Act of June 11 have already been abandoned." The Regional Forester at San Francisco states that even when the lands were not abandoned their use for agriculture was usually short-lived. "Today we know of very few instances where such home-steaded lands are being used for agricultural purposes."

The Stockraising Homestead Act of 1916 authorized the Secretary of the Interior to open for entry under the homestead laws not more than 640 acres per person of public lands the surface of which is chiefly valuable for grazing and raising of forage crops, which do not contain merchantable timber, which are not susceptible of irrigation from any known source of water supply, and which are of such a character that 640 acres are reasonably required for support of a family. Instead of cultivation, the entryman must make improvements to the extent of $1.25 per acre. The operation of the act has not been satisfactory, since ordinarily 640 acres of the kind of land described are not enough to support a family comfortably. Figures are not available on the area that has been patented in California.

Still another method of acquiring public land for agricultural purposes was authorized by the Desert Land Act of 1877. This act, as amended, provides for the sale in eleven western states and territories of 640 acres of nontimbered, nonmineral land unfit for cultivation without irrigation to any settler who will irrigate one-eighth of it within three years after filing. A payment of $0.25 per acre was to be made at the time of filing and of $1.00 at the time of final proof. Up to June 30, 1956, final entries under this act in California totaled 6,122 and covered 1,108,000 acres.

Timberlands

No legal method of acquiring timberlands which were not valuable for agriculture was available until 1878, when Congress passed the Timber and Stone Act. This act provided for the sale of 160 acres of surveyed, nonmineral land, chiefly valuable for timber or stone and unfit for cultivation, for not less than $2.50 per acre. The purchaser had to swear that the land was being acquired for his own use and benefit. If the object was to make timber legally available for lumbering, the maximum area of 160 acres that could be acquired by any one person was too small for economical, close utilization and permanent production. The inevitable result was the widespread use of fraud to build up large holdings of valuable timberlands. Where consolidation did not take place, the holding of large areas in small blocks by many owners has tended to prevent the adoption of sound cutting practices and sustained-yield management.

S. A. D. Puter, a native of Trinity County, California, who later became known as the "king of the Oregon land fraud ring," states that the first big fraud under the Timber and Stone Act was initiated in Humboldt County in 1882-1883. Persons in every walk of life who had never seen the land and who had no intention of ever using it were induced, for a consideration of $50 apiece, to sign applications and simultaneously to transfer their interests to the company. According to Commissioner Sparks of the General Land Office:

"Sailors were caught while in port and hurried into a saloon or to a certain notary public's office and induced to sign applications and convey the lands to a member of the firm. Farmers were stopped on their way to their homes, and merchants were called from their counters and persuaded to allow their names to be used to obtain title to the lands. The company's agent presented the applications to the register and receiver in blocks of as many as twenty-five at one time; paid the fees; had the proper notices published; hired men to make the proofs; paid for the lands and received the duplicate receipts; yet the register and receiver and some of the special agents appear to have been the only persons in the vicinity who were ignorant of the frauds."

In this case sufficient evidence was eventually obtained to result in cancellation of the claims, but such an outcome was the exception rather than the rule. Fraudulent use of the Preemption Act and the Homestead Act to obtain timberlands and mineral lands was also common; but the Timber and Stone Act apparently provided the more popular means of acquiring title to timberlands. Some

2,899,000 acres were patented under the latter act in California, or about 21 per cent of the total for the United States. The act was repealed in 1955.

Isolated, Mountainous, and Small Tracts

Public auction sales, which had never been used extensively in California, were abolished in 1891 except for isolated tracts, sale of which had been authorized in 1846. Sale of land which is mountainous or too rough for cultivation was authorized in 1912. The maximum areas which can now be sold are 1,520 acres for isolated tracts and 760 acres for mountainous tracts.

In 1938 Congress authorized the Secretary of the Interior to sell or lease not more than 5 acres of public lands which he may classify as chiefly valuable for home, cabin, health, convalescent, recreational, or business sites, subject to reservation to the United States of all oil, gas, and other mineral deposits. This Small Tract Act has generated considerable real-estate business and now constiutes the most popular means of obtaining title to public lands in California.

Mineral Lands

The gold rush highlighted the embarrassing fact that Congress had made no specific provision for the disposal of mineral lands, which were subject to sale and preemption in the same manner as other public lands. The forty-niners and their successors therefore framed their own regulations. These regulations had the force of law and were largely incorporated in the federal acts of 1866, 1870, and 1872 providing for the sale of placer claims at $2.50 per acre and of lode claims at $5.00 per acre. Patents have been issued to some 583,000 acres of mineral lands, but at least an equal area is undoubtedly held in mineral claims, which are legally transferable and which give the holder the right of occupation and exploitation.

In 1920 the Mineral Leasing Act stopped the sale of lands containing coal, phosphate, sodium, oil, oil shale, or gas and made them subject to lease. Later legislation extended the provisions of the act to lands containing potash or sulfur.

The Materials Disposal Act of July 1, 1947, authorized the Secretary of the Interior to dispose of sand, gravel, clay, timber, and other materials on public lands exclusive of national forests, national parks, national monuments, and Indian lands. A later act (July 23, 1955) added common pumice, pumicite, and cinders to this list and authorized the disposal of all such materials on both unreserved and reserved public lands except national parks, national monuments, and Indian lands. The 1955 act also specified that on unpatented mining claims thereafter located the United States shall have the right to dispose of the timber and other nonmineral resources, provided that such disposal shall not endanger or materially interfere with mining operations; and it established a procedure whereby the right to use the timber and other surface resources on existing, inactive mining claims may be canceled or waived.

Railroad Grants

The Pacific Railroad Act of July 1, 1862, granted the Union Pacific Railroad and the Central Pacific Railroad alternate, odd-numbered sections of land for 10 miles on each side of the road. This distance was increased in 1864 to 20 miles. A golden spike connecting the two railroads was driven at Promontory, Utah, on May 10, 1869. Similar grants were made in 1866 to the California and Oregon Railroad Company, the Western Pacific Railroad Company (not the present road of that name, which never received a land grant), the Southern Pacific Railroad Company, and the Atlantic and Pacific Railroad Company (later the Atchison, Topeka, and Santa Fe Railway Company).

The grant to the latter was forfeited in 1886 along the uncompleted portion of the main line, which included all of the grant in California. All of the other roads, together with their land grants, were taken over by the Southern Pacific Company on its incorporation in 1884. The area finally patented was about 11,588,000 acres, which comprised 13 per cent of the grants made directly to all railroad corporations and 8 per cent of the total grants, including those made to the states for the benefit of the railroads.

Summary

Grants and sales to the state, to corporations, and to individuals within California are summarized in Table 15 and Figure 13. The figures are compiled from information furnished by the Bureau of Land Management, and are in part estimates, since no complete tabulation of land disposals in California exists. Other compilers might reach different results, but the differences would seldom be significant.

The over-all picture as presented herewith is believed to be reasonably accurate. It shows total disposals of nearly 57 per cent of the

Table 15. Disposal of Public Domain in California to June 30, 1956.

METHOD OF DISPOSAL	ACRES		PER CENT	
Grants to the state				
For miscellaneous purposes	500,000		1	
For educational purposes	5,730,000		10	
For swamp reclamation	2,193,000		4	
For public buildings and parks	401,000		1	
		8,824,000		16
Grants to railroad corporations		11,588,000		20
Private land claims confirmed		8,850,000		16
Cash sales (chiefly public auction, private, preemption, and townsite sales)		8,631,000		15
Homestead entries (including commuted, forest, and stockraising homesteads)		11,433,000		20
Desert-land entries		1,108,000		2
Timber-culture entries		142,000		*
Timber and stone entries		2,899,000		5
Mineral entries		583,000		1
Ceded Indian lands		110,000		*
Other methods (chiefly scrip locations and military bounties)		2,400,000		4
		56,568,000[1]		100

* Less than 0.5 per cent.

[1] This figure is larger than the total area now in state and private ownership, since some of the land has been re-acquired by the Federal Government.

Source: Bureau of Land Management.

land area of the state. Of this amount, approximately one-fifth each went to railroad corporations and to homesteaders, and approximately one-sixth each to private claimants, to the State, and to cash purchasers.

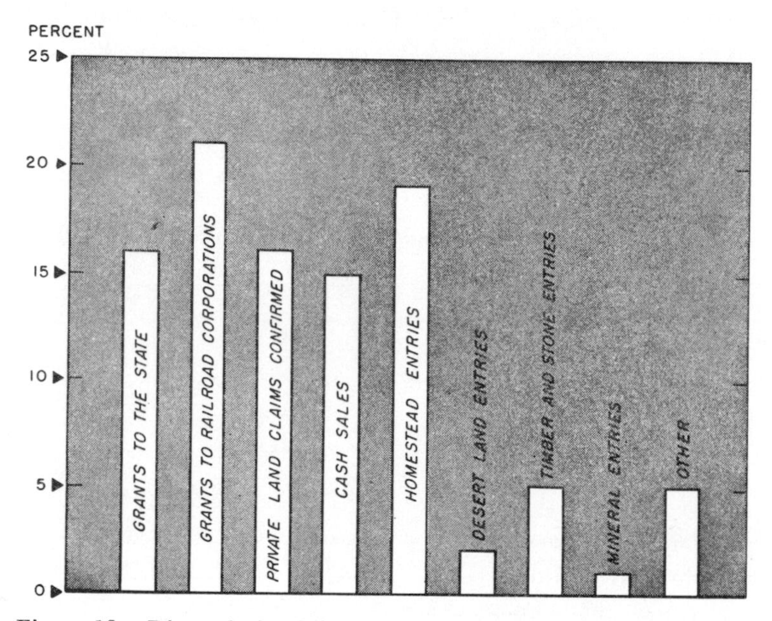

Figure 13. Disposal of public domain in California to June 30, 1956.

Reservations and Withdrawals

National Parks and Monuments

A change from the policy of disposing of public lands by grant and sale was foreshadowed in 1872, when Congress reserved the Yellowstone National Park "as a public park or pleasuring-ground for the benefit and enjoyment of the people." The next step came in 1890 with the establishment in California of three national parks — the Sequoia, the Yosemite, and the General Grant. Lassen Volcanic National Park was established in 1916. Kings Canyon National Park was created in 1940 by the absorption of the General Grant National Park and the transfer of a large area from the Sequoia National Forest and the Sierra National Forest. The Yosemite

National Park has been reduced from its original area of about 986,880 acres to an area of 760,951 acres as of December 31, 1956. The numerous changes that have been made in the boundaries of the three other national parks now in California have been mostly minor and in the direction of enlargement of the system.

Another, somewhat similar movement for the reservation of public lands started in 1906, when Congress authorized the President to establish national monuments for the preservation of features of historic, prehistoric, or scientific interest. Two national monuments — Muir Woods and Pinnacles — were established in California in 1908. They were subsequently followed by six others, of which Death Valley (1933) is much the largest.

National Forests

From the viewpoint of the area involved, a still more drastic departure from the disposal policy came in 1891, when Congress authorized the President to set aside as forest reserves public lands covered with timber or undergrowth. This authority was confirmed by the important act of June 4, 1897, which also stated the purposes for which forest reserves could be created and authorized the Secretary of the Interior to make rules and regulations for their administration.

The first forest reserve (the Yellowstone) was created within less than a month after passage of the act of March 3, 1891, and California was not far behind. On November 14, 1891, and December 7, 1892, President Harrison withdrew from entry a considerable area of public land in southern California, and on December 20, 1892, he proclaimed the establishment of the San Gabriel Forest Reserve of 555,520 acres. During the next few months he created additional reserves totaling 787,208 acres in southern California and 4,057,470 acres in the Sierra Nevada. President Cleveland's famous proclamation of February 22, 1897, added two reserves with an area of 1,428, 480 acres, and President McKinley created four more with an area of 1,985,921 acres. By the end of 1899 California had nine forest reserves with a total area of 8,814,599 acres, of which 3,929,594 acres were in the southern part of the state and 4,885,005 in the Sierra Nevada.

With Theodore Roosevelt in the White House, forest reserves (renamed "national forests" in 1907) expanded rapidly. Between 1901 and 1909 he created fifteen new national forests in California and made large additions to those already in existence. Net additions, including a small area in Nevada, totaled 19,624,000 acres, with the result that the gross area of national forests in California reached its peak in 1909 with 27,968,510 acres.

Up to this time the establishment of national forests in California, as in the rest of the country, had been almost a feverish process. Potentially suitable public lands covered an enormous area and were usualy difficult of access; the Forest Service staff was small; Roosevelt and his Forester, Gifford Pinchot, felt that time was running out. Inevitably, large areas were proclaimed as national forests with inadequate field examination, on the theory that it was better to reserve too much than too little.

Then came a period of readjustment, which has greatly slowed down in recent years but is still under way. As further information became available, boundaries were rectified and areas not clearly needed for national-forest purposes were eliminated. Although changes in name have been common, no new national forests have been created in California except for the Calaveras Big Tree National Forest of 379 acres which was authorized by Congress in 1909 and actually materialized in 1954. Net reductions in gross area by presidential proclamation were as follows:

President	Acres
William H. Taft	773,000
Woodrow Wilson	2,552,000
Warren G. Harding	7,000
Calvin Coolidge	68,000
Herbert Hoover	17,000
Franklin D. Roosevelt	10,000

In addition, several changes were made by Congress, the most important of which transferred about 781,000 acres from national forests to Lassen Volcanic, Sequoia, and Kings Canyon National Parks, with minor transfers from national parks to national forests.

In general, the trend since the large eliminations made by President Taft and President Wilson has been toward a stabilization of the gross area of national forests in the state at about 24 million acres, and of the net area at 19 to 20 million acres (Fig. 14).

Since 1912 the creation or enlargement of national forests in California has been possible only by act of Congress. This restriction was first applied in 1907 to Washington, Oregon, Montana, Idaho, Wyoming, and Colorado. It was later extended to California (1912), Arizona (1926), and New Mexico (1926), and was repealed with respect to Montana (1939).

Mineral Lands

Reservation of mineral lands in the public domain first centered around coal and oil lands. In California, some oil lands were withdrawn from agricultural entry in 1907, and in 1909 President Taft withdrew a gross area of 2,871,000 acres of oil land in the state from all forms of entry. These withdrawals were confirmed after passage of the act of June 25, 1910, authorizing the temporary withdrawal of public lands by the President – a power which the Supreme Court later ruled that he already possessed. During the next six years some additional withdrawals were made, while other lands which field examination showed unlikely to contain oil were restored to entry. Gross withdrawals of oil lands in California by January, 1916, amounted to some 1,508,000 acres, of which a considerable part was in private ownership.

A much more comprehensive and permanent reservation policy was adopted by Congress with passage of the Mineral Leasing Act of February 25, 1920. Under this act, as amended, public lands containing oil, oil shale, gas, coal, phosphate, sodium, potash, or sulfur are automatically withdrawn from sale and are available for exploitation only under leases from the federal government. Sale, lease, or other disposal of the surface of such lands, if not necessary for the use of the lessee, may be permitted by the Secretary of the Interior.

Range Lands

A step toward the reservation of public range lands was taken by the Taylor Grazing Act of June 28, 1934. In order to permit the highest use of the public land "pending its final disposal," the act authorized the Secretary of the Interior to establish grazing districts and to lease for grazing purposes any unreserved public lands so situated as not to justify their inclusion in a grazing district. In 1935 two grazing districts were established in California with a gross area of about 8 million acres, of which approximately half was in federal ownership. In addition, grazing leases are issued on nearly 6 million acres of unreserved public land not in grazing districts.

Blanket Withdrawals

On November 26, 1934, and February 5, 1935, President Franklin D. Roosevelt, acting under authority of the act of 1910, "temporarily" withdrew from entry, pending classification, practically all of the remaining unreserved and unappropriated public domain in the United States, including of course California. Section 7 of the Taylor Grazing Act, as amended, authorized the Secretary of the Interior to examine, classify, and open to entry any of these lands or any lands

Figure 15. Disposal of public land in California by various methods, 1947-1956.

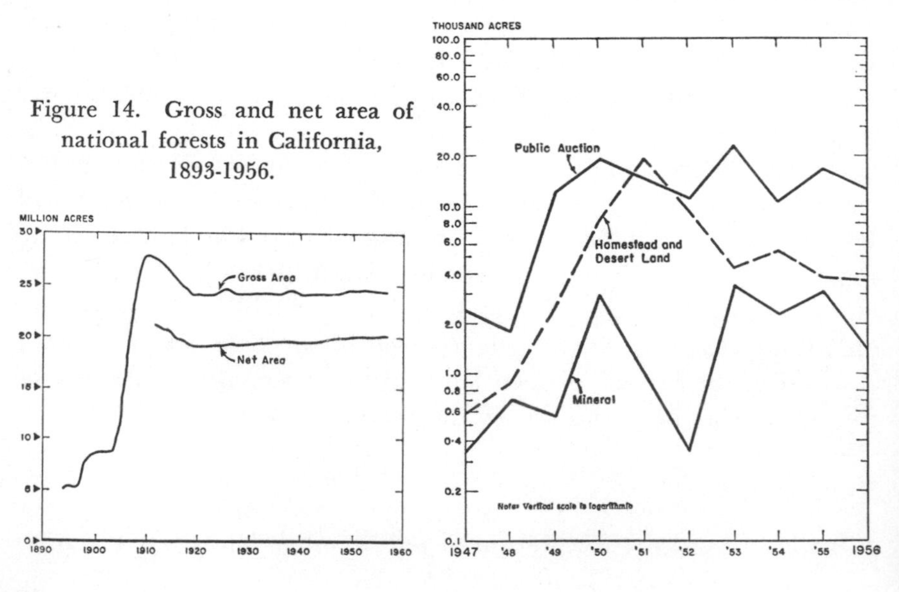

Figure 14. Gross and net area of national forests in California, 1893-1956.

Table 16. Patents to Public Land in California Issued under Various Forms of Entry and Sale, 1947 - 1956.

Year	Homestead	Desert land	Public auction	Mineral
	Acres			
1947	457	120	2,390	327
1948	200	680	1,829	713
1949	1,482	1,074	12,170	545
1950	4,687	4,360	19,047	3,070
1951	10,048	9,245	14,388	1,170
1952	5,208	2,806	11,219	297
1953	2,355	1,985	23,042	3,282
1954	2,306	3,038	10,215	2,161
1955	981	2,759	16,597	3,155
1956	230	3,362	12,632	1,407
	27,954	29,429	123,529	16,127

Source: Bureau of Land Management.

in grazing districts which are more valuable for the production of agricultural crops or for other purposes than for the production of native grasses and forage plants. Qualified persons may make application to enter any vacant, unreserved, and unappropriated public lands under applicable legislation, but until the lands have been classified and opened to entry, they are not subject to disposition, settlement, or occupation except under the mining laws.

That these withdrawals have not completely stopped the disposal of public lands is evident from Table 16 and Figure 15. The areas involved are, however, very small in relation to the total area of the unreserved public domain. Reclamation homesteads constituted the great bulk of the homesteads that went to patent during the last ten years. Only 3,900 acres were taken up under the original Homestead Act of 1862, only 390 acres under the Forest Homestead Act of 1906, and only 464 acres under the Stockraising Homestead Act of 1916. Mineral patents give very little idea of the area to which mineral claims were established.

Military Lands

Public lands have always been reserved from other uses when needed for military purposes, but the amounts so needed have increased strikingly in the last twenty years. Large purchases of land for military use have also been made. Comparable figures for different years are almost impossible to obtain, but such information as is available indicates that total holdings by the Department of Defense in the continental United States increased from 3.1 million acres in 1937 to 20.7 million acres in 1944, and to 27.6 million acres in 1956. In California, during this same period, reservations and withdrawals of public lands have approximated 1,800,000 acres for the Navy, have exceeded 600,000 for the Army, and have been less than 100,000 acres for the Air Force, or about 2,500,000 acres for the entire Department of Defense. Purchases have been only about half of this amount.

Indian Lands

What to do in the way of land for some 100,000 California Indians who, under the white man's law, had no right of ownership, and whose theoretical right of occupancy was largely ignored in practice, was a problem which Congress tried to meet by the appointment in 1850 of three commissioners to effect a just settlement with the Indians. The commissioners negotiated eighteen treaties with a considerable part of the Indian population under which the Indians relinquished their claims to land and in return were given the right to occupy certain areas specifically described and were also promised certain supplies and services. The treaties were vigorously opposed by the people, the press, and the legislature of the state, and on July 8, 1852, they were all rejected by the Senate of the United States.

This action left the Indians with little protection against the encroachments of miners and settlers. For years they were evicted, exploited, massacred, and driven from pillar to post. Bancroft remarks that "the California valley cannot grace her annals with a single Indian war bordering on respectability. It can boast, however, a hundred or two of as brutal butcherings, on the part of our honest miners and brave pioneers, as any area of equal extent in our republic."

Steadily decreasing numbers of Indians and steadily increasing areas of reservations, rancherias, and public domain set aside for their use by Congress, by Executive Order, and by purchase finally resulted in making some 600,000 acres available for occupancy and use by less than 10,000 Indians. The policy of making allotments of land to individual Indians was adopted in 1887 and rescinded in 1934. All Indians were made citizens of the United States in 1924, but those on reservations continued to be wards of the government.

In 1928 Congress authorized the State of California, in behalf of the Indians, to bring suit against the United States for its failure in 1852 to ratify the proposed treaties. In 1944 the Court of Claims made a net award to the Indians of $5,025,000, less $28,000 allowed the state for the expense incurred in conducting the litigation. In 1946 Congress set up an Indian Claims Commission to pass upon such further claims as Indians anywhere in the United States may have against the government.

Federal Acquisition and Exchange

Urban Land

Purchase of land needed for post offices, customs houses, offices, and other governmental activities has always been common practice. These purchases have been mostly in urban areas. In recent years the Department of Defense has also acquired large areas of urban land needed for the conduct of its various activities. In 1956 it held 85 per cent of the 1,350,538 acres of urban property in the United States owned by the Federal Government.

In California, urban federal holdings as of June 30, 1956, comprised 276,910 acres, most of which had been purchased. This area constituted a fifth of all federal urban property in the United States (Georgia came second with 252,146 acres), and represented an increase of nearly a third over the previous year. By way of comparison, it is interesting to note that federal ownership of rural property in the state decreased by 408,828 acres, or nearly 1 per cent, during the same time.

National Forests

Congress first authorized the acquisition of rural lands on any considerable scale with passage of the Weeks Act of March 1, 1911. This act, as amended by the Clarke-McNary Act of June 7, 1924, provides for the purchase by the government of land on the watersheds of navigable streams which is needed for the protection of the water supply or the production of timber. It marks an even more radical departure from the former policy of land disposal than did the act of 1891 which authorized the creation of forest reserves.

Although the original act was intended primarily for the establishment of national forests in the Southern Appalachians and the White Mountains, it contained no geographical limitation and has been used for the acquisition of forest lands in all parts of the country. Since 1936 the following purchases have been made in California:

UNIT	ACRES
Eldorado National Forest	9,474
Sequoia National Forest	22,242
Tahoe National Forest	84,514
Northern Redwood Purchase Unit	14,491
	130,721

Two redwood purchase units were established during the fiscal year 1936 in Del Norte and Mendocino Counties with a total area of 842,000 acres, which was later increased to 941,660 acres. To date, only 14,492 acres have been acquired (1 acre by gift) in the northern unit and none in the southern unit. Bills were introduced by Congresswoman Helen Gahagan Douglas in 1946 and 1949 to authorize the appropriation of $25,000,000 for the purchase of lands in Del Norte, Humboldt, and Mendocino Counties, with an estimated gross area of 2,385,000 acres. The acquired lands were to be known as the Franklin Delano Roosevelt Redwood Forest and were to include four memorial units to be administered by the National Park Service. The proposal received a favorable analysis by the Forset Service but was not reported out of committee in Congress.

Legislation passed in 1938 and 1940 authorized the use of receipts from the Angeles, Cleveland, San Bernardino, and Sequoia National Forests, when appropriated by Congress, for the purchase of lands within those forests. Purchases have been made under these authorizations as follows:

Unit	Acres
Angeles National Forest	1,382
Cleveland National Forest	6,091
San Bernardino National Forest	6,984
Sequoia National Forest	7,659
	22,116

No purchases from receipts have been made since 1953, although the authorizing legislation has not been repealed.

Interior Department Lands

Lands acquired by various units in the Department of the Interior which are not a part of the public domain were as follows up to June 30, 1956:

	Acres	Per cent
Geological Survey	7	*
Bureau of Indian Affairs[1]	1,387	*
Fish and Wildlife Service	30,008	8
National Park Service	97,702	27
Bureau of Reclamation	240,192	65
	369,296	100

* Less than 0.5 per cent.
[1] Does not include trust properties.

Lands acquired by the Bureau of Land Management by the exchange of public domain land are classified as "public domain," and are therefore not included in the above tabulation. Present public domain thus includes two classes of land – "original" public domain and "acquired" public domain.

Military Lands

According to an inventory prepared by the General Services Administration, acquisitions of land not a part of the public domain by the three departments in the Department of Defense totaled as follows up to June 30, 1956:

	ACRES	PER CENT
Army — military functions	407,812	32
Army — civil functions (Corps of Engineers)	41,162	3
Navy	462,125	37
Air Force	354,863	28
	1,265,962	100

Only 20 per cent of the total area under the jurisdiction of the Navy consists of acquired land, as compared with 40 per cent for the Army (military functions) and 82 per cent for the Air Force. Most of the acquisitions for military purposes, as well as the reservation of large areas of the public domain, have taken place within the last twenty years. They were obviously the result of World War II, the current "cold war," and the increased emphasis on air power and atomic weapons. California has been particularly affected by the need for military airfields, of which it has a larger area (834,682 acres) than any other state — 35 per cent of the total, with an additional 21 per cent in the adjacent state of Nevada.

Acquisition of land for military purposes has been offset in part since World War II by the cancellation of leases covering large areas of land, by the abandonment of reservations and withdrawals from the public domain, and by some sales of purchased land. The Army, for example, has released more than 450,000 acres in California, which has thus become available for use by private enterprise or by other public agencies; while acquisition has generally been limited to small sites required for anti-aircraft defense and for Army reserve training centers. The examination of lands suitable for disposal continues.

Other Agencies

Acquisition of land in California by all federal agencies outside of the Departments of Agriculture, Interior, and Defense has amounted to only 10,258 acres, or 0.5 per cent of the total. The combined holdings of these agencies, including public domain, comprise 49,039 acres, or 1.1 per cent of the entire federal ownership in California.

National Forest Exchanges

Acquisition and disposal of federal lands in California have been fairly extensive under the General Exchange Act of 1922. This act authorized the Secretary of Agriculture to exchange surveyed, nonmineral land or timber in national forests established from the public domain for privately owned or state land of equal value within national forests in the same state. In 1925 the provisions of the act were extended to apply also to lands acquired under the Weeks Act of 1911 or the Clarke-McNary Act of 1924.

The 1912 act forbidding the further creation or enlargement of national forests in California except by act of Congress does not prevent the acquisition of land within the exterior boundaries of existing national forests without action by Congress. Exchanges can, therefore, add to their net area. Furthermore, Congress in 1925 and 1938 authorized the addition to the Plumas, Eldorado, Stanislaus, Shasta, Tahoe, Modoc, Lassen, and Klamath National Forests of certain specified lands to be acquired by exchange or already in federal ownership.

Exchanges involving public-domain land or timber have been made in all of the national forests in California. Land so acquired, as in the case of the Bureau of Land Management, becomes a part of the public domain and is administered under the legislation applying to the federal property included in the exchange. The results of the approximately 430 exchanges that have been effected in California are summarized in Table 17.

Table 17. Summary of National-Forest Exchanges in California Involving Public-Domain Land or Timber.

	Federal acquisition		Federal disposal	
Area, acres	1,221,379		64,383	
Timber volume, M board feet	5,148,598		2,805,685	
Timber value	$7,419,206		$9,352,828	
Soil value	$4,161,062		$623,846	
Total value		$11,580,268		$9,976,674

Source: Forest Service.

The exchange program has resulted in a net addition to the area of national forests in California of 1,156,996 acres. This figure constitutes about 6 per cent of the total area administered by the Forest Service in California, as compared with a similar figure of less than 3 per cent for the entire United States. From another point of view, 23 per cent of the net area acquired by the government through the exchange process has been located in California.

The exchange program has been most active in the northern part of the state. This fact is illustrated by Table 18, which shows the national forests where the net area acquired by the government exceeds 50,000 acres.

Table 18. Net Area Acquired by Exchange in National Forests in California.

	Net area acquired			
National forest	Acres		Per cent of total	
Shasta	414,082		36	
Tahoe	146,328		13	
Modoc	118,861		10	
Plumas	87,849		8	
Stanislaus	83,790		7	
Eldorado	68,153		6	
Lassen	55,094		5	
Klamath	51,847		4	
		1,026,004		89
Others		130,992		11
Total		1,156,996		100

Source: Forest Service.

Siskiyou County shows by far the largest change from private to federal ownership as a result of the exchange program. The four national forests in southern California show a net gain through exchange of only 15,576 acres, or less than 0.5 per cent of their total area under federal administration.

The area added to national forests in California by exchanges involving acquired lands, as contrasted with public-domain land or timber, totals only 11,640 acres. Of this area, 65 per cent lies in the four southern forests.

Many more cases and much larger areas have been involved in the exchange of government timber for private land than in the exchange of land for land. This policy met with general approval during the depression days of the late 1920's and early 1930's, when carrying charges on private lands were high and profits were low or non-existent. Some owners complained that the government should never have permitted them to assume the "burden" of carrying large areas of old-growth timber, and a few even went so far as to say that the government should have retained title to all of the public domain not needed for agriculture or settlement.

PRESENT POLICY. With the return of prosperity and increased interest in the practice of forestry by private owners, these attitudes changed. The federal policy of exchanging stumpage for stumps came to be looked upon with less and less favor. Occasional charges were made that the Forest Service was using undue pressure to force private owners to trade on this basis. The changing situation led to a substantial modification of Forest Service policy with respect both to acquisitions and exchanges. The new policy was enunciated by the Chief of the Service in a letter of instructions dated July 2, 1953, from which the following are extracts:

"1. Until further study and consideration can be given this subject, all future land acquisition by purchase, and by exchange of national-forest timber for land, will meet at least one of the following requirements:

"(a) The land obtained by the Federal Government is to be used for research or for demonstration of forest management, and similar purposes. (This does not include acquisition of land for demonstration of national forest management, as in purchase units.)

"(b) The land is required for rights-of-way or other means of making public resources available for public use (e. g., timber-access roads and access to public hunting and fishing areas).

"(c) The land obtained requires national-forest status to prevent damage to adjoining national forest and private land, such as through excessive erosion or excessive fire hazard.

"(d) Small intermingled or adjacent tracts obtained to avoid excessive Federal expenditures for protection of adjoining national forest land and timber from theft and other trespass. (Ordinarily not in excess of 640 acres.)

" (e) Relatively small intermingled or adjacent tracts required to supplement the protection of special and specific recreational, community-watershed or similar public values.

" (f) Small administrative sites required for administration of Forest Service activities.

" (g) Small intermingled tracts the acquisition of which will permit economies in public services (e. g., where county governments are trying to avoid construction and maintenance of roads, schools, etc., for isolated settlers).

"2. In addition to the foregoing criteria, land-for-land exchanges will continue to be authorized to consolidate public and private holdings, to consolidate Federal and State holdings, to permit urban and industrial development, and to permit similar adjustments in ownership clearly in the public interest.

"3. These policies will not limit action otherwise authorized in relation to:

" (a) Transfer of land already in Federal ownership to national forest jurisdiction.

" (b) Acquisitions in harmony with specific congressional directives (e. g., the International Wilderness Area of the Superior National Forest, Minnesota).

"4. Until further notice, exchange of national forest timber for private land, in addition to meeting one or more of the criteria listed under (1), are to have the prior approval of this office.

"Exchange of national forest timber for land, especially "tripartite" exchanges, will be considered if this procedure is the only practical method of accomplishing an exchange which is definitely and obviously in the public interest . . .

"5. Prior approval by or notification of county officials is essential. The Weeks Law forest land purchase item in the F. Y. 1954 Appropriation Bill contains the proviso, 'that no part of this appropriation shall be used for the acquisition of any land without the approval of the local government concerned.' This necessitates advance affirmative action by the County Board or appropriate local governmental agency before 1954 Weeks Law land purchase cases are approved . . .

"Existing administrative restrictions provide that in each (2/20/22) exchange case where the value of the national forest land or stumpage is $5,000 or more, each County Board shall be given advance notice in writing of the proposal. In addition, any other exchange proposal which it is anticipated may be objected to by any local group, should be explained to and discussed in advance with the County Boards in which the land or timber is located.

"6. There may be special cases and exceptions to these policies which you may want to bring to our attention, such as:

" (a) Old cases in process for a considerable period of time, which do not fall into any of the above classes but the rejection of which would be grossly unfair to the proponent.

" (b) New cases which the Regional Forester feels clearly justify an exception to the above classification may be submitted — before making commitments — with suitable explanation . . ."

The new policy, which is still in effect, has materially curtailed exchanges of timber for land. In California, only one such exchange has been effected. It involved 9,650 acres of land owned by the Clover Valley Lumber Company, with which a precutting agreement had been effected prior to the enunciation of the change in policy.

Future exchange activities, in California as elsewhere throughout the country, will be facilitated by an appropriation of $165,000 made by Congress in 1957 to help cover the cost of administration, for which no specific funds had previously been available.

State Land Policy

When California entered the Union in 1850, the entire land area of the state except for that in valid Spanish and Mexican grants became a part of the public domain and therefore subject to the control of the federal government. Subsequent grants to the state, most of which were made between 1850 and 1862, totaled 8,824,000 acres. This area (nearly 9 per cent of the land area of the state) is almost the same as that included in confirmed private grants (8,850,000 acres).

LAND SALES

From the beginning California followed the policy of selling the land granted to it by the Federal Government as rapidly as title could be obtained and purchasers found. That the policy was successful in bringing about the prompt transfer of large areas from state to private ownership is indicated by the following comments by Bancroft:

"In relation to the several grants of land, in 1869, all of the 500,000 acre grant [for permanent improvements] had been sold, excepting 10,000 acres, represented by outstanding school warrants. All of the seventy-two sections [for a 'seminary of learning'], and ten sections [for public buildings], had been sold. Very little swamp land remained, and only the least desirable of the surveyed common-school lands. The agricultural-college grant [of 150,000 acres] was converted to the use of the state university by an act of the legislature of 1868. By an act of the same body, provision was made for the sale of all lands of every kind owned by the state, or in which she had any interest, the maximum price being fixed at $1.25 per acre.

"Thus in eighteen years the state had disposed of her vast landed possessions, making no attempt to increase their value by improvements, nor leaving any to rise in value along with the development of the country about them. The money realized was appropriated in the manner heretofore shown, a large part of it having been dissipated by the extravagance of the early legislatures, or fraudulently disposed of by political tricksters in collusion with dishonest officials. The funds created have been borrowed by the state, the interest on the money obtained by sacrificing the state's lands taking the place of the income which should have been derived from a judicious care of them."

Administration subsequently improved, but the policy of land disposal continued. Of the original federal grants, little is now left except about 850,000 acres of school lands, of which some 150,000 acres are unsurveyed. Sales and leases of schools lands have built up the present school trust fund with total resources as of June 30, 1957, of about 22 million dollars, the interest on which is used under Article IX, Section 4 of the Constitution for the support of the common schools of the state.

Park Program

The first state park in the nation was established in California in 1864, when Congress granted the Yosemite Valley and the Mariposa Big Tree Grove to the State "to be held forever for public use, resort, and recreation." After creation of the Yosemite National Park in 1890 jurisdictional difficulties arose, and in 1906 Congress accepted recession of these areas by the California State Legislature to the Federal Government.

In 1902 the first permanent state park was acquired by purchase in Santa Cruz County. Known first as the California State Redwood Park, it is now the Big Basin Redwoods State Park. The next important step, a direct result of the establishment of the Save-the-Redwoods League in 1918, was the acquisition in 1921 of the first groves of what is now the Humboldt Redwoods State Park in Humboldt County. The establishment of both these coast redwood parks stemmed largely from public reaction to the destructive logging practices which prevailed at that time. About a dozen other widely scattered park properties had also been acquired by the state during these years.

Acquisition of land for park purposes assumed greatly increased importance in 1927, when the legislature created a State Park Commission; established a Division of Parks (changed in 1945 to the Division of Beaches and Parks) in the Department of Natural Resources; authorized a bond issue of $6,000,000 for the acquisition of state parks, to be matched dollar for dollar from sources other than the state in cash or land; and authorized a state park site survey, which was conducted by Frederick Law Olmsted. Since the state had previously reserved no land that might be suitable for park purposes, acquisition had to be effected by gift or purchase. The program has been so well supported that in thirty years the state's system of beaches and parks has grown from a few thousand acres to more than 500,000 acres.

The bond money authorized by the legislature in 1927 and approved by the people in 1928 was exhausted in 1940, and during World War II the park acquisition program was at a standstill. Because of the rapidly growing need for park areas and recreational facilities, the legislature in 1938 had allocated for park acquisition and development, subject to appropriation, 30 per cent of the royalties derived from state-owned tidelands. In 1941 this amount was increased to 70 per cent, of which one-third was allocated to a State Beach Fund and two-thirds to a State Park Fund. Then in 1945 the legislature, anticipating greater postwar activity, appropriated $15,000,000 from the general fund, subject to matching like the 1928 bond money. One-third of this amount was for the acquisition of interior parks and two-thirds for the acquisition of beaches, subject to completion by the coastal counties of master acquisition plans and their approval by the state.

The decision by the United States Supreme Court in 1947 that the Federal Government has paramount interest in the tidelands resulted in the impoundment of the oil royalties until after passage by Congress of the act of May 2, 1953, confirming the titles of the states to lands beneath navigable waters within state boundaries and to the natural resources within such lands and waters. Meanwhile the state park system was operated by loans from the general fund, which were paid back upon release of the oil royalties.

In anticipation of the return of the impounded funds, the State Park Commission in 1952 approved preparation of a 5-year master plan for park acquisition and development, which was later revised and extended. In 1955 the legislature appropriated $17,500,000 of oil royalty funds for specific new park projects, in addition to $6,000,000 for operation, maintenance, and construction in the already large park system. The Governor, however, vetoed the acquisition appropriation, without prejudice, in order to make possible fuller consideration of certain policies involved. For the 1956 budget session of the legislature the 5-year master plan was again revised, and special appropriations for park acquisition of more than $32,000,000 were included in the regular budget of the Division of Beaches and

Parks. At the same time, the legislature placed a ceiling of $7,000,000 a year on the accrual of 70 per cent of the oil royalties to the park and beach funds.

That portion of the 1945 appropriation designated for beach acquisition was almost totally committed by 1955; but the allocation for interior parks, owing to lack of matching money, was not, and the legislature caused the uncommitted funds to revert. In 1956 the matching principle was definitely abandoned in favor of outright state appropriations, although the Save-the-Redwoods League still obtains contributions and gifts to assist in the establishment of state parks.

Additional park acquisition funds in the amount of $6,585,000, plus nearly $9,000,000 for construction, were appropriated by the 1957 legislature, which also raised the one-year-old ceiling on annual oil royalty accrual to $12,000,000. But even the very substantial appropriations of recent years have not been able to meet fully the rapidly expanding demand for recreational facilities.

As in the case of national parks and monuments, the physical resources of the state park system are in general not available for commercial utilization. Like the federal areas, state parks may be regarded as limited multiple-use properties providing watershed protection, game reserves, and natural areas for scientific observation, in addition to recreation and the preservation of natural scenic values. That the program in general meets with popular approval is indicated by the phenomenal support it has received.

Wildlife Program

In the field of wildlife conservation, California's efforts for many years were concentrated on the passage of legislation designed to control hunting and fishing. In 1870, however, the legislature established the first wildlife refuge in the United States at Lake Merritt, now supported and maintained by the City of Oakland. A few years later, in 1878, an area on Mt. Diablo for three miles about the summit was made a refuge.

Game preserves, for which the State was authorized to accept land from private owners, were legalized in 1907, and in 1915 the State Constitution was amended to provide for game refuges. The turning point in the acquisition of land for game-management purposes came some fifteen years later, when the following refuges were purchased at a cost of nearly $400,000:

Refuge	County	Year	Acres
Los Banos	Merced	1929	3,000
Gray Lodge	Butte	1931	2,542
Finney-Ramer Unit of Imperial Refuge	Imperial	1931 - 1932	2,064
Suisun	Solano	1932	1,887

Still more substantial progress in the establishment of refuges, waterfowl areas, and deer ranges came in the 1940's after the Pittman — Robertson Act of 1937 made federal funds available, among other things, for the purchase of refuges. The entire wildlife program was further strengthened greatly by passage of the California Wildlife Conservation Act of 1947, which reads in part as follows:

"It is hereby declared that the preservation, protection and restoration of wildlife within the State of California is an inseparable part of providing adequate recreation for our people in the interest of public welfare; and it is further declared to be the policy of the state to acquire and restore to the highest possible level, and maintain in a state of high productivity those areas that can be most successfully used to sustain wildlife and which will provide adequate and suitable recreation. To carry out the aforesaid purposes, a single and coordinated program for the acquisition of land and facilities suitable for recreational purposes and adaptable for conservation, propagation and utilization of the fish and game resources of the state is hereby established . . .

". . . [the Wildlife Conservation Board] shall determine what areas, lands or rights in lands or waters should be acquired by the state in order to effectuate a coordinated and balanced program resulting in the maximum revival of wildlife in the state and in the maximum recreational advantages to the people of the state. The board shall authorize the acquisition of such lands, rights in land, water, or water rights as may be necessary to carry out the purposes of this act."

In the same year the legislature created the Wildlife Restoration Fund to carry out the purposes of this act. Subsequent appropriations have provided more than $14,000,000 for the fund.

Under these acts, and with the help of federal grants-in-aid, the area of wildlife refuges has increased to more than 100,000 acres. Further recognition of the importance of wildlife was intended by the Fish and Game Reorganization Act of 1951, which changed the Division of Fish and Game in the Department of Natural Resources into a separate Department of Fish and Game.

STATE FOREST PROGRAM

Although California created a State Board of Forestry as early as 1885, it took no steps until recently to establish state forests either by the reservation of lands already in state ownership or by the acquisition of lands that had passed into private ownership. In 1945 the California Forestry Study Committee created by the legislature in 1943 reported that "California is the only western forest state without state forests . . . We do have three small tracts acquired by gift and purchase but they are not of state forest calibre. One is an administrative site; one is useful primarily as a recreation site and the third is very remote and inaccessible."

The three tracts referred to were as follows:

Mount Zion State Forest, Amador County, 164 acres, acquired by gift and purchase in 1930 and 1932.

Las Posadas State Forest, Napa County, 796 acres, acquired by gift in 1930.

Ellen Pickett State Forest, Trinity County, 160 acres, acquired by gift in 1940.

Another tract of 9,013 acres in Shasta County, known as the Latour Forest, was protected by the State Division of Forestry but was not regarded as a state forest since it was under the control of the State Lands Commission. It was obtained by the exchange of scattered school lands within national forest boundaries for a compact tract of federal land in the Lassen National Forest.

Lack of progress was not due to lack of interest on the part of the state's own forestry officials. In 1910 the State Forester in Vol. 4 of the Transactions of the Commonwealth Club of California stated: "The advantage of having the state acquire cutover lands would lie, first, in the certainty that a commercial forest would again be produced on the area; second, the present owners would be relieved of the burden of holding the land through the long period that it would be unprofitable." In 1919 the State Board of Forestry recommended "acquirement of logged-off areas, both in the redwoods and pine forests, as a nucleus for state forests for future timber supply." Another board repeated the recommendation in 1923, but took no steps to put in into effect.

In 1941 the State Board of Forestry was requested to renew its efforts to obtain the establishment of state forests and the next year delegated a staff member to report on possible purchase areas. His report was followed by the introduction in the legislature of bills authorizing the acquisition of state forests. These failed of approval but led to the creation in 1943 of the California Forestry Study Committee.

Forestry Study Committee and 1945 Legislation

That committee made a thorough study of the situation, and in 1945 submitted a comprehensive report in which the subject of state forests received prominent attention. The committee concluded that "several million acres of forest lands [are] now idle or largely so because of poor restocking," and that "it is not likely for a long time that many private owners will undertake their reforestation. Some of the lands may be sold for other and less permanent uses and thus be entirely lost to timber production. Others will be abandoned for taxes. Consequently if the State must have the timber these lands should grow, it will have to acquire the lands and reforest them itself . . .

"In area, State forest units should be as large as possible to reduce the per-acre costs of administration and protection. Blocks of 10,000 to 50,000 acres are preferable. Smaller areas not too distant from the main blocks should not be overlooked, where road systems permit quick and easy access. Areas as small as 40's or quarter sections, if near ranger stations would be large enough for local demonstration areas. Inasmuch as there is much private cutover land inside the National forests, consideration should be given it as well as that outside. Forest Service officials assure us that they will not oppose such acquisitions. Eventually such lands may be traded in such a way that both the Forest Service and the State could block out boundaries of manageable units.

"A total of 1,000,000 acres should be the present goal. Initial purchases and until an administrative and technical force can be organized should total about 200,000 acres." Further comment on the areas suggested for purchase is contained elsewhere in the report: "By purchasing 200,000 acres of these cutover lands most promising of success, and reforesting them, valuable experience will be gained which should be effective in interesting private owners or investors in reforesting other land. However if private owners do not become interested in a long-term investment such as reforestation involves, the State may have to acquire considerably more than 200,000 acres, perhaps beyond 1,000,000 acres."

The committee also emphasized the need for "demonstration areas," which "should meet the same general requirements as set forth for State forests except that they may be smaller, situated so that they will serve as an easily reached local demonstration for private owners and where they can be administered and protected readily by local State rangers. There is great need for such areas for trying out and demonstrating different methods of reforestation and forest management; determining the adaptability of exotic species for commercial timber, especially hardwoods now not well represented naturally, and similar work. Demonstration areas need not be large. For a new plantation, 20 acres may suffice although 40 to 160 acres is preferable."

The committee called attention to the fact that legislation authorizing the acquisition of land for state forests had been enacted in 1937 to enable the state to take advantage of the federal Fulmer Act of 1935, which had never become operative. Repeal of these particular sections of the Public Resources Code did not seem necessary to the committee, but it did feel that "a new article should be added to the code providing solely for State acquisition and management and for declaring the standards to be followed in purchases."

The committee's efforts bore fruit in passage of the act of May 10, 1945, providing for the acquisition and management of state forests. The act declared it "to be the policy of the State to acquire by purchase, exchange, lease or grant (1) such cutoverlands, the reforestation of which is not assured under private ownership, to reforest such lands during periods of unemployment and at other times, and (2) virgin and other timber lands deemed suitable by the State Board of Forestry for use as areas for the demonstration, protection and management of cutting and logging practices designed to promote reforestation; and to protect and manage such lands to the end that they will produce as nearly as possible their maximum yield of useful forest products on a basis of continuous production."

Acquisition of forest land is to be effected only upon approval by a State Forest Purchase Committee composed of the Governor, the Director of Finance, the Director of Natural Resources, and the Chairman of the State Board of Forestry, and upon recommendation of the board of supervisors of the county in which the land is situated. Rules and regulations for the administration of state forests, prepared by the State Forester and approved by the board, "shall be in conformity with forest management practices designed to promote continuous forest production with due regard to the preservation of soil, watershed, scenic, wildlife and recreational values. The sale of timber and other forest products is limited to raw materials only."

"State owned lands classified by the State Forester and approved by the State Board of Forestry as not suited to the growing of forest products, or necessary to the management of the forest, shall be sold according to State laws . . . To each county in which lands acquired for State forest purposes are situated, an amount equivalent to taxes levied by the county on similar land similarly situated in the county shall be paid the county . . . Tax-deeded lands classified as forest lands . . . may be acquired for State forest purposes through the usual procedure governing the sale of tax-deeded lands."

The legislature in 1945 made specific appropriations of $100,000 for the purchase of the Latour Forest of 9,013 acres in Shasta County, and of $600,000 for the purchase of the Mountain Home Tract of 4,560 acres in Tulare County. It directed that the Mountain Home Tract "shall be preserved as nearly as possible in virgin state, and shall be devoted to multiple public use for hunting, fishing and recreation," and that its area shall not be reduced below 4,000 acres. A blanket appropriation of $2,000,000 for the purchase of state forests was made in 1946.

Aside from these two tracts, the only purchases have been as follows:

Boggs Mountain State Forest, Lake County, 3,433 acres, 1949;
Jackson State Forest, Mendocino County, 52,042 acres, 1947-1953.

No further appropriations have been made by the legislature, and no further purchases appear to be contemplated at this time.

Mineral Lands

In 1921 the legislature decided to retain title to the mineral resources in state-owned lands. It consequently reserved from sale except upon a rental and royalty basis all coal, oil, oil shale, gas, phosphate, sodium, and other mineral deposits on lands belonging to the state other than tax-deeded lands. Specific provision was made for the prospecting and leasing of mineral lands, including reservation to the state of the right to sell, lease, or otherwise dispose of the surface of the lands covered by mineral leases so far as use of the surface is not necessary in extracting mineral deposits.

In 1938 the State Lands Act, which subsequently became Division 6 of the Public Resources Code, revised and codified existing legislation relating to state lands, including mineral lands. In addition to again declaring that all mineral deposits "are reserved from sale except upon a rental and royalty basis," it provided that purchasers of any lands belonging to the state acquire no title, right, or interest to any mineral deposits therein.

The 1938 act also created the State Lands Commission consisting of the State Controller, the Lieutenant Governor, and the Director of Finance. One of the many responsibilities assigned to the commission was authority to issue leases for the utilization of minerals on state-owned lands. Receipts were made available to cover costs of administration and to reimburse the school fund for leases involving school lands. Of the remaining balance, 30 per cent was transferred to the State Park Maintenance and Acquisition Fund created by the act. In 1941 this amount was increased to 70 per cent.

That the production of oil and gas may sometimes jeopardize scenic and recreational values was recognized in two acts passed in 1955. One act authorized the State Lands Commission to refuse to grant permits for the erection on tidelands or submerged lands of any structure that might interfere with the recreational use of such lands. The other prohibited the lease for the production of oil and gas from state-owned tide and submerged lands in certain areas in Los Angeles County, Santa Barbara County, and San Luis Obispo County.

Agricultural Colonization

California's only venture into the field of agricultural land ownership was motivated by its desire to assist in the settlement of agricultural lands. In 1918 and 1919 land was purchased for the establishment of colonies at Durham in Butte County and at Delhi in Merced County. The project was plagued by one difficulty after another, and was abandoned in 1931 at an estimated loss to the state in excess of $2,500,000. The Division of Land Settlement in the State Department of Agriculture, in its final report on the project, summarized its conclusions as follows:

"There seems to be good reason to conclude that had the engineering and administrative features been perfectly accomplished and had no serious depression developed or other factors contributing toward failure intervened the principle involved of government paternalism, with its extreme tendency to destroy individual effort and initiative and in many instances to break down the very self-respect of the subject of its beneficence, would, in itself, have been sufficient to bring about ultimate failure of the venture as a whole . . .

"It cannot be gainsaid that there was a serious land colonization problem facing the State at the time the State land settlements were started, and that there is still a definite service to be performed by the State government along colonization lines, but that service apparently can best be carried out through rigid State regulation of those private agencies seeking to colonize the lands of the State for profit, as the demand for settlement develops and conditions affecting agricultural activity warrant."

Summary

In summary, the state's basic policy has been one of land disposal. So rapid was the process that by the beginning of the present century, when the nation was beginning to think in terms of public-land reservation, California's holdings were reduced to a relatively small area of scattered and largely unsurveyed school sections. Consequently the system of parks and wildlife refuges, in which it has become increasingly interested, has had to be acquired almost entirely by purchase and at considerable expense. Interest in state forests was a later development and has resulted in hardly more than a token acquisition for that purpose. Mineral lands continue to be sold, but title to the minerals themselves since 1921 has been retained by the state. No lands have been reserved or acquired primarily for range management.

Private Land Policy

Size of Holdings

Somewhat more than half of the total land area of California has passed from public to private ownership as a result of Spanish and Mexican land grants, federal grants and sales, and state sales. The Spanish and Mexican grants were often of large size and included predominantly agricultural and grazing land. Breaking up of the large grants resulted chiefly from the economic pressure to which owners were subject during the period when they were forced to prove the validity of their claims, from the gradually changing emphasis in land use from stockraising to cultivation, and from the multiplication of heirs. Their disappearance has, however, been far from complete. On the basis of information furnished by county assessors, Dr. Frank Adams of the University of California reported in 1944 that 20 of the original grants were still intact, that 12 grants were held to the extent of two-thirds or more of their extent in one ownership, and that 6 grants were held to the extent of one-third to two-thirds of their extent in a single ownership.

In the early years of statehood large estates were also built up by other means, among which manipulation of the federal and state land laws played a prominent part. One of the best known "land barons" of those days was Henry Miller, who came to California in 1850 as a penniless immigrant from Germany. With his partner, Charles Lux, he is credited with having acquired 1,000,000 acres. A holding of similar size is attributed to William S. Chapman, one of the most notorious and powerful speculators of the period. Holdings in excess of 100,000 acres were not uncommon.

Farms and Ranches

These enormous estates included, for the most part, land suitable primarily for the grazing of livestock or the production of harvested crops. In many cases they have been broken up into smaller farms and ranches as population has swelled, but large holdings are still common. Today California has some of the smallest and some of the largest farms in the United States. Bureau of the Census figures for 1954 show that 34,138 farms under 10 acres in size included 28 per cent of the total number of farms but less than 1 per cent of the total area in farms; while 6,248 farms 1,000 acres or more in size included only 5 per cent of the total number of farms but 74 per cent of the total area in farms. The large number of small farms results from the combination of irrigation and a favorable climate which make intensive cultivation of a small area a profitable enterprise.

Many of the large farms are really ranches which were built up when the state's economy was primarily a pastoral one. Although grazing on the open range in private ownership will doubtless continue to be an important activity, the present tendency on the part of both cattlemen and sheepmen is to rely more and more heavily on improved and irrigated pasture to supply the bulk of the feed for their livestock. With cultivated crops, two opposite tendencies exist. Large farms are being broken up to make room for the small farmer with relatively little capital, and at the same time they are being built up because of the advantage they offer in the use of mechanized equipment and in the pumping of water from ever-deepening wells.

Forest Lands

Large private holdings of forest land by private owners arose chiefly from railroad grants, from manipulation of federal homestead, preemption, and timber and stone legislation, and from sales of state school lands. Grants to railroads totaled 11,587,732 acres, not including approximately 1,750,000 acres released to the government under the Railroad Transportation Act of 1940. A total of 9,410,534 acres was sold by the grantees to other owners. All or part of the holdings of five of the present nineteen large ownerships of 50,000 acres or more of forest land resulted from these sales. The residual, single owner of the railroad grants still has 2,175,000 acres, of which 464,000 acres may be classified as commercial forest land.

No legislation providing for the acquisition of timberlands as such was passed by Congress until 1878, when the Timber and Stone Act permitted the purchase of not more than 160 acres per person in the Pacific Coast states. Under this limitation holdings of sufficient size to appeal to the larger operators could be built up only through evading the law by the use of dummy entrymen and other methods, including perversion of the preemption and homestead laws. These practices were gradually stopped by government prosecutions, particularly in the early 1900's, with a consequent slowing down in the consolidation of large holdings. Enforcement of the law has sometimes been characterized as unfortunate from the conservation viewpoint, since it interfered with the building up of properties large enough to permit a logical pattern of logging and to make close utilization and sustained-yield management practicable.

A temporary reversal of the trend toward the building up of larger ownerships by processing companies occurred during the depression years. A few companies were forced to sell their properties to obtain ready cash. Others, in the vicinity of national forests, traded cutover lands for stumpage. This "stumps for stumpage" policy and other forms of land exchange resulted in a net increase in national forest area of about a million acres between 1922 and 1956, but mainly during the depression years of the late twenties and the thirties. Both large and small owners were involved.

Current Trends

At present there is again a definite trend toward enlargement of private holdings in forest lands. Nine of the nineteen large ownerships have expressed at least a desire to enlarge. All of the remaining ten large owners intend to maintain their present size except for involuntary losses to highways, parks, and reservoirs. One or two are prevented from any large-scale acquisition because their lands are contiguous to other large ownerships with the same objective. An interesting development of the last few years has been the merger of already sizeable companies or the absorption of one by another.

Returns from the medium-sized owners (with holdings of 5,000 to 49,999 acres) sampled in this study indicate that somewhat more than half of them are interested in enlargement. Only 20 per cent of the remainder did not commit themselves to a definite policy of at least retaining their present size.

Current studies at the School of Forestry of the University of California indicate that, for Mendocino County, ownerships of less than 5,000 acres are trending in two directions—consolidation with larger ownerships and division into a larger number of smaller ownerships. Presumably an important factor in this development is the character and location of the particular property. If it is primarily useful for forestry purposes, the trend will probably be toward consolidation with larger ownerships. If it has considerable value for such use as a summer home site, the trend will undoubtedly be toward smaller ownerships. A striking feature of this size class is the more rapid turnover in ownership than occurs in the medium and large size classes. In other words, there is much less stability of ownership among the smaller properties.

The consolidation of timberlands into larger ownerships will undoubtedly continue as a natural concomitant of the trend toward fiberization of wood and the desire of the processors to have integrated production. The capital required for this type of production makes it almost imperative for the processor to safeguard his investment by having control over a large part of his required raw materials. Therefore there will be increasing competition among the larger processors for available smaller ownerships.

A highly significant recent development in the policy of private owners is their increasing adoption of improved methods of forest management. During the 1920's there was considerable interest in better management in the redwood region, and at about the same time at least one company began less destructive logging practices in the pine region. Some revival of interest followed the depression of the early 1930's and the move to establish rules of forest practice under Article X of the Lumber Code. The first serious step toward really intensive management, however, came in the early 1940's, and for several years the pioneer in this direction found few followers. More recently, economic forces and improved technologies have resulted in more rapid progress.

In 1945 the chairman of the California Forestry Study Committee stated: "We found that very little of the cutover lands are being reforested. Much of the best timber growing land is idle and covered with brush. In some areas nature has done a good job reforesting but more by chance than by assistance by man . . . The committee recommends that where private owners of timberlands are unable or unwilling to reforest their cutover lands that the State should acquire them and bring them back into production . . . If the State fails to acquire State forests the inevitable results will be complete ownership by the Federal Government of all forest lands in the State."

This situation led in the same year to the passage of legislation authorizing the acquisition of state forests and providing some control over cutting practices on private lands. Shortly thereafter the interest of private owners in forest management became intensified in both the redwood and the pine regions, and started the present rather widespread movement toward the adoption of long-range plans and improved cutting practices.

PART III

PRESENT PATTERN OF LAND OWNERSHIP

The present pattern of land ownership in California is the result of a continuing evolution that has involved varying policies and innumerable transfers of title among federal, state, other public, and private owners.

Over-all View

In less than a century the federal government reduced its holdings from 100 per cent to about 45 per cent of the total area of the state. The reduction was accomplished by confirmation of claims originating from Spanish and Mexican land grants, by grants to the state, and by grants and sales to individuals and corporations. Beginning in the 1890's, the policy of disposal was gradually succeeded by a policy of extensive reservation and withdrawal of public lands from private entry, and still later by a policy of limited acquisition, chiefly for national forests and military reservations. As a net result of these developments, federal ownership now comprises about 47 per cent of the land area of the state.

Grants to the state totaled nearly 9 per cent of its area, of which about two-thirds was for the support of common schools and about one-fourth for the reclamation of swamplands. The state proceeded to dispose of most of these grants to private owners except for about 850,000 acres of school lands, or less than 1 per cent of the area of the state. As in the case of the Federal Government, numerous acquisitions have been made in recent years, primarily for public works and parks, with the result that the state now owns somewhat more than 2 million acres, or about 2 per cent of its land area.

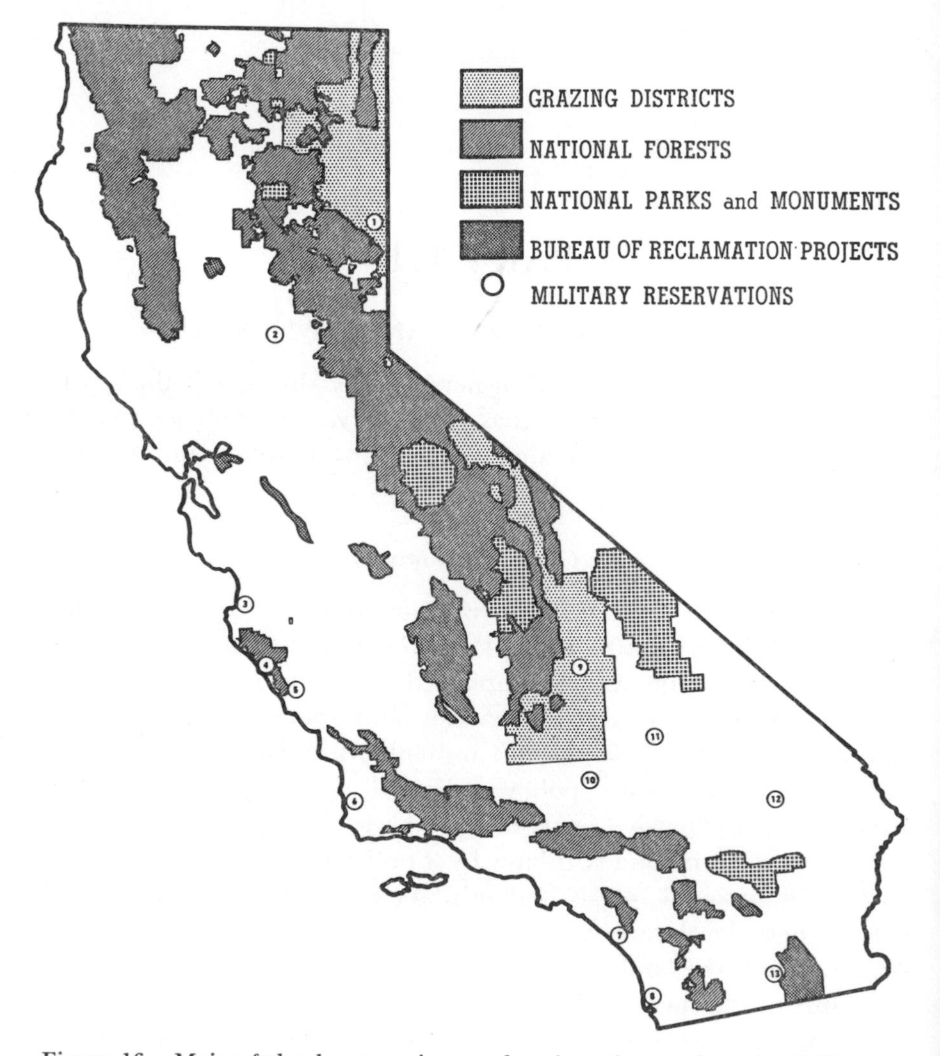

Figure 16. Major federal reservations and reclamation projects in California, based on a map of the United States published by the Bureau of Land Management, 1953. Not shown are wildlife refuges, Indian reservations, military reservations of less than 20,000 acres, and unreserved public domain outside of grazing districts. Boundaries of the military reservations shown are not available; for their area, see tabulation in the text (p. 87). Courtesy Bureau of Land Management, U.S.D.I.

County, municipal, and other local public ownership embraces many parcels of land, but their aggregate area is probably under 1 per cent of the total area of the state. Approximately 50 per cent of California lands are therefore in the hands of a large number of private owners. Urban, suburban, and agricultural lands are nearly all in private ownership; deserts and mountain tops are mostly in public ownership; while forest and range lands are more evenly divided between the two classes of owners.

Federal Lands

Federal ownership of land in California as of June 30, 1956, excluding trust properties, is summarized in Table 19. Most of the federal holdings (99.4 per cent) are rural in character, with the great bulk of the urban holdings under the jurisdiction of the Department of Defense. With respect to origin of title, 96 per cent of the federal holdings are classed as public domain — 98 per cent each for Interior and Agriculture, 67 per cent for Defense, and 79 per cent for other departments and agencies.

Table 19. Federal Ownership in California by Departments, Exclusive of Trust Properties, as of June 30, 1956.

Department	Acres	Per cent of federal holdings	Per cent of state
Department of the Interior	23,011,944	49	23
Department of Agriculture	19,977,415	42	20
Department of Defense	3,816,786	9	4
Other departments and agencies	49,039	*	*
Total	46,855,184	100	47

* Less than 1 per cent.

Source: Inventory prepared by General Services Administration.

Major federal reservations (including grazing districts) and reclamation projects as of 1953 are shown in Figure 16. The uses to which federal holdings were put as of June 30, 1956, are shown in Table 20 and Figure 17. Of the total area in federal ownership, 80 per cent was used for forests, wildlife, and grazing, and an additional

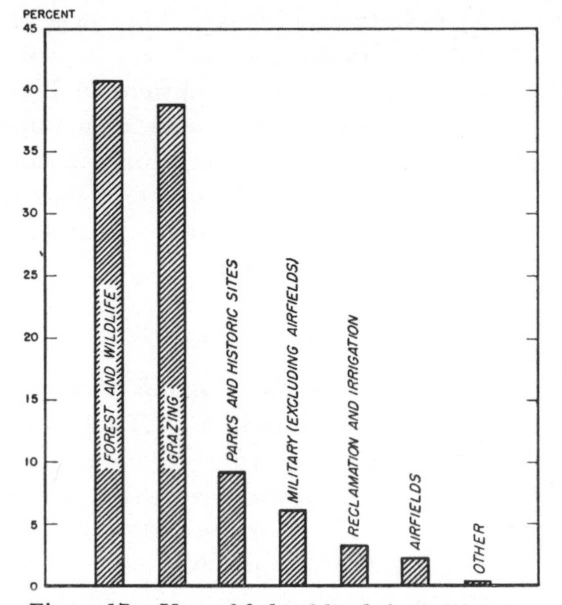

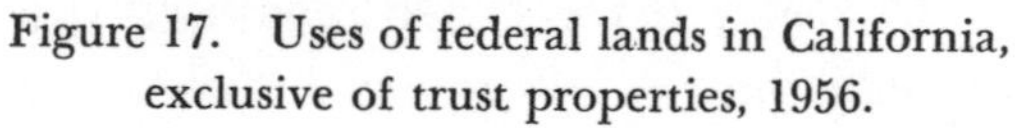

Figure 17. Uses of federal lands in California, exclusive of trust properties, 1956.

Table 20. Uses of Federal Lands in California, Exclusive of Trust Properties, as of June 30, 1956.

Use	Acres	Per cent of federal holdings	Per cent of state
Forests and wildlife	19,142,305	41	19
Grazing	18,141,498	39	18
Parks and historic sites	4.074,856	9	4
Military (excluding airfields)	2,831,793	6	3
Reclamation and irrigation	1,350,765	3	1
Airfields	834,682	2	1
Storage	85,640	*	*
Flood control and navigation	69,497	*	*
Industrial	45,242	*	*
Power development and distribution	19,903	*	*
Other	259,003	**	*
Total	46,855,184	100	47

* Less than 0.3 per cent.

** Less than 0.6 per cent.

Source: Inventory prepared by General Services Administration.

9 per cent for parks and historic sites. From another point of view, the area devoted to these uses, which are typical of "wildlands," constitutes 41 per cent of the total area of the state.

The distribution of federal lands by agencies and counties, as reported by the California Senate Interim Committee on Public Lands in January, 1955, is shown in Table 21 and Figure 18. In no county did the area used by other federal agencies than the three listed reach 0.5 per cent of the total area of the county. The total area in federal ownership has increased somewhat since these figures were compiled, particularly in the Department of Defense, but the changes would not alter materially the percentages of ownership by counties.

Table 21. Distribution of Federal Holdings in California by Departments and Counties.

County	Interior[1]	Agriculture	Defense	Total
	Per cent of County Area			
Alameda	*	*	2	2
Alpine	12	88	0	100[2]
Amador	2	18	0	20
Butte	2	12	0	14
Calaveras	5	14	0	19
Colusa	6	9	0	15
Contra Costa	*	0	2	2
Del Norte	1	67	*	68
El Dorado	4	42	*	46
Fresno	13	26	*	39
Glenn	3	22	0	25
Humboldt	5	14	*	19
Imperial	63	*	2	65
Inyo	77	12	7	96
Kern	16	7	3	26
Kings	1	0	0	1
Lake	14	30	0	44
Lassen	25	21	1	47
Los Angeles	2	25	1	28
Madera	8	29	0	37
Marin	*	0	1	1
Mariposa	32	16	0	48
Mendocino	7	7	0	14

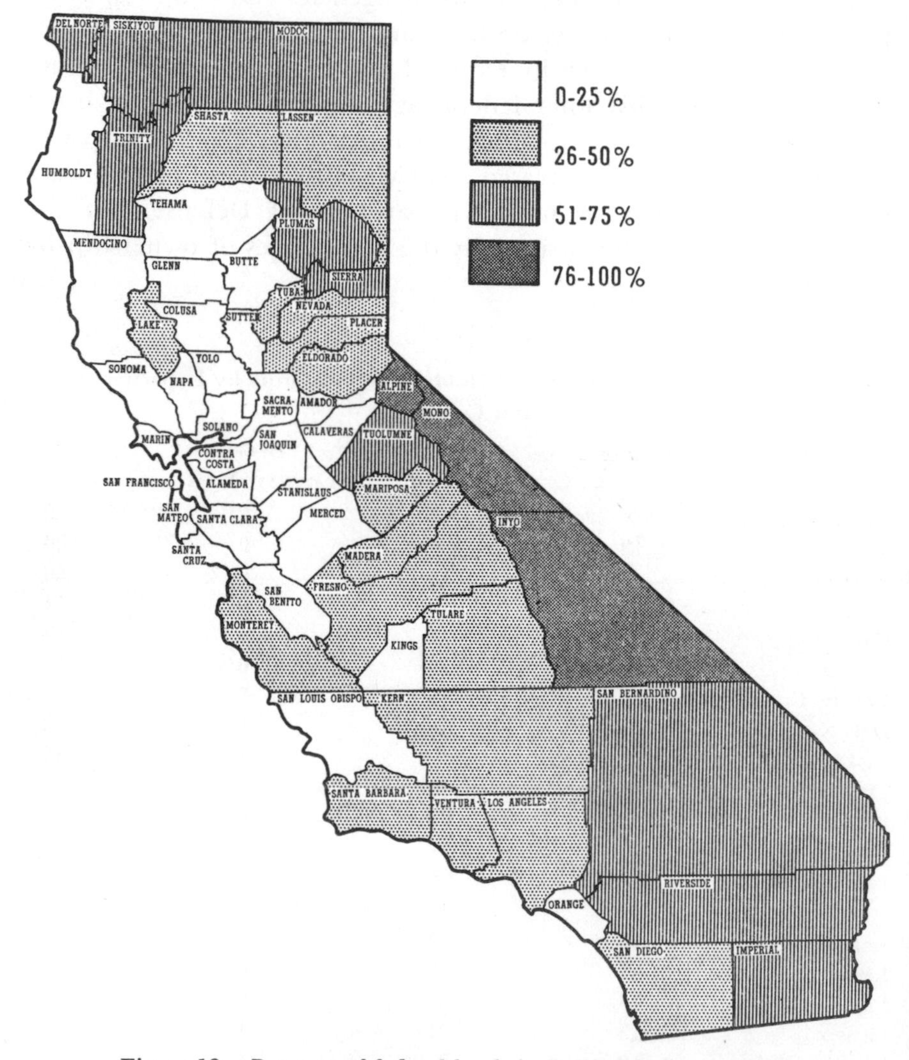

Figure 18. Per cent of federal lands in California by counties.

County	Interior[1]	Agriculture	Defense	Total
	Per cent of County Area			
Merced	1	0	*	1
Modoc	15	52	0	67
Mono	21	59	0	80
Monterey	4	15	13	32
Napa	13	*	*	13
Nevada	3	23	14	40
Orange	*	9	2	12
Placer	3	29	*	32
Plumas	3	68	0	71
Riverside	46	5	2	53
Sacramento	*	0	2	2
San Benito	14	0	0	14
San Bernardino	64	3	7	74
San Diego	14	10	7	31
San Francisco	*	0	12	12
San Joaquin	*	*	*	1
San Luis Obispo	6	9	1	16
San Mateo	*	0	*	*
Santa Barbara	2	35	6	43
Santa Clara	3	*	*	3
Santa Cruz	*	0	0	*
Shasta	12	26	*	38
Sierra	1	59	0	60
Siskiyou	5	57	0	62
Solano	*	0	2	2
Sonoma	2	0	*	2
Stanislaus	2	0	*	2
Sutter	*	0	0	*
Tehama	3	20	0	23
Trinity	4	67	0	71
Tulare	21	29	0	50
Tuolumne	32	43	0	75
Ventura	*	47	1	48
Yolo	5	0	0	5
Yuba	1	12	16	29
	24	20	2	46

* Less than 0.5 per cent.

[1] Including Indian lands.

[2] The committee's report shows the combined areas of federal and state lands in Alpine County to be greater than the entire area of the county. It comments that "the reclamation figure is probably too high."

Source: Senate Interim Committee on Public Lands.

As would be expected, federal holdings are smallest in the counties which are primarily urban and agricultural in character. In seven counties — Kings, Marin, Merced, San Joaquin, San Mateo, Santa Cruz, and Sutter — federal ownership is 1 per cent or less of the total area. By way of contrast, in four counties lying wholly or largely east of the Sierra Nevada — Alpine, Inyo, Mono, and Tuolumne — federal ownership runs up to 75 per cent or more of the area.

DEPARTMENT OF DEFENSE

Land holdings of the Department of Defense in California as of June 30, 1956, are shown in Table 22. Some 750,000 acres were also being used under permits, leases, and easements, chiefly by the Navy. In addition, applications for the withdrawal of about 3,000,000 acres of public land were pending with the Bureau of Land Management on December 31, 1956. As of June 30, 1957, the Department of Defense had control over 5,384,029 acres in California, of which 49 per cent was public domain, 22 per cent was "owned" land (chiefly purchased), and 29 per cent was land under lease, easement, or temporary use.

Table 22. Ownership of Land in California by the Department of Defense as of June 30, 1956.

UNIT	PUBLIC DOMAIN	OTHER LAND	TOTAL
		ACRES	
Army — military functions	624,703	407,812	1,032,515
Army — civil functions (Corps of Engineers)	9,770	41,162	50,932
Navy	1,838,288	462,125	2,300,413
Air Force	78,063	354,863	432,926
Total	2,550,824	1,265,962	3,816,786

Source: Inventory prepared by General Services Administration.

The importance of California in the military picture is indicated by the fact that the area in the state held by the Department of Defense for military purposes (excluding the Corps of Engineers) is greater than that in any other state. The Navy's holdings constitute nearly two-thirds of those in the entire country; those of the Army are second only to New Mexico; while those of the Air Force are exceeded by several other states, notably Nevada.

The areas of military reservations covering more than 20,000 acres each, as of June 30, 1957, are shown in Table 23. The approximate location of the reservations is indicated by corresponding numbers on the map showing major federal reservations (Fig. 16). The areas given include all land under the control of the department indicated, and not merely public domain and acquired land.

Well over half of the area controlled by the Department of Defense is in the desert portions of Inyo, San Bernardino, and Riverside Counties. These lands are used chiefly for ordnance testing and for aircraft gunnery ranges. There are only seven counties in which the department controls more than 5 per cent of the area of the county (Inyo, Monterey, Nevada, San Bernardino, San Diego, Santa Barbara, and Yuba), and in 37 counties its holdings are less than 1 per cent.

Table 23. Military Reservations of more than 20,000 Acres in California as of June 30, 1957.

		Acres
Army		
1.	Sierra Ordnance Depot	97,759
3.	Fort Ord	28,547
4.	Hunter Liggett Military Reservation	259,763
5.	Camp Roberts	44,433
6.	Camp Cooke	83,583
11.	Camp Irwin	628,728
Air Force		
2.	Beale Air Force Base	35,982
10.	Edwards Air Force Base	300,012
Navy		
7.	Camp Pendleton Marine Corps Base	126,333
8.	Camp Elliott	29,240
9.	China Lake Ordnance Test Station	1,207,426
12.	Twenty-nine Palms Marine Corps Base	594,741
13.	El Centro Air Station	702,721

Source: Real Estate Division, Department of Defense.

From the standpoint of land use, single-purpose management of Department of Defense lands — for military objectives — tends to prevail, particularly during periods of high military activity. Outside of urban centers and airfields, the bulk of the land is brushy, desert, or mountainous. Some of it is suitable for grazing, and there is a negligible amount of commercial forest land. There is considerable use of military lands for grazing, but relatively little for mining or recreation. Recreational use is, however, encouraged on civil works installations. Naturally, wherever an element of danger is introduced, as in the testing of weapons, all non-military uses are prohibited.

Department of the Interior

Land ownership in California by the Department of the Interior as of July 1, 1956, is shown in Table 24. The preponderance of public-domain land —98 per cent of the total — is particularly striking.

Table 24. Ownership of Land in California by the Department of the Interior as of June 30, 1956, Exclusive of Trust Properties.

Unit	Public domain	Other land	Total
		Acres	
Bureau of Land Management	17,506,578	—	17,506,578
National Park Service	3,977,147	97,702	4,074,849
Bureau of Reclamation	1,147,384	240,192	1,387,576
Bureau of Sport Fisheries and Wildlife	1,605	30,008	31,613
Bureau of Indian Affairs[1]	9,914	1,387	11,301
Geological Survey	20	7	27
Total	22,642,648	369,296	23,011,944

[1] Excluding tribal and allotted lands held in trust by the United States.

Source: Inventory prepared by General Services Administration.

Bureau of Land Management

About three-fourths of the land under the jurisdiction of the Department of the Interior is administered by the Bureau of Land Management. Of this area, nearly a fourth is inside of grazing districts and about three-fourths outside. Private and public ownership within the districts is distributed as shown in Table 25. A small percentage of the public lands within the districts is administered by other federal agencies.

Public ownership clearly predominates in the Mojave and Virginia City Districts in the southeastern and east-central parts of the state, and private ownership in the Honey Lake District in the northwestern part of the state. Legally, private and state lands could be leased for administration by the Bureau of Land Management, but actually only 1,118 acres are so leased.

Table 25. Ownership of Grazing Districts in California as of June 30, 1956.

GRAZING DISTRICT	FEDERAL		PRIVATE AND STATE		TOTAL
	ACRES	PER CENT	ACRES	PER CENT	ACRES
C-1 (Mojave)	3,044,391	72	1,184,409	28	4,228,800
C-2 (Honey Lake)	1,022,135	41	1,456,845	59	2,478,980
N-3 (Virginia City)[1]	281,780	70	122,016	30	403,796
State	4,348,306	61	2,763,270	39	7,111,576

[1] Most of this district is in Nevada.

Source: Bureau of Land Management.

Vacant, unreserved public lands outside of grazing districts occur in every county in the state except eight — Alpine, Lassen, Marin, Orange, San Francisco, San Joaquin, San Mateo, and Sutter. They are, however, pretty well concentrated in three counties on the east side of the state, as shown in Table 26.

Table 26. Unreserved Public Domain outside of Grazing Districts as of June 30, 1956.

COUNTY	ACRES	PER CENT
San Bernardino	7,683,429	57
Inyo	1,971,233	15
Riverside	1,351,369	10
	11,006,031	82
Others	2,493,414	18
	13,499,445	100

Source: Bureau of Land Management. Because of differences in reporting the data, the figures given here and in Table 25 differ slightly from the inventory prepared by the General Services Administration.

Some 5,813,866 acres, or 42 per cent, of this area were leased in 1956 under Section 15 of the Taylor Grazing Act of 1934, at a rental of $69,612. Leases under Section 15 of the act cover an area that is greater by 1,465,560 acres than the area organized in grazing districts under Section 3 of the act. They bring in receipts that are greater by $15,419.

Unreserved public lands both in and out of grazing districts are open to entry under applicable land laws when classified by the Bureau of Land Management as suitable for the purpose for which application is made. Table 27 shows the area which was examined during the fiscal year 1956 and was found suitable or unsuitable for the purpose specified by the applicant. The large percentage of the lands examined which were found unsuitable for homestead and for desert-land entry is striking.

Table 27. Results of Land Classification in California, Fiscal Year 1956.

Purpose	Found suitable		Found unsuitable		Total
	Acres	Per cent	Acres	Per cent	Acres
Homestead	1,024	23	3,354	77	4,378
Public sale	23,225	82	5,182	18	28,407
Exchange	2,018	93	160	7	2,178
Desert land	12,224	10	106,892	90	119,116
Other	17,835	56	14,155	44	31,990
	56,326	30	129,743	70	186,069

Source: Bureau of Land Management.

Public-land business is particularly active in California under the Small Tract Act of 1938, which authorizes the sale or lease of not more than 5 acres for home, recreation, business, and other purposes, subject to a reservation to the United States of all mineral deposits. The popularity of the act in California is indicated by the fact that up to June 30, 1956, the area classified in that state was 55 per cent greater than in all the rest of the United States and Alaska put together. Interest is particularly keen in the southern part of the state and includes desert lands that a few years ago would have been regarded as valueless.

Table 28 shows the areas classified as suitable for small-tract purposes up to June 30, 1956. San Bernardino County, with 83 per cent of the total, ranks so high largely because public interest has led the Bureau of Land Management to concentrate its efforts in that county.

Table 28. Areas Classified under the Small Tract Act in California to June 30, 1956.

County	— Area classified — Acres	Per cent
Calaveras	118	*
Imperial	54	*
Inyo	3,302	2
Kern	5,474	3
Lake	480	*
Los Angeles	6,111	4
Placer	40	*
Riverside	10,185	6
San Bernardino	142,653	83
San Diego	2,706	2
Shasta	135	*
Sierra	20	*
Tulare	20	*
	171,298[1]	100

* Less than 0.5 per cent.

[1] Does not include a considerable area of "accommodation" classifications of scattered tracts not published in the Federal Register.

Source: Bureau of Land Management.

Commercial forest lands under the jurisdiction of the Bureau of Land Management are estimated by the Forest Service in the Timber Resource Review at 324,000 acres. Much of this land is in small tracts but there are some sizeable blocks. Timber sales during the fiscal year 1956 included 18,091 M board feet, with a value of $451,-778. An additional $47,259 was collected for 4,656 M board feet cut in trespass. Although grazing constitutes by far the greatest use of unreserved public lands from the standpoint of area involved, receipts from timber sales in 1956 were nearly four times as much as receipts from grazing leases both inside and outside of grazing districts. The really big money from the public lands comes from mineral leases and permits. In 1956 receipts from this source totaled $9,620,034, of which 85 per cent came from oil and gas and 8 per cent from potash.

NATIONAL PARK SERVICE. Table 29 shows the net area of lands under the jurisdiction of the National Park Service as of December 31, 1956, with the percentage of each unit in federal ownership. The total figure is slightly less than that in the inventory of June 30, 1956, prepared by the General Services Administration.

The very high percentage of federal ownership is striking, particularly in view of the fact that 98 per cent of the net area consists of public domain, and that only 2 per cent has been acquired by purchase. The explanation probably lies in the early establishment of the Yosemite, General Grant, and Sequoia National Parks (1890), and also of the several national forests from which sizeable transfers were later made to the present Sequoia, Kings Canyon, and Lassen Volcanic National Parks.

This situation is likewise true of the Devils Postpile and Lava Beds National Monuments, both of which were formerly parts of national forests. The two large national monuments – Death Valley and Joshua Tree – were established considerably later, but for the most part in areas that were not attractive for private ownership.

The Millerton Lake National Recreation Area includes the lands surrounding the reservoir created by Friant Dam as part of the Central Valley Project. It is one of three such areas in the United States (the other two are at Coulee Dam and Lake Mead) established by agreement between the Bureau of Reclamation and the National Park Service. Arrangements have recently been completed to transfer administration of the Millerton Lake Area from the National Park Service to the State Division of Beaches and Parks, under a new agreement with the Bureau of Reclamation.

Commercial utilization of the resources of the national parks and monuments is not permitted except for a very limited amount of grazing and some salvage of insect-killed timber. They may, however, to a limited degree be regarded as multi-use properties, since in addition to preserving the natural scenery they provide recreation, watershed protection, and natural areas that may be used for scientific study. The Forest Service estimates that the four national parks in California contain 443,000 acres that would be classified as commercial forest land if it were available for utilization. There is, of course, considerable development of commercial facilities to meet the needs and desires of visitors.

Table 29. Area of National Parks and National Monuments in California as of December 31, 1956.

	Net area, acres		Per cent of gross area	
National Parks				
Kings Canyon	453,718		99.8	
Lassen Volcanic	104,481		98.6	
Sequoia	385,258		99.9	
Yosemite	757,991		99.6	
		1,701,448		99.6
National Monuments				
Cabrillo	0.5		100.0	
Channel Islands[1]	1,120		100.0	
Death Valley[2]	1,750,298		97.8	
Devils Postpile	798		100.0	
Joshua Tree	490,599		87.9	
Lava Beds	46,239		100.0	
Muir Woods	485		96.2	
Pinnacles	12,818		88.4	
		2,302,357		95.6
National Recreation Area				
Millerton Lake		11,605		90.9
		4,015,410		97.2

[1] Includes land area only.

[2] Area includes only land in California; percentage is based on total area.

Source: National Park Service.

Bureau of Reclamation. The Bureau of Reclamation had jurisdiction over 1,387,576 acres of federal lands in California as of June 30, 1956, according to the inventory prepared by the General Services Administration. Of this area, 83 per cent was public domain and

17 per cent acquired land. The latter (240,192 acres) constitutes about two-thirds of the entire area acquired by the Department of the Interior.

The Bureau's two major projects in the state are the Central Valley Project in the Sacramento and San Joaquin Valleys and the All-American Canal System of the Boulder Canyon Project in southeastern California. Three of the installations – Keswick, Shasta, and Siphon Drop (at Yuma) – include hydroelectric plants; and several installations constitute important sources of municipal and industrial water supplies.

Recreational use of reclamation reservoirs and of the land surrounding them is strongly encouraged. So far as practicable the Bureau of Reclamation turns over the administration of recreational activities to local, state, or other federal agencies. The Cachuma Project in Santa Barbara County furnishes a good illustration of the way in which the participation of local agencies can be effected. Here plans were first developed by the county planning commission, and later approved by the county board of supervisors, which proved satisfactory to all concerned.

In addition to the recent transfer of the administration of recreational activities at Millerton Lake to the State Division of Beaches and Parks, arrangements have been completed for state administration of recreation on lands surrounding the reservoir created by Folsom Dam. Land surrounding the reservoir created by Shasta Dam was added to the Shasta National Forest by Congress in 1948 in order to place recreational activities on it under the administration of the Forest Service.

Bureau of Sport Fisheries and Wildlife. Lands in California over which the Bureau of Sport Fisheries and Wildlife has sole control comprised only 31,613 acres on June 30, 1956 (General Services Administration), 95 per cent of which had been acquired by purchase. However, lands under the primary administration of some other agency, plus leased lands, bring the total area over which it has complete or partial jurisdiction to 188,259 acres. Of this area, more than 99 per cent is in the eleven migratory bird refuges. The six largest refuges (constituting nearly 90 per cent of the total refuge area) are the Lower Klamath, Tule Lake, and Clear Lake Refuges in Siskiyou and Modoc Counties in the extreme northeastern part of the state, and the Imperial, Salton Sea, and Havasu Lake Refuges in Imperial and San Bernardino Counties in the extreme southeastern part of the state.

The great bulk of the land in migratory bird refuges is on reclamation projects. They furnish an excellent example of mutiple land use and of cooperation between two federal agencies. Federal lands at Honey Lake, Madeline Plains, and Topaz Lake totaling 1,514 acres are administered by the Cooperative Wildlife Research Unit at the University of California. Purchases by the Bureau of Sport Fisheries and Wildlife have been almost entirely for migratory bird refuges.

Bureau of Indian Affairs. "Indian lands" are for the most part owned by the Indians, in the form of either tribal lands or allotted lands, but are administered by the federal government in its capacity as trustee. There is a much smaller area of rancherias[1], of public-domain allotments, and of public lands used by the government for administrative purposes.

The Bureau of Indian Affairs estimates that the area under its jurisdiction in California as of June 30, 1957, totaled 576,009 acres, of which tribal lands and rancherias comprised 87 per cent, allotted lands more than 12 per cent, and government-owned lands used for administrative purposes less than 1 per cent. Although California's 120 reservations far exceed in number those in any other state, they constitute only 1 per cent of the total area under the jurisdiction of the Bureau in the continental United States. Some 36 per cent of the reservations and rancherias are less than 100 acres in size, and 70 per cent are less than 1,000 acres.

The reservations are widely distributed throughout the state, but

[1] "Rancherias" are lands purchased by the United States for use by groups of landless Indians. Since they are owned by the government, their legal status differs from that of "reservations," which the government holds in trust for the Indians. Administration of the two classes of land is, however, similar, and they are often referred to collectively as "reservations."

there are 25 counties in which they do not occur. San Diego, Riverside, Humboldt, Tulare, San Bernardino, and Mendocino Counties, each with more than 30,000 acres of reservations, together contain more than four-fifths of the total area in reservations. The two largest reservations (Hoopa Valley and Tule River) are located in Humboldt and Tulare Counties. San Diego County has the largest number of reservations, mostly in the form of rancherias.

Commercial forest lands are estimated by the Forest Service at 133,000 acres and provide an important source of revenue. Cash sales in the calendar year 1955 amounted to 33,604 M board feet with a value of $344,871. These figures compare favorably with sales of $451,778 from the considerably larger area of commercial forest land in the unreserved public domain.

On August 1, 1953, Congress resolved "That it is declared to be the sense of Congress that, at the earliest possible time, all of the Indian tribes and the individual members thereof located within the States of California . . . should be freed from federal supervision and control," and that after such action has been taken "all offices of the Bureau of Indian Affairs in the States of California . . . whose primary purpose was to serve any Indian tribe or individual Indian freed from federal supervision should be abolished." No definite action has yet been taken to effectuate this proposal, although several bills on the subject have been introduced in Congress. A first step in that direction was, however, taken by an act of August 15, 1953, which transferred to California and to several other states both criminal and civil jurisdiction over Indians in "all Indian country within the state" to the same extent that the state has jurisdiction elsewhere.

Department of Agriculture—Forest Service

All except a few hundred acres of the land under the jurisdiction of the Department of Agriculture is administered by the Forest Service. The net area of each unit as of June 30, 1956, and the percentage which that area constitutes of the gross area are shown in Table 30. The figures include some minor duplications in national monuments and in reclamation withdrawals.

Table 30. National Forests and Related Areas in California as of June 30, 1956.

NATIONAL FORESTS	NET AREA, ACRES		PER CENT OF GROSS AREA	
Angeles	648,274		94	
Calaveras Big Tree	379		100	
Cleveland	391,562		69	
Eldorado	640,632		72	
Inyo	1,774,329		97	
Klamath	1,371,918		88	
Lassen	1,046,491		76	
Los Padres	1,768,182		88	
Mendocino	867,272		80	
Modoc	1,688,877		82	
Plumas	1,138,008		81	
Rogue River	49,261		88	
San Bernardino	614,783		76	
Sequoia	1,118,579		95	
Shasta	1,282,535		68	
Sierra	1,295,962		92	
Siskiyou	31,740		82	
Six Rivers	935,267		86	
Stanislaus	896,165		82	
Tahoe	694,217		58	
Toiyabe	629,745		91	
Trinity	1,049,893		87	
		19,934,071		83
PURCHASE UNITS				
Northern Redwood	14,492		6	
Southern Redwood	0		0	
		14,492		2
EXPERIMENTAL AREAS				
Institute of Forest Genetics	116		100	
San Joaquin Range	4,580		100	
		4,696		100
LAND UTILIZATION PROJECTS				
Butte Valley	18,315		100	
San Joaquin	5,157		100	
		23,472		100
ADMINISTRATIVE SITES		51		100
		19,976,782		80

Source: Forest Service.

Of the total area, nearly 93 per cent consists of withdrawals from the "original" public domain. Some 6 per cent has been acquired by exchange of public-domain land or timber (and is therefore classified as "acquired" public domain), and less than 1 per cent by purchase. Only 2 per cent of the land in the two purchase units in the redwood region has so far been acquired (all in the northern unit), and the southern unit was abolished in May, 1957. Additional areas within national forests in process of acquisition in early 1957 included 27,446 acres, of which more than half was in the Lassen and Plumas National Forests.

Aside from the tiny Calaveras Big Tree National Forest of 379 acres, the percentage of the gross area in federal ownership varies from a low of 58 per cent in the Tahoe to a high of 97 per cent in the Inyo. Railroad land grants still in private ownership constitute a prominent part of the land ownership pattern in the Tahoe, Eldorado, San Bernardino, Shasta-Trinity, and Klamath National Forests.

According to the Timber Resource Review, the national forests in California contain 8,573,000 acres of commercial forest land. This area comprises 43 per cent of the net area of national forests and 49 per cent of the entire commercial forest area of the state.

The remainder of the area consists of noncommercial forest land, brush land, range land, and barren land. In terms of volume, the national forests contain 50 per cent of the sawtimber and 48 per cent of the growing stock in the state.

The status of the 17 primitive, wilderness, and wild areas in California is summarized in Table 31.

The high percentage of public lands in all but two of these areas is in large part an indication of their inaccessibility. Even a small percentage of private ownership may, however, be a serious detriment in areas of this character. Their total area comprises nearly 8 per cent of the net area of national forest land in the state.

Four "natural areas" have been established in national forests in California as follows:

Devil's Garden Natural Area of 1,600 acres, Modoc National Forest, established February 28, 1933, to preserve an example of juniper forest.

Table 31. Primitive, Wilderness, and Wild Areas in National Forests in California as of June 30, 1956.

Areas and national forests in which located	Net area: Acres	Net area: Per cent of gross area
Agua Tibia – Cleveland	26,225[1]	97.7
Caribou Peak – Lassen	16,403	99.8
Cucamonga – San Bernardino	5,000	100.0
Desolation Valley – Eldorado	40,700	98.4
Devil Canyon-Bear Canyon – Angeles	36,200	100.0
Emigrant Basin – Stanislaus	97,020	99.0
High Sierra – Inyo, Sequoia, Sierra	393,899	100.0
Marble Mountains – Klamath	243,561	99.2
Middle Eel-Yolla Bolly – Mendocino, Trinity	136,106	94.9
Mt. Dana-Minarets – Inyo, Sierra	82,181	99.8
Salmon-Trinity Alps – Klamath, Shasta, Trinity	220,999	77.4
San Gorgonio – San Bernardino	27,178	78.3
San Jacinto – San Bernardino	20,343[2]	60.5
San Rafael – Los Padres	74,160	98.9
South Warner – Modoc	68,242	96.5
Thousand Lakes Valley – Lassen	15,485	94.9
Ventana – Los Padres	52,894	94.6
	1,556,596	93.7

[1] Includes reserved Indian lands.

[2] Does not include San Jacinto State Park of 12,228 acres; combined area of federal and state land equals 96.8 per cent of the gross area.

Source: Forest Service.

Harvey Munroe Hall Natural Area of 4,250 acres, Inyo National Forest, established January 6, 1933, to preserve an example of High Sierra alpine and subalpine life zones.

Indiana Summit Natural Area of 1,000 acres, Inyo National Forest, established June 23, 1932, to preserve an example of virgin Jeffrey pine forest.

White Mountain Natural Area of 2,330 acres, Inyo National Forest, established November 13, 1953, to preserve an unusual stand of extremely ancient bristlecone pine.

Since natural areas are specifically set aside for scientific study, public use is not encouraged. It is not prohibited, however, so long as it does not noticeably disturb the natural condition of the area. A request for the withdrawal from mineral entry of the four established areas has been on record with the Department of the Interior since May 9, 1955.

State Lands

The three classes of state-owned land recognized by the California Senate Interim Committee on Public Lands, with the 1954 area of each as reported by the committee, are shown in Table 32.

Table 32. State-owned Lands in California, 1954.

Class	Area Acres	Per cent of State-owned area	Per cent of Total state area
Lands under departmental jurisdiction	998,693	44.0	1.0
Tax-deeded lands	417,291	18.4	0.4
State lands (mostly school lands)	852,889	37.6	0.9
	2,268,873	100.0	2.3

Source: Senate Interim Committee on Public Lands.

Departmental Lands

Lands under the jurisdiction of the various departments of state government, commonly known as "proprietary" lands, comprise considerably the largest area. The rate at which they were acquired is shown in Figure 19, which is based on the 1955 report of the Senate Interim Committee on Public Lands. Twenty different agencies are involved, but the three departments of Natural Resources, Public Works, and Fish and Game control 92 per cent of the area (Table 33 and Fig. 20).

Most of the departmental lands have been acquired by purchase or gift. Of the area controlled by the Division of Beaches and Parks, approximately 70 per cent (426,596 acres) is in the Anza Desert and Borrego State Parks, chiefly in eastern San Diego County. More than 95 per cent of these large parks was obtained through transfer to the state by Congress of federal public-domain lands. Humboldt

County, with 34,167 acres, contains the second largest area of state park land, two-thirds of which is in the Humboldt Redwoods State Park.

Table 33. Departmental Control of State-owned Lands in California, 1954.

DEPARTMENT	ACRES		PER CENT OF TOTAL	
Natural Resources				
Division of Beaches and Parks	560,628		56	
Division of Forestry	71,060		7	
		631,688		63
Public Works		200,437		20
Fish and Game		89,996		9
Others		76,572		8
		998,693		100

Source: Senate Interim Committee on Public Lands.

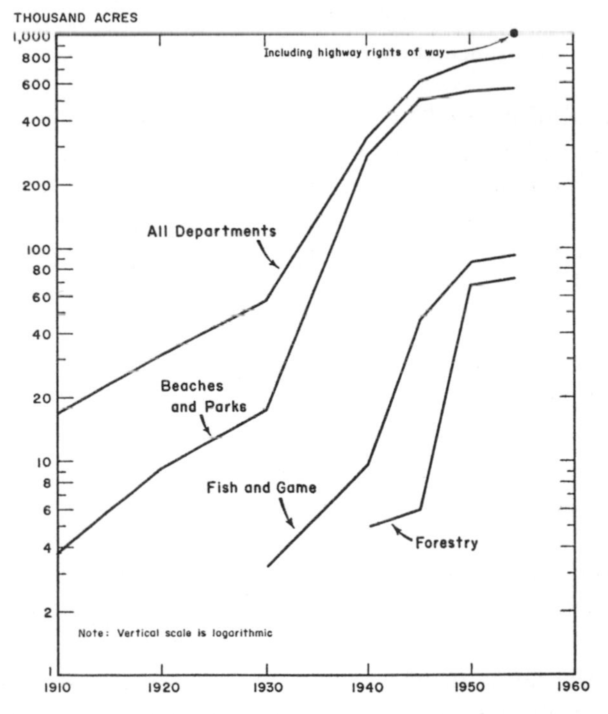

Figure 19. Departmental holdings by chief state land management agencies, 1910-1954.

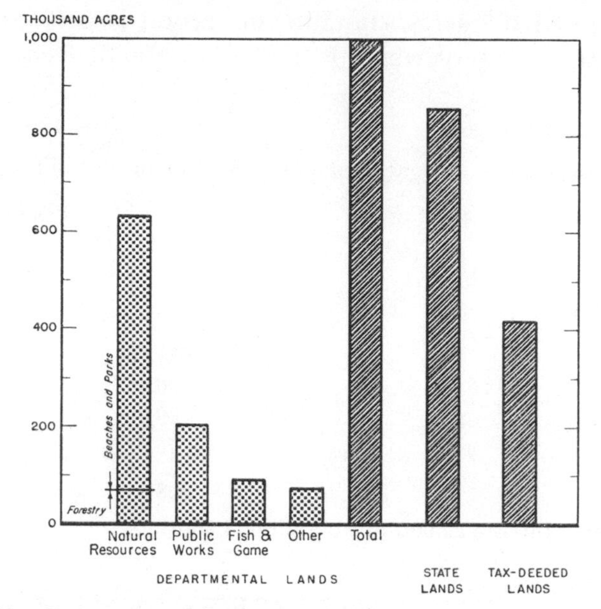

Figure 20. Departmental lands, state lands, and tax-deeded lands, 1954.

Property administered by the Division of Forestry consists chiefly of state forests. The Jackson State Forest (52,042 acres) in Mendocino County constitutes 73 per cent of the area in this category.

Recent additions bring the total area administered by the Department of Fish and Game to 104,141 acres, divided as follows:

	Acres	Per cent
Deer Ranges	56,400	54
Waterfowl Areas	47,198	45
Game Farms, Fish Hatcheries, and Others	543	1
	104,141	100

The Tehama Deer Range of 42,897 acres is located in Tehama County and the Doyle Deer Range of 13,503 acres in Lassen County. Waterfowl refuges and management areas are scattered from Siskiyou County in the north to Imperial County in the south. Practically all of the lands in deer ranges and waterfowl areas have been purchased, chiefly from state funds but with considerable assistance from Pittman-Robertson funds.

The State Department of Fish and Game works in close cooperation with the Federal Bureau of Sport Fisheries and Wildlife in its programs of land and water management. The three areas of cooperative wildlife units administered by the state were withdrawn at the request of the Department. Requests were pending in 1957 for the withdrawal by the federal government of an additional 554,742 acres of public land in 23 different areas to be administered by the state for wildlife purposes. Favorable action on these requests would increase by more than five times the area now under state administration.

The great bulk of the land held by the Department of Public Works is in the form of highway rights of way (98.6 per cent). Such land is located in every county in the state, with a minimum of 591 acres in San Francisco County and a maximum of 18,918 acres in San Bernardino County. From the standpoint of land management the chief problems connected with its administration are esthetic and recreational. An important program is the development by the Division of Beaches and Parks of wayside rest areas.

Tax-deeded Lands

The area of tax-deeded lands is in a state of more or less constant change. As of January 1, 1956, it had decreased from the figure given by the Senate Interim Committee on Public Lands to 280,680 acres, exclusive of the area in 106,996 lots. The land is for the most part marginal or submarginal in character, with little value for agriculture, timber production, grazing, or recreation. Current annual receipts are about $25,000, which goes to the counties concerned.

School Lands

"State lands" consist almost entirely of school lands. What few swamp and overflowed lands still remain in state ownership are also included but not submerged lands. Although the school lands are widely scattered, nearly 30 per cent of them are located in San Bernardino County. There they aggregate 371,757 acres, or nearly 3 per cent of the total area of the county. In four other counties —

Imperial, Inyo, Lassen, and Siskiyou – they approximate 2 per cent of the area of the county, but nowhere else do they exceed 1 per cent.

Some 150,000 acres of school lands are still unsurveyed, and nearly 100,000 acres are in military reservations. They contain the major part of the 186,000 acres of commercial forest land estimated by the Forest Service to be in state ownership (1 per cent of the commercial forest area of the state). A considerable area is suitable for grazing and is leased for that purpose. Receipts from sales and leases, excluding oil and gas, during the eight fiscal years from 1947 to 1954 averaged about $126,000, with substantial increases in recent years. Lands which are suitable for cultivation can be sold only to actual settlers, and mineral rights are reserved in all sales. Effective management is seriously handicapped by the scattered character of the lands and the fact that state ownership of most of them is regarded as temporary.

County, Regional, and City Lands

No figures are available on county ownership, but the total area of forest and range land involved is certainly small. The Forest Service estimates the area of commercial forest land held by counties and municipalities at 8,000 acres, nearly all of which is in San Mateo, Humboldt, Mendocino, and Santa Clara Counties. The bulk of the area is held for watershed and recreational purposes.

The East Bay Regional Parks constitute the only regional park district in the state. The district was formed in 1934 by the cities of Oakland, Berkeley, Alameda, Piedmont, Albany, Emeryville, and San Leandro. In 1957 it contained about 8,200 acres. The parks "are maintained as a semi-wildwood area designed to protect, preserve, and increase native plant and animal life in addition to furnishing recreational areas of varied interest to all age groups." The success of the district suggests the desirability of more widespread use of this method of providing recreational facilities.

The City of Los Angeles (Department of Water and Power) owns about 62,000 acres in Mono County and about 238,000 acres in Inyo County. Much of this area was formerly ranch or pasture land which has reverted to brush since the water once used locally has been diverted to Los Angeles via the aqueduct. Special-use permits from the Forest Service and the Bureau of Land Management have made it unnecessary for the city to take advantage of a 1936 act authorizing it to purchase at $1.25 per acre lands in Mono County "which may be necessary" in connection with the development and utilization of the water supply.

The City of San Francisco owns about 52,000 acres, largely in Alameda and Contra Costa Counties, which it holds for the protection of its water supply. Some 55,000 acres of land are held by the East Bay Water District, and there are doubtless many small areas in the hands of other districts and municipalities in various parts of the state.

Table 34. Summary of Public and Private Land Ownership in California.

Class	Acres		Per cent	
Public ownership				
Federal, including trust properties (General Services Administration and Bureau of Indian Affairs)	47,421,000		47	
State (Senate Interim Committee)	2,269,000		2	
County, regional, and municipal (Estimated)	260,000		*	
		49,950,000		50
Private ownership				
Farm land (1954 Census)	37,795,000		38	
Commercial forest land not in farms (Forest Service)	6,467,000		6	
Other rural, urban, and suburban land (Calculated)	6,102,000		6	
		50,364,000		50
		100,314,000		100

* Less than 0.5 per cent.

Source: As indicated in parenthesis following each item. Not all estimates are of the same date.

PRIVATE LANDS

AREA AND CHARACTER

Private ownership of land in California is estimated roughly at 50,364,000 acres, as shown in Table 34. The area of "other rural, urban, and suburban land" was derived by subtracting the sum of the preceding five items from the total area of the state. "Other rural" land includes all that in private ownership outside of farms and commercial forest areas. It consists chiefly of noncommercial forest land, range land, and waste land, such as deserts and mountain tops.

Available information is not adequate to permit assignment of an acreage to each of these classes of land, but their relative productive capacity cannot be large. Yields from noncommercial forest and waste lands are obviously small, and the great bulk of the productive range land must be included in the 19,889,000 acres of nonwoodland on farms and ranches which was reported by the Census to be "pastured" in 1954.

The extent to which grazing is concentrated on the larger farms, commonly known as ranches, is indicated by 1954 Census figures for farms of 1,000 acres or more in size:

	ACRES	PER CENT OF ALL FARMS
Cropland used only for pasture	1,871,797	62
Woodland pastured	4,488,860	87
Other pasture (not cropland or woodland)	15,236,360	90
	21,597,017	86

The fact that 86 per cent of the total area grazed is comprised in farms of 1,000 acres or more in size is clear evidence of the concentration of grazing on the ranch type of farm. So also is the fact that 91 per cent of all land pastured consists of woodland pasture and "other pasture" (not cropland). It is in these two types of pasture that "brush" constitutes so serious a problem.

Commercial Forest Lands

Much the most detailed information concerning wildland in private ownership is that for commercial forest land provided by the Timber Resource Review. This appraisal of the timber situation is both more complete and more accurate than the appraisals presented in three earlier studies by the Forest Service: "Timber Depletion, Lumber Exports, and Concentration of Timber Ownership" (Capper Report, 1920), "A National Plan for American Forestry" (Copeland Report, 1933), and "A Reappraisal of the Forest Situation" (Reappraisal Report, 1946). While all four reports have received some criticism because of the presentation and interpretation of the findings by the Forest Service, there is general agreement that better sampling methods, the more effective use of photogrammetry, and more widespread cooperation by both public and private agencies make the Timber Resource Review the most reliable source of information yet available on forest areas, volumes, growth, and drain.

The Timber Resource Review gives the following division of commercial forest land in private ownership by classes of owners:

Class	Acres	Per cent
Farmers	1,586,000	20
Wood-using industries	3,389,000	42
Other	3,078,000	38
	8,053,000	100

It is difficult to reconcile the figure of 1,586,000 acres for farms with the figure of 5,855,000 acres of woodland in farms given by the 1954 Census. Since the Census reports 5,142,000 acres of woodland pastured (88 per cent of the total farm woodland), it is probable that much of the area classified by the Census as woodland was classified by the Forest Service as either noncommercial forest land or non-forest land. This conclusion seems to be further substantiated by the fact that the Census reported 123,000 farms in 1954, while the Forest Service estimated the number of farm owners of commercial forest land at only 2,675 in 1953. Returns of

$4,020,000 to farmers from forest products in 1954 give a return of only $0.69 per acre on the basis of Census estimates of acreage, and of $2.53 on the basis of Forest Service estimates. Either figure indicates the current low productivity of farm woodlands.

Situation by Size Classes

Supplementary information on ownership by the size classes recognized by the Forest Service was obtained in connection with the present study. Data for the large ownerships (50,000 acres or more) were obtained by personal contacts with responsible representatives of each owner. Medium-sized ownerships (5,000 to 49,999 acres) were sampled by questionnaires to 50 owners, to which 21 replies were received. Information on small ownerships (less than 5,000 acres) was obtained from the Regional Office of the Forest Service at San Francisco, the California State Division of Forestry, and foresters employed by private operators. Adjustments to reflect current conditions were then made on the basis of further information supplied by service foresters in the State Division of Forestry and several county assessors' offices.

The adjusted figures for private ownership by size classes are given in Table 35 (see also Fig. 21). The data for the large ownerships are considerably more accurate than those for the medium-sized and small ownerships, particularly the latter. This situation is an inevitable result of the large number of owners involved and the current rapid fluctuations in ownership. It does not invalidate the reliability of the general picture which the figures present.

Table 35. Private Ownership of Commercial Forest Land in California by Size Classes, 1953.

	Owners		Area	
Class of ownership	Number	Per cent	Acres	Per cent
Small (less than 5,000 acres)	10,000	98.4	2,616,000	32.5
Medium (5,000 to 49,999 acres)	138	1.4	2,350,000	29.2
Large (50,000 acres or more)	19	0.2	3,087,000	38.3
	10,157	100.0	8,053,000	100.0

Source: "Timber Resource Review," Forest Service, and present study.

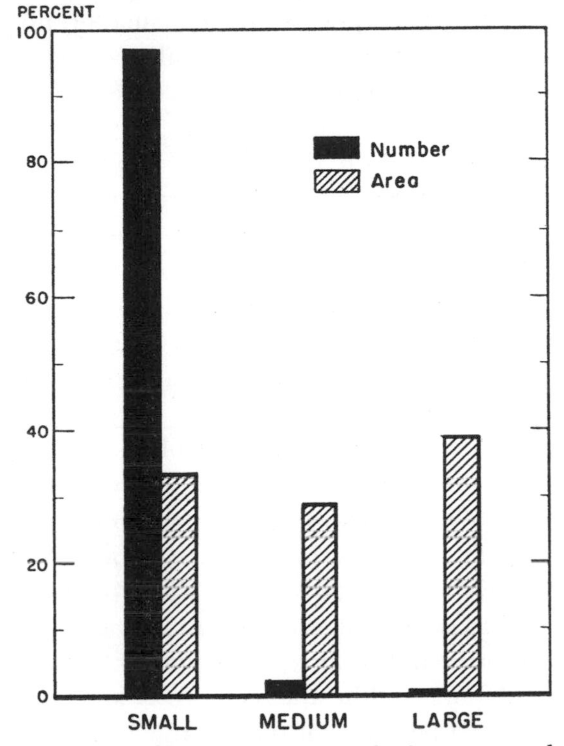

Figure 21. Per cent of number of owners and of area owned by size classes for commercial forest land in private ownership, 1953.

Small owners, with nearly a third of the commercial forest area of the state in private ownership, comprise a highly important group. They include a wide variety of types which are found throughout the range of areas in this size class, from a few acres up to the maximum of 4,999 acres. In some cases, the forest land is part of an operating ranch; in others, it is separate from the ranch proper but is still rancher-owned. A large number of the properties undoubtedly belong to absentee owners. As a group, this class of ownership, by sheer force of numbers, is difficult to analyze. Current studies by the School of Forestry of the University of California confirm the opinion expressed in many parts of the state that small ownerships are changing hands very rapidly. In some cases they are being split up into still smaller ownerships, while in other cases they are being consolidated into larger holdings.

Medium-sized forest properties are far smaller in number and slightly less in area than those in the small size class. It is equally difficult to generalize as to their characteristics. Ownerships in the lower quartile of the range resemble those in the upper quartile of the small ownerships, while those in the upper quartile of the medium-sized group have many of the characteristics of large ownerships. One of these characteristics is the possession of processing plants. Returns from the sample used in this study show that about 55 per cent of the owners of medium-sized properties have processing plants and control approximately 65 per cent of the area in this classification. The sample also shows that corporations comprise about 60 per cent of the total number of owners and hold 73 per cent of the area. No information is available as to the percentage of corporation ownership that is family dominated or controlled.

Large ownerships increased by 3, or nearly 20 per cent, during the four years from 1953 to 1957. They now number 19. With only 0.2 per cent of the total number of owners, they control 38 per cent of the commercial forest area of the state in private ownership. They range in size from near the lower limit of 50,000 acres to slightly more than 700,000 acres. The median size is approximately 70,000 acres. Fourteen, or 74 per cent, of the 19 large owners have their own processing plants, but control only about 54 per cent of the forest land in this classification. Five owners are actively engaged in selling stumpage, one to a processing plant under the same management. Several mergers involving ownerships in both the large and medium-sized classifications have taken place within the last two years.

PART IV

PROBLEMS IN LAND OWNERSHIP

Origin of Problems

Land ownership controls land management. The pattern of ownership and its effect on management are therefore matters of major importance. In California, as elsewhere in the United States, that pattern has resulted from constantly changing policies on the part of both public and private owners. Whether or not policies that in retrospect would have proved more satisfactory could have been devised, adopted, and carried out is open to debate.

During the first century and more of the Republic's existence people were relatively few. Natural resources were not only relatively abundant; they were apparently inexhaustible. That their utilization might result in dust bowls, timber shortages, depleted ranges, scarcity of wildlife, and exhaustion of mineral deposits never occurred to the average American. A rampant individualism insisted on the right of every man to own a piece of land and to do with it as he pleased. Cameron[1] has summed up the situation as follows:

". . . the hard fact remains that the story of the Anglo-Saxon in America, when reduced to its simplest terms, is nothing but the story of a raging spirit of adventure with an uncontrollable westward urge, a spirit so intoxicated by the spaciousness amid which it found itself that it had scant patience with law and authority and

[1] Cameron, Jenks: "The Development of Governmental Forest Control in the United States," The Johns Hopkins Press, Baltimore, Md., 1928.

custom but insisted on hewing its way westward in its own sweet fashion. A spirit of Adventure, in other words, so little restrained by Order that Order in truth dared not attempt to control too rigidly." Such attempts at control as government did make were often ill-advised and usually of little avail. When legislation interfered with development, its violation by the pioneer was seldom regarded as a moral offense.

The conquest of the continent was inevitably marked by "exploitation" rather than "conservation." The westward march, according to Cameron, "was bound in the course of its glacierly, irresistible progress to ride down certain things which lay in its path. The Indian was one, the buffalo another, timber, a third – to mention but a few of them . . . The American people squandered their patrimony. The American people alone are to blame. But at that did they not come pretty close to getting value received?"

Certainly the United States was settled, natural resources were put to work, and industries were developed in record time. Moreover, the American people proved sufficiently adaptable and their land policies sufficiently flexible to meet changing physical, economic, and social conditions. When widespread depletion of natural resources began to make its appearance, the drive to transfer all public lands to private ownership was checked. Lands remaining in federal ownership were gradually reserved or withdrawn from entry, and their area was increased by purchase and exchange. Management practices by all classes of owners improved, sometimes slowly but none the less surely, as population pressures, increased values, and technological advances made management profitable.

For present purposes, the important result of past policies is that today's pattern of land ownership in California, outside of urban and farm areas, is one of scattered holdings by federal, state, and private agencies alike, with wide variation in the effectiveness of management. School grants of Sections 16 and 36, grants of scattered swamp and overflowed lands, railroad grants of alternate sections, and the limitation of individual acquisitions under the preemption, homestead,[1] and timber and stone laws to 160 acres made it difficult

[1] The Enlarged Homestead Act of 1909 increasing the area that could be acquired to 320 acres was extended to California in 1912.

for both private and public owners to acquire or to retain solid blocks of sufficient size for the most effective administration and management. The large area of public (chiefly federal) land also complicates financial and jurisdictional relationships among the federal, state, and local governments. The question is: what changes in the situation would give better results in terms of better land management, and how can they be brought about?

Basic Considerations

Underlying Philosophies

A wide range of philosophies exists with respect to land ownership. At one extreme are the few who believe that under the private enterprise system all land should be in private ownership except that needed for the discharge of strictly governmental functions. At the other extreme are the few who believe that all land, because it is the creation of nature and not of man, should be in public ownership; or, if for practical reasons a limited amount of private ownership is permitted, that all economic "rent" should be collected by the state in the form of the "single tax." Between these two extremes, the overwhelming majority believe that both private and public ownership have their place, but with wide difference of opinion as to the best combination of the two types of ownership in any particular set of circumstances.

All would probably agree that the ultimate objective in the ownership, use, and management of natural resources ("land") is to promote the public interest. Even with private property, where profit is a necessary accompaniment of continued private ownership, management practices which are inimical to the public interest are almost certain to result in demands for some form of public control or for a transfer to public ownership. But "public interest" is difficult to define, impossible to measure by any mathematical formula, and approachable by more than one road. Few doubt that governmental agencies have an important part to play in its achievement; or that governmental action may appropriately take the form of public education of and assistance to private owners, public regulation of their activities, and public ownership of land. Just what are the responsibilities of different levels of government in each of these fields of action is far less clear.

Correct decisions as to ownership, uses, and management of land are particularly important because of its limited amount and because of the difficulty of changing from one use to another. That all land, including that now considered "waste," will some day be valuable for some purpose seems as certain as that competition for its control between different owners and different uses will continue to increase. Wise choices depend not only on knowledge of the physical characteristics of land and of the results of its past and present use, but also on foresight in gauging the probable influence of changing technological, economic, and social forces.

Evaluation of Costs and Returns

The acid test of the soundness of any activity is – does it pay, are returns of all kinds greater than costs of all kinds? Even in private activity the answer is often far from clear, as is witnessed by the numerous failures in the business world; but for the most part a common measuring stick – the dollar – can be applied to both costs and returns. With many kinds of public activity no such measuring stick exists. How does one compare costs and returns in such activities as the maintenance of schools, public libraries, police forces, and public health services; national defense and foreign aid; and land management to control erosion, to check floods, and to provide opportunities for recreation, including hunting and fishing? How accurately can future returns and costs be foreseen and estimated?

How does one identify, as well as evaluate, the social costs and returns connected with private ownership, and the private costs and returns connected with public ownership? For example, does logging on private land affect favorably or unfavorably the water supply and opportunities for recreation; to what extent does public ownership and management help or hinder the stabilization of forest and wood-using industries and the communities dependent thereon? These questions lead into the subject of multiple use – what it is, what are its advantages and disadvantages from both the public and private point of view, and by what agencies it is most effectively practiced. They also emphasize the fact that every use affects every other use. Timber management, range management, watershed management, and recreation management are inextricably intertwined.

National and State Approaches

Most land use problems have national as well as state and local significance. This is especially, but not exclusively, true when federal ownership, regulation, or cooperation is involved. Just as different land uses are interrelated, so are national, state, and local interests. The progressive abbreviation of time and space has made it more difficult than ever to draw a sharp line between federal and state rights and responsibilities. "One nation" is today much nearer a reality than "one world."

These facts led the American Forestry Association in its 1954 Program for American Forestry to recommend concurrent national and state-by-state studies of land ownership patterns and problems throughout the country. This dual approach recognizes that every state has its own pattern and problems which must be considered not only by themselves but as part of the national picture. The present exploratory study constitutes a first step toward more thorough consideration of the situation in California, with due regard to both state and national interests.

That situation and its historical background have been described briefly in earlier portions of this report. It is undoubtedly a different situation from that which would exist if the last century could be relived with full knowledge of what has actually happened. Since that is impossible, we must of necessity start from where we are. Changes are justified only if they promise to improve the situation. Ownership studies should therefore attempt to identify the strong and the weak points in the present setup, and to devise means for its improvement.

Priority of Uses

The task is a highly difficult and complicated one because of the many agencies, the many land uses, and the many economic, social, political, and philosophical factors involved. The objective of evolving an ownership pattern that will assure the most productive use of the wildland resources of the state in the "public interest" is clear, but not the pattern itself.

Water is the state's most valuable natural resource. As such, it deserves, and should receive, primary consideration in land management. With the expansion of population, agriculture, and industry, conservation of the water supply will become an increasingly urgent problem unless and until fresh water from the ocean can be supplied to distant points at a price to compete with natural supplies of fresh water. Even in that eventuality, an ample supply of surface runoff and of ground water will continue to be a major asset, and the control of erosion and floods will be as imperative as ever.

The generalization in the preceding paragraph is, of course, subject to many local exceptions. There are considerable areas where for topographic, climatic, scenic, biologic, or other reasons wood, forage, or recreation may have a higher priority as the main objective of management. Their relative importance will vary widely from place to place, depending on the characteristics of the land and on economic and social considerations.

Mineral resources rank high in value, but they occur in commercial quantities over a relatively small area and their exploitation is commonly compatible with other, surface uses of the land. There are, however, situations where conflicts arise between the utilization of minerals and other resources, as for example scenic values, and where priorities must therefore be established.

Research in several fields is urgently needed to guide both private and public owners in making sound policy and managerial decisions with respect to objectives and practices, including the particular use or combination of uses that will result in the optimum yield of the various goods and services which the land is capable of producing.

Multiple Use

"Multiple use" has come to be regarded by many as the key to the solution of all of our wildland problems. Like "selective cutting," it is looked upon as a panacea and a guarantee of virtue. Consequently most owners, no matter what their primary objective, now claim that they are practicing multiple use, which may or may not be the result of deliberate planning. The assumption is common that good management for one purpose automatically serves other purposes, and particularly protection of the water supply. Good timber management, range management, and recreation management, for example, are generally accepted as being also good watershed management.

Actually, we know relatively little concerning the potentialities and limitations of multiple use, which means simply planned management with due regard to all of the various values involved. It does not mean the use of every acre, or even of an entire tract, for all possible purposes, but rather the combination of uses that will yield the most satisfactory results in the management of any given administrative unit from the standpoint of its owner. The degree to which different uses are developed therefore depends in large part on the objectives of the owner.

Much needs to be learned about the extent to which different uses are compatible or incompatible, and about the precise methods of management that will permit the optimum combination of uses. For example, sound watershed management in any given area may or may not be consistent with sound timber management or range management. On the one hand, the logging techniques which seem to be acceptable to most forest managers, with the use of heavy equipment, extensive road construction, and even the skidding of logs directly down stream channels, would not be satisfactory where water quality is important. On the other hand, it is probable that in some areas effective watershed management for high water yield will call for fewer trees per acre than the timber manager would like to see.

Similarly, carefully conducted logging operations might not only be unobjectionable but even desirable from the standpoint of certain groups of recreationists such as picnickers, campers, hunters, and fishermen, while they would be wholly unacceptable to the wilderness lover. From the standpoint of the landowner, recreational use may be too dangerous at certain seasons and in certain areas but entirely acceptable at other times and places. These are samples of problems that need study under the widely varying conditions that exist in different parts of the state such as the redwood region, the pine region, and the chaparral region of southern California.

The successful application of multiple use requires not only decision as to what activities will be encouraged, and where, but also provision of machinery to facilitate their effective administration. Two important items are roads and fences. Access roads are needed by every class of user, from the timber operator, stockman, hunters, fishermen, and other recreationists to the fire fighter and the administrator. Fences establish definite boundary lines, help to control livestock, both for the good of the range and for the protection of recreation areas, and are often useful in other ways. Location of roads and trails with due regard to the needs of all the uses involved is a major factor in obtaining their effective coordination.

The problem of multiple use is inseparable from that of values. As accurate knowledge as practicable of probable returns and costs is essential for sound judgment as to the best use or combination of uses for a particular piece of land, and as to the type of ownership best suited to achieve the purposes in view. The returns which may be expected from any given form of management can be estimated fairly accurately in terms of timber and forage values, somewhat less so in terms of water values (including protection from erosion and floods), and far less so in terms of recreational values. Recreation as an activity (picnicking, camping, skiing, hunting, fishing, etc.) needs to be distinguished from the "re-creation" that results from the activity in the form of improved physical, mental, and spiritual health.

Monetary measurement of the activity is possible, although there is room for considerable improvement in the methods now in use. There is as yet nothing that even approaches a satisfactory quantitative measure of the extent to which the activity makes the recreationist a more highly developed human being, a more productive worker, and a better citizen; yet these are values for which the activity is undertaken. Even though it may never be possible to put a dollar sign on them, we certainly need to be able to identify them and to evaluate at least in broad terms their magnitude and duration.

Opinion Surveys

That we shall ever be able to make any accurate financial comparison of the net returns from different forms of wildland use where social and intangible values and costs are involved seems highly unlikely. Therefore, decisions as to what uses should be favored, and under what ownership, will have to based on judgment after consideration of all available facts. Present owners, managers, administrators, and legislators will make the decisions in the first instance; but in the long run they will be made either directly or indirectly by the voters — county-wide, state-wide, and nation-wide. In other words, the judgment of the community as to relative values, and as to the best means of realizing them, will be the final arbiter, just as it is in education and other activities where social and intangible values are important.

This situation emphasizes the need to obtain and to make generally available as much information as possible on the many complex factors involved. Only an informed public can be relied upon to make intelligent judgments. There is also need for administrators and legislators to have current knowledge as to people's views with respect to matters of public policy and practice. Efficiently conducted public-opinion surveys could be very helpful in providing information as to the kind of recreation that the people themselves prefer, and as to their attitude with respect to such programs as the preservation of wilderness areas, whether or not they personally ever expect to use them. Studies along these lines can fill a real need.

Techniques of Land Management

Efficient management of land for the production of whatever combination of goods and services may be the objective of the owner clearly depends on knowledge, and application, of the appropriate techniques. It is beyond the scope of this report to attempt any enumeration of the manifold technical problems involved in the skillful handling of natural resources of all kinds. The research programs of federal, state, and private agencies attest their variety and difficulty.

It is, however, pertinent to emphasize the opportunities that exist for all classes of owners to take advantage of the latent but unused productive capacity of large areas of land. A single illustration from the field of timber production will give some idea of the possibilities.

Forest Service estimates show the following areas and percentages of poorly stocked commercial forest land in California:

Class of land	M acres	Per cent of class
Young sawtimber stands	898	32
Poletimber stands	497	44
Seedling and sapling stands	29	66
	1,424	36

In addition, there is an area of 2,113,000 acres that is nonstocked. These figures mean that nearly three-fifths (58 per cent) of the total commercial forest area of the state, exclusive of old-growth sawtimber stands, is either poorly stocked or nonstocked. Truly staggering opportunities therefore exist for increasing the production of timber on lands already cut over, and also on lands bearing old-growth stands as cutting reaches them, through improved protection from fire, insects, and disease and through more intensive silvicultural practices (including planting).

Table 36 compares the area of plantable commercial and noncommercial forest land in California with the area of acceptable plantations so far made by various classes of owners as of 1952. "Plantable" areas, as defined by the Forest Service, include "nonstocked or poorly stocked forest land or nonforest land: (a) on which the establishment or interplanting of forest tree cover is desirable and practicable, and (b) on which regeneration will not occur naturally to a desirable density within a reasonable time."

Acceptable plantations, more than half of which are on national-forest land, constitute only 0.6 per cent of the 4 million acres of commercial forest land that still needs planting, and only 0.1 per cent of the 3 million acres of noncommercial forest land (chiefly brush and open woodland). Comparable figures for the continental United States are 10 per cent and 2 per cent. It is interesting to note that

California is credited with having 12 per cent of the plantable forest area in the country and 57 per cent of that in the West.

Table 36. Area of Plantable Forest Land and of Acceptable Forest Plantations in California by Classes of Owners, 1952.

Class of owner	Commercial forest land: Plantable	Commercial forest land: Acceptable plantations	Noncommercial forest land: Plantable	Noncommercial forest land: Acceptable plantations	Total: Plantable	Total: Acceptable plantations
	Thousand Acres					
Federal	1,987	17	1,867	*	3,854	17
State, county, and municipal	39	—	40	*	79	*
Private	2,078	9	1,200	5	3,278	14[1]
	4,104	26	3,107	5	7,211	31

* Less than 50 acres.

[1] In addition, there are 5,000 acres of acceptable shelterbelt plantings, mostly for the protection of citrus groves.

Source: "Timber Resource Review," Forest Service, 1955.

In much of California, climatic conditions make the rehabilitation of poorly stocked and nonstocked forest lands very difficult. Repeated attempts to reforest brush fields have had little success, and even under more favorable conditions planting has resulted in many failures. The 1957 legislature recognized this situation by appropriating $9,500 to enable the State Forester to "undertake experiments and studies pertinent to determining costs and feasible methods of reforestation by planting, seeding, release of natural seedlings from competing brush, or other procedures deemed promising of the desired results, and involving also brush removal and control, soil preparation and control of rodents or other destructive organisms."

Similar opportunities and needs for increasing production or improving services exist with other natural resources. Although practice in general lags behind knowledge in range management, wildlife management, watershed management, and recreation management, and in the utilization of minerals, failure to obtain greater yields often results from lack of know-how. All owners are dependent on research in the biological, physical, and engineering sciences to place at their disposal the techniques which alone make intensive management possible. The extent to which these techniques will be practiced depends on many factors. Of prime importance so far as private owners are concerned, are economic considerations and public policy with respect to education and other forms of assistance.

Efficiency of Different Classes of Owners

The criterion of the effectiveness of any form of ownership — federal, state, corporation, individual — is the results actually obtained by the owner in the management of the land. Public owners appraise results primarily from the standpoint of their overall contribution to the "public interest." Private owners appraise them primarily from the point of view of their financial profitability, not only currently but in the case of sustained-yield management for an indefinite period of time. The two points of view are not necessarily in conflict. Public ownership should certainly yield returns (economic and social, tangible and intangible) in excess of costs; private ownership, through its investment of capital, employment of labor, and production of useful goods, automatically contributes in many ways to the public interest. There is, however, normally a difference in emphasis on immediate objectives.

Society is interested in different kinds of ownership from the standpoint both of objectives and of efficiency of administration. What is the record of various federal and state agencies, of corporations, of farmers, and of other individuals in providing the water, recreation, wood, and forage needed by an increasing population with a rising standard of living and an expanding economy? This is a question which it is important but difficult to answer.

Even the tangible results of managerial practices are often difficult to measure, as is evidenced by the failure of two attempts by the Forest Service to devise a method for appraising the productivity of cutover forest lands which meets with general approval. When it comes to determining the effect of management on the quality, quantity, and distribution of the water runoff, or the provision of satisfactory opportunities for hunting, fishing, and other forms of recreation, the task is much more difficult. Until research in such fields as these is much further advanced, comparisons will have to be based largely on general impressions by those whose training and experience lend weight to their judgment.

Some aspects of administration can be appraised more readily. Fifteen years ago the Forest Service was the recognized leader in the management of forest and range lands. The states did little outside of the field of fire control, where their efforts were often relatively weak. Private owners employed few foresters and gave them little responsibility. Today state fire-control activities are so effective that the California State Association of County Supervisors has recently urged that federal activities be brought up to state standards. Some of the larger private owners are now practicing forestry of an intensity that the Forest Service finds it hard to match. Range management on private lands has improved greatly. Recreational facilities in state parks, notably in California, are often superior to those in national parks and national forests, where the situation has become so serious that the National Park Service and the Forest Service have been forced to dramatize their needs in "Mission 66" and "Operation Outdoors."

Leaders of the Forest Service believe that it is laboring under the handicap of inadequate federal appropriations and salary scales. They state that on some national forests the funds available for fire control are about half those needed for effective protection. In 1955 there was an overload of 39 per cent on the recreational facilities on national forests throughout the country, and the situation was certainly no better in California. Timber sale work is handicapped by inadequate funds for estimating, appraising, and marking the timber to be sold. Salary scales make it difficult for federal agencies to compete with state and private agencies for the best men, particularly in the professional grades.

On the other hand, there are those who believe that the Forest Service and other bureaus (federal and state) tend to be less efficient than private owners: that they spread the job out thinner, offer less incentive to complete it expeditiously, engage in more paper work, and in general get less return per dollar of expenditure. Persons with this point of view argue that, while public agencies may need more funds for certain activities, the need for greater efficiency is even more acute.

Study is needed to determine to what extent these generalizations are supported by facts. Many complications, including the frequent differences in objectives, make the task a difficult but nonetheless urgent one. The effect of appropriations, salary scales, and administrative competence on the relative efficiency of different classes of owners, when all factors are taken into consideration, is obviously of major importance.

Research dealing with such subjects as multiple use, social and intangible values, costs and returns, techniques of land management, and relative efficiency of management by different classes of owners is highly important but will inevitably be slow in producing conclusive information. Meanwhile it is desirable to study some aspects of the land ownership situation in the light of the considerable knowledge which we already have and which can be obtained by relatively short-time investigations. Some of the specific problems that need current attention are discussed in the following pages.

Federal Land Problems

Problems connected with federal ownership will be taken up by classes of land, followed by a general consideration of the subjects of contributions in lieu of taxes and of federal jurisdiction.

Unreserved Public Domain

The unreserved public domain in California comprises 17,848,000 acres, of which 24 per cent is inside and 76 per cent outside of grazing districts. The entire area is withdrawn from entry except under the mining laws; but any land may be classified and opened to entry by the Secretary of the Interior under applicable laws. The most important of these laws are the Homestead Act, the Desert-land Act, the Small-tract Act, and the acts authorizing the sale of isolated and mountainous tracts. Sale of materials, including timber, without disposal of the land, is also authorized.

GRAZING DISTRICTS. A major question concerns the future of the grazing districts, which are sometimes referred to as "reserves that are not reserves." Under the Taylor Grazing Act of 1934 the Secretary of the Interior is authorized to establish such districts pending "final disposal" of the land. A trial of more than twenty years would seem to provide adequate experience for a definite decision as to whether they should be abolished or made permanent. The repeated failure of attempts to transfer them to the states or to private owners indicates an intention on the part of Congress to retain them in federal ownership. If that is the case, action to change them from withdrawals to reservations would clear up the uncertainty that surrounds their present status and would give them a stability that would strengthen their administration. The problem is, of course, not one that is peculiar to California, but is common to the ten western states in which grazing districts are located.

A related question that is peculiar to California concerns the desirability of establishing as grazing districts all or part of the 5,814,000 acres in the unreserved public domain that are leased for grazing under Section 15 of the Taylor Grazing Act. Such action is now (1957) under consideration by the Bureau of Land Management in consultation with the users of the range. It would reduce the proportion of receipts from leases paid to the counties in lieu of taxes, but would provide uniformity of treatment of similar lands and presumably greater stability of administration.

A third question concerning grazing districts arises from the fact that 28 per cent of the Mojave Grazing District and 59 per cent of the Honey Lake Grazing District are not in federal ownership. A greater blocking up of the various ownerships through the exchange process would seem desirable from the point of view of all concerned.

LAND CLASSIFICATION. A needed activity that is well under way is classification of the unreserved public domain to determine the uses for which the land is best suited and whether or not it should be opened to entry. The Bureau of Land Management believes that current appropriations are as large as it can handle effectively in view of the need to train men for the work. It is essential that the classification be thorough, that it be based on economic and social as well as physical factors, and that it consider both present and prospective conditions and needs.

SMALL TRACTS. One aspect of this program that should have special consideration is the classification of land for lease or sale under the Small Tract Act of 1938. That act authorizes the Secretary of the Interior, in his discretion, to lease or sell vacant, unreserved public lands in tracts not exceeding 5 acres, which he may classify as chiefly valuable for residence, recreation, business, or community sites.

Final sales during the eight years from 1949 to 1956 (there were no sales prior to 1949) are shown in Table 37 and Figure 22. In addition, 30,566 leases covering 164,491 acres were in force on June 30, 1956. So keen is interest in acquisition of land under this act in southern California that there is a backlog of many thousands of applications on which the Bureau of Land Management has not yet been able to take action.

Table 37.—Final Entries Approved for Small Tract Sales in California, 1949-1956.

YEAR	NUMBER	ACRES	PURCHASE MONEY
1949	34	170	$5,500
1950	38	195	3,723
1951	73	364	6,675
1952	240	1,202	27,766
1953	185	862	18,876
1954	476	2,268	42,702
1955	1,362	6,472	121,609
1956	1,653	7,533	141,394
	4,061	19,066	$368,445

Many feel that this act, like the Stockraising Homestead Act of 1916, is an example of ill-considered legislation that encourages people to take up land for a purpose for which no real need exists or under conditions that will be inimical to the long-run public interest. They believe that it often results in the alienation of land that should remain in public ownership, in the breaking up of livestock ranges, in the creation of rural slums, and in widespread specula-

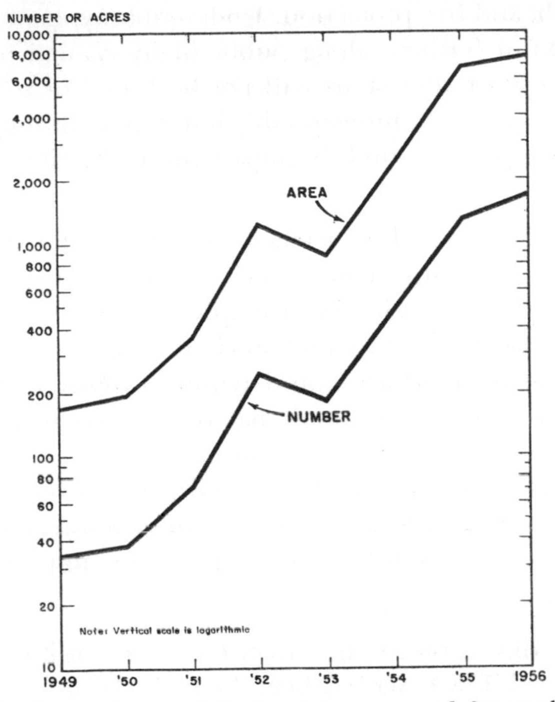

Figure 22. Number and area of final entries approved for small-tract sales in California, 1949-1956.

tion. In other words, they believe that in practice the Department of the Interior has not achieved the high ideals embodied in its statement of policy:

"It is the policy of the Secretary in the administration of the act of June 1, 1938, to promote the beneficial utilization of the public lands subject to the terms thereof, and at the same time to safeguard the public interest in the lands. To this end small tract sites will be considered in the light of their effect upon the conservation of natural resources and upon the communities or area involved. Lands will not be leased or sold, for example, which would lead to private ownership or control of scenic attractions, or water resources, or other areas that should be kept open to public use. Nor will isolated or scattered settlement be permitted which would impose heavy burdens upon State or local governments for roads, schools, and police, health, and fire protection. Undesirable types of construction for settlement or business along public highways and parkways will be guarded against, and lands will not be leased or sold under the act if such action would unreasonably interfere with the use of water for grazing purposes or unduly impair the protection of watershed areas."

A major cause for such deficiencies as exist in the administration of the act is the pressure under which the Bureau of Land Management has had to work. It has been simply swamped with applications to open up areas which had not previously been classified and the wise development of which would require careful study and planning of a high order. The result has often been premature settlement, with improper location of roads; inadequate provision for water supply, sanitation, schools, fire and police protection, and recreation areas; and, in general, lack of any comprehensive plan to assure satisfactory standards of housing, layout, improvements, and maintenance.

San Bernardino County, in which the great bulk of the activity under the Small Tract Act has been located, claims that is has been unable to exercise the control over matters of this kind which it exercises over the development of land in private ownership, and that it has found itself faced with the responsibility for providing services for which it has had no opportunity to make adequate preparation, either financial or otherwise. The county has prepared an itemized statement of the difficulties it has encountered in trying to cope with the problems created by the act, together with a detailed list of the steps which it believes should be taken to improve the situation.

Thorough study is needed to determine what changes are desirable in the law, in its administration, or in county policies and practices. Prompt action is in order because of the tremendous pressure on the Bureau of Land Management to speed up its classification activities and to open additional areas to entry both in localities where considerable development has already taken place and in new locations; and because any initial mistakes in land development are difficult if not impossible to correct. It would help to minimize such mistakes if classification were handled in close cooperation with local agencies.

FOREST LANDS. Still another problem has to do with the 324,000 acres of commercial forest land in the unreserved public domain. The fact that much of this area consists of scattered and relatively small blocks makes it subject to considerable trespass and otherwise increases the difficulty of administration. Figure 23 illustrates the distribution of the unreserved public domain in relation to other federal lands, Indian lands, and state lands in one part of the state — northwestern California. The Pacific Southwest Field Committee of the Department of the Interior, by which the map was prepared, estimates that 55 per cent of the 170,000 acres of public domain covered by the study cannot be profitably administered by the Bureau of Land Management and is eligible for disposal. The remaining 45 per cent is occupied by stands of timber with a total volume of 2 billion board feet and an annual cut of 30 million board feet.

A clear-cut decision should be reached with respect to the future of such lands as these. They can be added to national forests, sold or exchanged with the state or private owners, or continued in their present administrative setup. In the latter case they should receive more intensive management and be given a reserved status.

Legislation would be necessary or desirable in connection with any of these alternatives. Exterior boundaries of national forests in California can be extended, or a new type of reserves created, only by act of Congress. If the land were to be sold in blocks of sufficient size to make economic management units, as would be desirable, the present limit of 1,520 acres on the maximum size of isolated tracts that can be sold would have to be raised. A pertinent question in this connection is whether a higher limit is desirable for all types of land, of course with continuation in the Secretary of the Interior of full power to decide whether or not any sale should be made.

MILITARY LANDS

Events during and following World War II resulted in the acquisition or withdrawal of more than 4 million acres of land in California for use by the Department of Defense. This material expan-

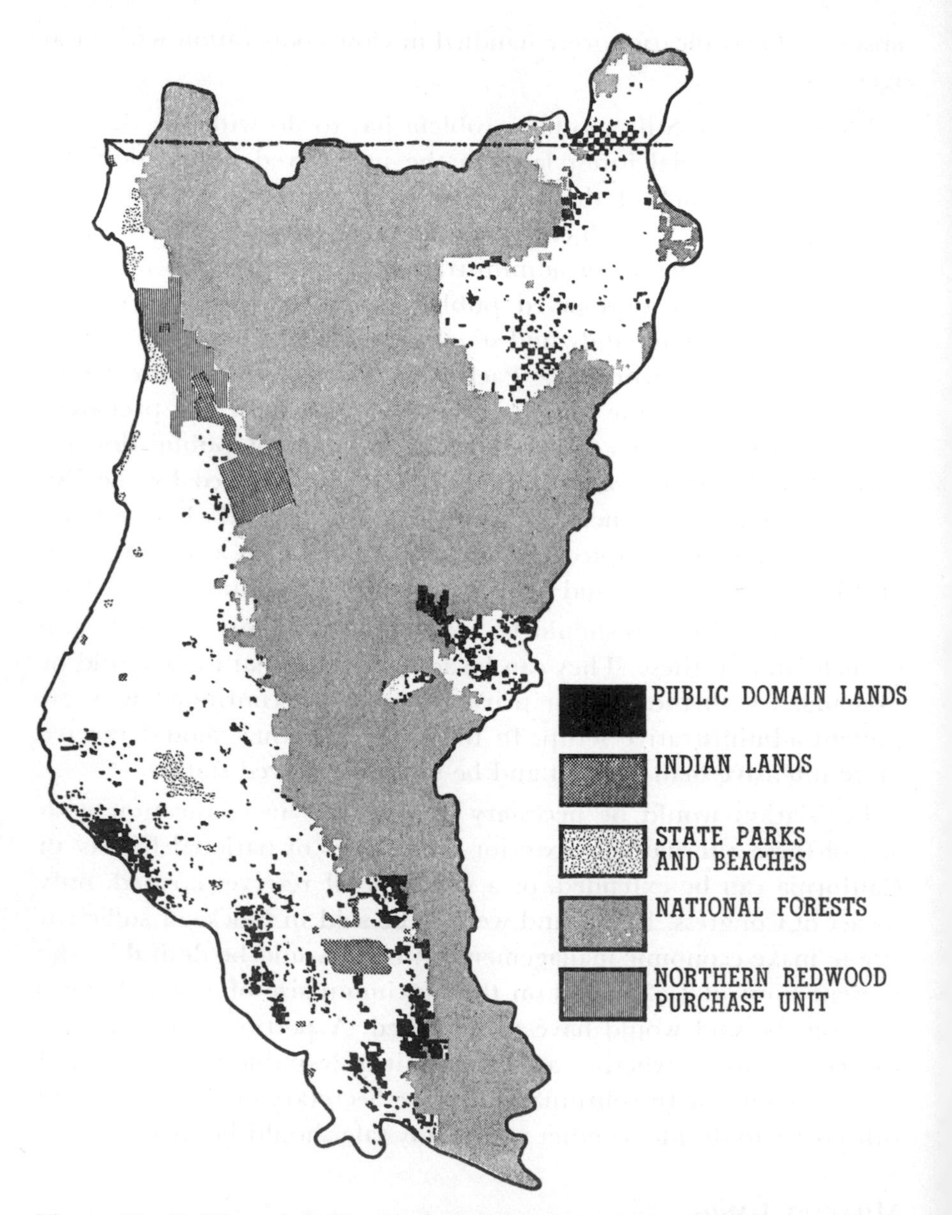

Figure 23. Public and Indian lands in part of northwestern California, 1956. From *Natural Resources of Northwestern California,* U. S. Department of the Interior, Pacific Southwest Field Committee, Northwestern California Investigations.

sion of its holdings has led to occasional accusations that its constituent departments are "land grabbers." The critics recognize that large areas are needed for maneuvers, bombing ranges, and other military purposes, but question whether some of the areas acquired and withdrawn are not excessive in size or so located as to interfere unnecessarily with other uses. Their concern has led to the introduction and passage of legislation to prohibit the withdrawal of additional tracts of 5,000 acres or more without the approval of Congress.

On the contrary, the military representatives point out that many of the installations are too small to provide adequate range for modern weapons and sufficient room for the enlarged maneuvers required in training for atomic warfare. It is admitted that there may be times when for short periods the military agencies retain more lands than are currently required, but a suitable cushion must be maintained to meet sudden increases in military activity. Even in such cases, the leasing of lands for non-military uses during periods of reduced military activity provides a public service. Finally, the military representatives point out that approval by Congress is required for all purchases and interservice exchanges.

For obvious reasons fairly sizeable portions of the area reserved for military purposes are not ordinarily available for other uses such as grazing, mining, logging, hunting, and fishing. Even after military operations cease, other uses may be prevented or greatly restricted for some time because of "contamination" of the land by unexploded shells and bombs, and in some cases, although not to an appreciable extent in California, by radioactive materials such as strontium 90. It is therefore urgent that plans for the withdrawal of lands for military purposes continue to be worked out through the fullest possible cooperation among the various units in the Department of Defense and with other federal and state agencies whose activities may be affected by the proposed withdrawals, in order to make sure that both the area involved and the interference with other uses are kept to a minimum consistent with the actual needs for military purposes. At the same time it must be recognized frankly that in an atomic age military needs for space tend to increase.

National Forests

From time to time it has been proposed that considerable areas of national-forest land should be transferred to state or private ownership. Among the many factors responsible for this proposal are the mounting value of the timber and forage resources of the national forests; the growing dependence of the wood-using industries on the national forests for their timber supply; the increasing use of good forest practices by the larger timberland owners; the current reaction against federal ownership and activity in general; doubt whether some national-forest lands really serve the "national interest"; and the belief that national forests should include only lands whose major value is for timber production and watershed protection, which are specified by the act of 1897 as the primary purposes for which national forests may be created.

The proposal is vigorously opposed by those who believe that federal ownership offers the best long-run prospect for stable and effective management, and that the increasing value of national-forest resources is an argument in favor of their retention rather than of their disposal. They emphasize the importance of an integrated program for the best use of *all* resources, and point to the fact that Congress both by substantive legislation and by appropriations has repeatedly recognized the production of forage and the provision of opportunities for recreation as important functions of the national forests. They take a liberal view of what constitutes the "national interest" in an age when all parts of the country are constantly being drawn closer together, and ask whether, in southern California for example, it is not as legitimate a function of the federal government to assist in protection from floods by land management as by the construction of engineering works.

The arguments pro and con obviously apply, with varying weights, in all parts of the country where national forests are located. So far as California is concerned, the following statement by the Senate Interim Committee on Public Lands (1955) is probably fairly representative of public opinion:

"There is no evidence of any objection on the part of the Californians to the [original] forest withdrawals, and an objection today is surely a very minor voice. However, it must be remembered that these withdrawals were blanket withdrawals. Of the 19,000,000 acres of land in California bearing the name of national forest, some of the lands have never, and probably will never, see a tree . . .

"Almost all of the landholding agencies of the federal government are to some extent in checkerboard pattern, and these agencies feel that private lands within this pattern constitute a menace to the proper management of their holdings. Time after time, the reason given for the taking of state and private land is 'to round out the management program.' If this concept is carried to its extreme, we can envisage the small amount of land that will be left in which Californians might live and work . . .

"The extent to which the State and Federal Governments hold land is not just another academic argument. It is important to the individual, important to local government, that is to say, counties, school districts and other municipal corporations, and important to the state itself . . . Inasmuch as government-owned land is exempt from taxation by both the State and Federal constitutions, the individual taxpayer must absorb the loss of tax revenue to local government by an increased tax levy on his real property, or an increased taxation of his income to help the State and Federal Government assist local governmental agencies in providing local governmental services."

With respect to federal lands in general, and to national forests in particular, these comments emphasize the need for the basic studies previously suggested of the potentialities and limitations of multiple use; the evaluation of social and intangible costs and returns; and the relative efficiency of public and private owners in attaining the objectives of land management. These objectives will naturally vary widely from place to place and from time to time. Such studies will need to be continued indefinitely and conclusive results will not be obtained overnight. Meanwhile there is room for many shorter term studies and for action that may materially improve the present situation.

BOUNDARY ADJUSTMENTS. An illustration of this situation is the abolition by the National Forest Reservation Commission on May 6, 1957, of the Southern Redwood Purchase Unit of 600,000 acres and the reduction of the area of the Northern Redwood Purchase Unit from 263,000 acres to 148,000 acres. Although these purchase units were established during the fiscal year 1936, only 14,492 acres have been acquired in the northern unit, while in the southern unit no land has been acquired or even approved for purchase. Lack of progress in effectuating the original program was presumably due to lack of appropriations and to improved management by private owners which lessened the need for federal acquisition that apparently existed twenty years ago. Under these circumstances the action taken by the Commission, which was doubtless recommended by the Forest Service, is both understandable and commendable.

Of prime importance is consideration of both exterior and interior boundaries of the long-established national forests — a process in which the Forest Service has been continuously engaged for many years. For example, since 1954 the regional office has made a study of the boundaries of all national forests in California, as a result of which it has recommended certain changes in boundaries that are now before the Washington office for action. The fact that the subject continues to receive intensive consideration is evidence that there is nothing "sacred" about existing boundaries and nothing necessarily permanent about the status quo at any given time or place. Cases doubtless exist where land could advantageously be put to other uses and administration strengthened by the elimination of isolated blocks of national forest land and the straightening of irregular boundaries. Another possibility is the elimination of larger areas of non-timbered land along the exterior boundaries of national forests, provided there is reasonable assurance that the land will be managed as well or better under other ownership from the standpoint of the "public interest," including that of the local community as well as of the state and the nation. Decisions are often difficult to reach.

Town sites that have developed on national forest lands under special use permits constitute another problem. There are now some 25 communities in some 13 national forests in which practically all of the land is occupied by residences and business establishments. Private ownership of such land is clearly desirable but can now be effected only by the process of exchange, which is often difficult to arrange. Elimination of the land from the national forests is possible by Presidential proclamation or by act of Congress, but such action would restore the land to the unreserved public domain, from which it could be acquired by private owners only under the Town Sites Act or the Small Tract Act.

A preferable alternative would seem to be the enactment of legislation authorizing the sale of town sites by the Secretary of Agriculture under suitable safeguards. Such legislation, which is embodied in bills now before Congress, might also advantageously include authority to sell isolated parcels or projecting strips of national-forest land, similar to that which the Secretary of the Interior now has for unreserved public-domain lands. Study is needed to determine the precise provisions that would best meet the situation in California and elsewhere.

A more difficult and more important problem is that which the California Senate Interim Committee viewed with so much concern – the adjustment of interior boundaries. Certainly intermingled holdings, particularly when of checkerboard pattern, create so many difficulties of administration and management for both public and private owners that possible remedies of the situation deserve the most careful study. The Tahoe National Forest, with a roughly equal division of ownership between the federal government and several private owners, mostly checkerboard, furnishes the most conspicuous but not the only example of the chaotic situation that the past land policy of the government sometimes produced. (See Fig. 24.)

The whole subject needs careful reconsideration, on a national as well as a state basis. Should the policy of exchanging timber for land be permanently abandoned? Should more areas of strategic importance for national-forest administration be acquired under the Weeks Law or out of national-forest receipts? Should the proposed authority to sell isolated and projecting strips of national forest land be extended to interior holdings, with such limitations as Congress might see fit to impose? Whatever procedure is adopted, the objec-

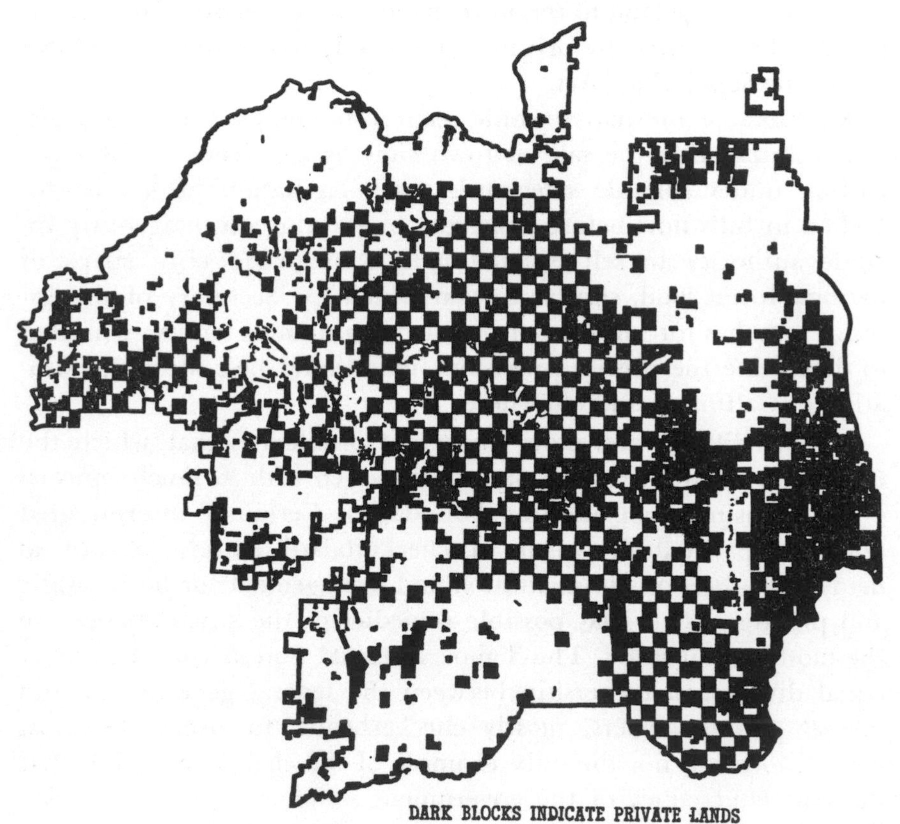

Figure 24. Checkerboard pattern of federal and private holdings in part of the Tahoe National Forest, 1955. Courtesy, Forest Service, U. S. Department of Agriculture.

tive would be to bring about an ownership pattern that would facilitate the sustained-yield management of timber and range lands by both public and private agencies, and that would assure the safeguarding of watershed and recreational values. Would it be a serious matter if the blocking-up process resulted in increasing the area of one national forest and decreasing that of another? Full cooperation among federal, state, and private agencies is essential to find a satisfactory solution.

SUSTAINED-YIELD UNITS. Another attempt to promote stability in the forest and wood-using industries and the communities dependent thereon is the Sustained-Yield Forest Management Act of 1944. This act is thought by some to have outlived its usefulness. Only one sustained-yield federal unit has been established in California (1950) — the Big Valley Unit of 82,185 acres on the Modoc National Forest; and it is clear that a second federal unit proposed by the Board of Supervisors of Modoc County will not materialize.

There are no cooperative sustained-yield units, although in 1948 a public hearing was held on a proposal for the establishment of the Woodleaf Cooperative Sustained-Yield Unit which would have involved nearly 16,000 acres of private land and approximately 40,000 acres of national-forest land in Butte, Plumas, Sierra, and Yuba Counties. This proposal was rejected because of vigorous opposition by local interests. Another proposal, which would involve 40,677 acres of national-forest land and 25,210 acres owned by the Placerville Lumber Company, has been pending since 1948, with no prospect of approval.

The position of the present administration was made clear in July, 1957, when the Secretary of Agriculture informed the Senate Committee on Agriculture and Forestry that "it has been determined to discontinue, for the foreseeable future, further establishment of both Federal and Cooperative Sustained Yield Units under the Act of March 29, 1944," and that he has no objection to the enactment of bills now before Congress which would repeal that act but would not affect existing units. This attitude is not shared by some landowners and local communities, who feel that repeal of the act would be unwise.

WILDERNESS AREAS. "Wilderness areas" and "wild areas" (the successors to "primitive areas") constitute a particularly difficult problem in the application of the multiple-use policy in national-forest administration. The basic concept is reasonably clear, and the Forest Service definition is specific with respect to size and excluded uses. But the definition leaves many questions unanswered. Just where should the boundaries of a potential wilderness (or wild) area be drawn so as to attain the desired objective without undue sacrifice of other objectives, such as timber production and utilization and mass recreation? How much management does a wilderness require for its own protection and that of surrounding lands, and how much management will it stand without losing its distinctive character? What kinds of uses, including recreational uses, can be allowed before overutilization and consequent deterioration occur? Forest Service comments on such questions as these are very much to the point:

"It is exceedingly difficult to calculate the total area of wilderness required to meet either the present or the prospective need because this need cannot be measured. From the standpoint of the wilderness lover it is unquestionably true that the more of these areas that are set aside and the larger they are, the better; consequently, it would appear from the viewpoint of the wilderness lover alone if every area of 100,000 acres or more on the national forests which yet remains uninvaded by roads were set aside as a wilderness it would be none too much. However, the management of national forests must meet the needs of many people. No one sort of use can be considered to the exclusion of others, except on small areas. Setting aside 100,000 acres for a wilderness may preclude too many other types of use to make arbitrary action possible. It is necessary first to consider all competing values.

"The great majority of those who go to the forest for recreation do not have either the ability or the desire to get away from the easy travel made possible by roads, and penetrate into the back country. To the extent that the land therein is suitable for nonwilderness recreation, the establishment of a wilderness means closing just so much of the national forests to the use of those who came there to seek recreation in the form of touring, picnicking, camping near their cars, or stopping at resorts, organization camps, or summer homes."

The conflict between different kinds of recreational use recalls a comment by James Truslow Adams in an article in Harper's Magazine for April, 1930, entitled "Diminishing Returns in Modern Life." After pointing out that a beautiful spot on Long Island which used to be visited by only a few was now frequented by thousands, he continued: "I admit that according to the Declaration of Independence and the New Testament there was no reason why only a privileged few should enjoy the solitude and beauty of the Point . . . Theory, however, has nothing to do with it . . . The point is that by the mere fact that eight thousand people tried to enjoy the solitude and beauty of Montauk at once, the solitude and beauty evaporated . . . 'the many' did not get what 'the few' had had . . . What the many got was something entirely different from what the few had got. Which of those, for the whole human race for generations to come, might be the better would baffle the mathematics of even an Einstein to figure out."

When mathematics fails, recourse must be had to judgment, initially of the legislator and the administrator and eventually of the community. Hence the importance of the public-opinion surveys previously suggested, together with studies that will make possible the more accurate identification and appraisal of personal and social values. The position of the Forest Service is that "the safe general rule to be followed in case of doubt is to withhold development until the proper course of action is evident, because once such an area is invaded by conflicting uses, the true wilderness conditions can rarely be restored in any period short of centuries."

Aside from overuse, the greatest dangers to which wilderness areas are exposed are the establishment of mining claims and the construction of roads to private property. Here is one situation where there can be no question as to the desirability of eliminating inholdings by exchange or if necessary by purchase. At least equally important is the closing of wilderness areas to mineral entry, but not necessarily to prospecting, until mineral values clearly exceed wilderness values. Careful study will be necessary to frame legislation that will accomplish this objective without injustice to the mining industries or danger to the nation's mineral requirements.

A lesser, but by no means negligible, danger is that water storage may depreciate or even destroy wilderness values. The danger arises not only from the change in the natural landscape effected by such storage but also from the usual necessity of building and maintaining a road to the water development.

National Parks

The outstanding problem in the management of national parks was created by Congress in 1916 when it directed that they should be enjoyed by as many people as possible and at the same time be kept unimpaired for the enjoyment of future generations. One means of attempting to attain both objectives is to concentrate visitors in certain portions of the parks and to retain the primeval character of the remaining area by keeping it free from roads. This policy might be strengthened by formally establishing as wilderness areas the parts of the parks that are to be kept relatively inaccessible. Whether such action should be taken by the Secretary of the Interior or by Congress, as is proposed in pending legislation for both national parks and national forests, is a question that needs thorough consideration. In any event, the elimination of interior private holdings is important to preserve the integrity of the parks. So, too, is the avoidance of uses detrimental to the purposes for which the parks were established.

The National Park Service is now engaged in a comprehensive, nation-wide study aimed at achieving a well-rounded national-park system through the addition of areas of outstanding scenic, natural, and historic significance which are not now included in it and through the elimination of existing areas found to be of less than national significance. This study raises specifically the question as to what adjustments, if any, of existing boundaries between national parks and national forests are in order, in California as well as elsewhere — a question on which the views of the general public as well as of the two administrative agencies directly involved are important.

The problem is basically one of policy rather than of administration. To what extent, and where, should specific limitations be placed on practical application of the theory of multiple use? In national parks and national monuments, existing limitations virtually prevent logging, grazing, mining, reservoir construction, and hunting. In national forests, the very fact that these activities are permitted limits their use and value as museum pieces and for certain forms of recreation. In both types of reservations, there is multiple use, but multiple use of a radically different kind and scope.

The decision as to what kind of multiple use should be favored in a given situation involves a comparison of social and economic values for which there is no common measuring stick. It must therefore be based on the judgment of Congress — a judgment that will inevitably be influenced by the views not only of the National Park Service and the Forest Service but of organizations such as the Sierra Club, the Western Pine Association, the California Wool Growers Association, the County Supervisors Association of California, and the California State Chamber of Commerce, and of individuals in all walks of life. These views will have a firmer basis, and Congress will be more likely to reach a sound judgment, as the research urged earlier in this report permits identification and, to a greater extent than is now possible, measurement of the values at stake.

An impartial bystander, if such a person exists, might wonder whether the tendency to multiply the number of categories into which federal lands are divided really contributes to the most effective land management; and whether a single category of federal wildlands (exclusive of those reserved for military purposes), each administrative division of which would be managed for the combination of uses to which it is best suited from the point of view of the overall "public interest," might not give better results. If he were to express such views, he would doubtless be attacked by every pressure group in the country, each of which would fear that its particular objective would be menaced by such a setup. They would, however, presumably agree, in theory at least, that both policy and administration in the management of federal lands should be based on as many facts as it is possible to obtain on the relative costs and returns of all kinds resulting from different uses.

Reclamation and Flood-Control Projects

The major problem of land use connected with projects of the Bureau of Reclamation and the Army Corps of Engineers has to do with the acquisition and administration for recreational purposes of lands surrounding the reservoirs. The present joint policy of the Department of the Interior and the Department of the Army regarding land acquisition states that: "Except as authorized by law, no title to land will be acquired for purposes of preservation of wildlife or forests, restoration or replacement of such values destroyed by reservoirs or for creating additional values of like nature, or for recreational purposes." Such authorization is sometimes given by Congress in connection with specific projects, but there is need for a more general grant of authority to assure full realization of the multiple-use potentialities of reclamation, flood-control, and other reservoirs, among which recreation ranks high.

The present policy of both departments of delegating administration of recreational areas so far as possible to local, state, or other federal agencies seems to be working well.

A related matter which has caused concern in some quarters is the fact that a few hundred thousand acres of the federal land in California which the Bureau of Reclamation has under withdrawal for possible reservoir sites and project works are in national forests and at relatively high elevations. There is fear that the future construction of reservoirs on these sites will seriously impair the primeval character of the areas, whether or not they are in formally established wilderness areas. On the other hand, it is reasonably certain that many of the sites will never be used for reservoirs. Such withdrawals also remove the withdrawn lands from mineral entry, although mining may be allowed under special-use permit until the land is needed for other purposes.

The problem can be met in large part if it is jointly recognized and given sympathetic consideration by the various agencies engaged in river-basin planning. Coordinated planning is essential to make sure that reservoir construction gives adequate consideration not only to recreation but also to timber production and road location. Water development, in spite of its intrinsic importance and high priority, should not be allowed needlessly to affect adversely other land uses — a result which it is particularly important to avoid because of the relative permanence of the engineering works involved.

Indian Lands

When Congress in 1953 declared its intention to free the Indian tribes in California and elsewhere from federal supervision and control, it paved the way for the development of a new problem in land use. Only somewhat more than 7,000 Indians and less than 600,000 acres of land in California will be affected if the intention is carried into action, but both the human and the physical resources involved are of major value. The reservations include varying proportions of agricultural, range, forest, and waste land, and water rights are everywhere an item of importance. Commercial forest land is estimated by the Forest Service at 133,000 acres, with a sawtimber stand of about 4 billion board feet.

Although the Senate Interim Committee on California Indian Affairs has already explored some of the human and natural-resource problems that will have to be faced both by the state and federal government when federal withdrawal actually takes place, much more study will be needed to find satisfactory solutions. Present attempts to liquidate the Klamath Indian Reservation in Oregon illustrate vividly the difficulty of finding methods of disposing of the land to federal, state, or private agencies that will be fair to the Indians and that at the same time will assure the continued productivity of the land at a high level. Although the areas of Indian reservations in California are much smaller than that of the Klamath Reservation, some of them such as the Hoopa Valley, Hoopa Extension, Tule River, Round Valley, and Ft. Bidwell Reservations in the northern part of the state are sufficiently large and contain sufficient timber to present similar problems. Different but still difficult problems are presented by the many small reservations in the southern part of the state.[1]

[1] The scattered character of Indian reservations in California and their generally small size are shown in a map and tables accompanying the 1955 report of the Senate Interim Committee on California Indian Affairs.

Contributions in Lieu of Taxes

Kind and Extent. The fact that federal property is exempt from taxation has led to much complaint that federal ownership therefore places a heavy burden on the local taxpayer. Actually the federal government makes large contributions to local communities in lieu of taxes, but the situation varies so greatly from agency to agency, from time to time, and from place to place that no generalization is possible. So far as California is concerned, federal contributions are for the most part in the form of revenue sharing. The arrangements now in force are summarized in Table 38.

In addition to the direct payments to counties, 10 per cent of the gross receipts from national forests is earmarked for the construction of roads and trails within national forests in the state, and much larger specific appropriations are made for the construction of forest highways and forest development roads and trails. Federal appropriations are also made for the construction of roads in national parks, Indian reservations, and the unreserved public domain. Contributions to the Reclamation Fund resulting from federal ownership and receipts are eventually spent, when appropriated by Congress, on approved projects in the reclamation states, including of course California. They are not earmarked for expenditure in the state of origin.

Another contribution to the state for aid in highway construction is based on the ratio of the unappropriated and unreserved public lands and nontaxable Indian lands in the state to the total land area of the state. The federal share of the cost of highway projects is increased by the product of this ratio and the percentage of the total cost normally payable by the state (that percentage is 10 per cent for highways in the National System of Interstate Highways and 50 per cent for other federal-aid highways). With more than 18 per cent of the total area of the state in unreserved public land and Indian land, and with allocations to California for the fiscal year 1958 of $96,947,850 for interstate highways and $45,708,438 for other highways, the amounts involved are considerable.

This increase in the percentage of the total cost of joint highway projects that will be borne by the federal government does not in-

Table 38. Federal Contributions in Lieu of Taxes from Different Classes of Land.

Source of receipts	Per cent of receipts earmarked for			
	States and counties	Reclamation funds	Indian trust funds	U. S. Treasury
Taylor Act grazing districts				
Grazing Fee				
Public lands	12.5	—	—	87.5
Ceded Indian lands	33.3	—	66.7	—
Leased lands	—	—	—	100.0
Range improvement fee	—	—	—	100.0
Taylor Act grazing leases				
Public lands	50.0	—	—	50.0
Ceded Indian lands	—	—	100.0	—
Mineral leases and permits	37.5	52.5	—	10.0
Outer continental shelf lands	—	—	—	100.0
Reclamation land sales	—	100.0	—	—
Sales of other public lands and materials therefrom	5.0	95.0	—	—
National forests	25.0	—	—	75.0
Land utilization projects	25.0	—	—	75.0
National parks	—	—	—	100.0
Wildlife refuges	25.0	—	—	75.0
Lands acquired for flood control purposes (Army Engineers)	75.0	—	—	25.0
Military installations	—	—	—	100.0
Federal Power Commission licenses on national forests and public lands	37.5	—	—	62.5
Indian lands (trust properties)	—	—	100.0	—

Source: Bureau of Land Management.

crease the total allocation of federal funds to the state, which is based on (1) the ratio of the area of the state to the area of the nation, (2) the ratio of the population of the state to the population of the nation, and (3) the ratio of the state's mileage of rural delivery and star routes to the state's total road mileage. It does, however, reduce the amount of matching funds required of the state and thus releases a substantial amount of state funds for use on other projects or for other purposes.

Still another form of expenditure made by the federal government in its capacity as a landowner is for the protection of federal lands from fire. Under the California system of fire protection, this is an expenditure which would have to be made by the state if the land were in private or state ownership. In other words, the state accepts the basic responsibility for the protection of wildlands from fire but excepts federal lands, presumably because the government does not pay taxes on them. The assumption by the federal government of this responsibility may therefore be regarded as in effect a contribution in lieu of taxes, even though the actual expenditure of the funds is made by the government.

Federal payments to California counties in the form of shared revenues, plus direct expenditures for road construction and fire control incurred because of federal land ownership, were approximately as follows for the fiscal year 1956:

Shared revenues	$ 8,866,000
Road construction	10,551,000
Fire control	9,947,000
	$29,364,000

Each of these items is discussed in more detail below.

SHARED REVENUES. Contribution in lieu of taxes in the form of shared revenues, that is, in cash payments to the state and counties, for the fiscal year 1956 are given in Table 39.

Table 39. Federal Payments to the State and Counties in the Form of Shared Revenues, Fiscal Year 1956.

SOURCE	AMOUNT	PER CENT
Taylor Act grazing districts	$5,084	*
Taylor Act grazing leases	33,848	*
National forests	5,294,356	60
Sales of public lands and timber	21,180	*
Mineral leases and permits	3,511,205	40
	$8,865,673	100

* Less than 0.5 per cent.

Source: Bureau of Land Management and Forest Service.

In round numbers, 100 per cent of the total payments came from receipts from national forests and from mineral leases and permits. Table 40 itemizes the payments of 25 per cent of the gross receipts from national forests to individual counties for the period from 1950 to 1956, inclusive.

The source of the receipts – from timber sales, grazing fees, land uses (mostly special-use permits), and power permits – is shown in Figure 25. Particularly striking are the great increase in receipts from timber sales (more than 500 per cent from 1947 to 1956), the steady increase in receipts from land use (about 150 per cent), and the recent decrease in receipts from grazing, which are now at almost exactly the same level as 10 years ago. In 1957, receipts from timber sales were down about a fourth, and from power permits up about a fourth, as compared with 1956.

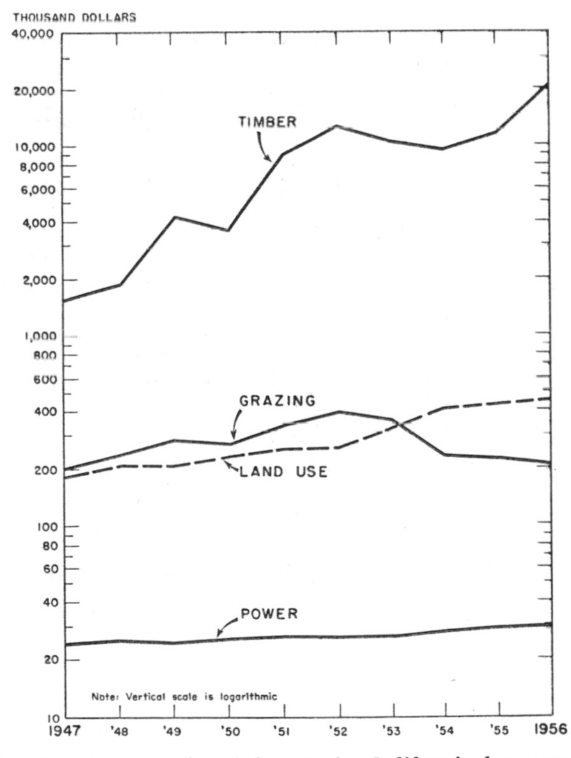

Figure 25. Receipts from national forests in California by sources, 1947-1956.

Table 40. Contribution of 25 Per Cent of National Forest Receipts to Counties, 1950 to 1956.

County	1950	1951	1952	1953	1954
Alpine	$ 26,270	$ 38,603	$ 57,074	$ 53,688	$ 42,642
Amador	5,021	12,951	27,500	24,996	16,805
Butte	27,138	68,386	74,043	61,672	40,931
Calaveras	14,979	19,197	24,042	23,180	19,986
Colusa	3,229	5,549	2,902	5,909	6,102
Del Norte	3,253	23,774	43,071	25,481	64,755
El Dorado	33,324	86,694	185,494	168,566	113,197
Fresno	54,645	118,944	102,028	138,277	153,201
Glenn	9,114	15,664	8,191	16,780	17,311
Humboldt	1,322	13,455	21,439	15,192	25,305
Inyo	7,957	8,585	17,286	16,083	5,645
Kern	4,363	16,204	15,901	11,862	26,323
Lake	12,040	20,692	10,820	22,059	22,699
Lassen	66,308	173,975	316,239	235,152	185,547
Los Angeles	2,513	3,256	3,502	8,785	15,918
Madera	24,703	52,345	44,492	55,925	58,953
Mariposa	14,483	23,167	24,411	27,857	26,856
Mendocino	8,221	14,129	7,395	15,215	15,666
Modoc	47,466	112,516	386,423	135,700	203,924
Mono	10,382	11,197	19,829	18,331	7,820
Monterey	954	1,314	1,350	1,360	1,248
Nevada	10,210	32,754	37,348	37,168	46,579
Orange	447	534	657	637	666
Placer	19,473	60,628	77,015	75,242	85,333
Plumas	293,678	725,902	666,549	564,684	355,214
Riverside	12	22	– – –	8,391	9,425
San Bernardino	8,827	9,288	9,434	16,927	19,218
San Diego	1,267	1,758	2,449	3,533	3,688
San Luis Obispo	568	782	803	809	742
Santa Barbara	1,905	2,623	2,696	2,715	2,491
Shasta	33,230	103,270	179,463	149,784	124,776
Sierra	33,584	98,156	103,797	99,994	112,190
Siskiyou	28,447	133,901	240,995	264,716	259,984
Tehama	28,115	72,376	132,650	108,202	87,730
Trinity	11,810	66,583	216,735	135,659	142,184
Tulare	12,102	40,705	42,078	31,999	64,551
Tuolumne	100,069	128,255	161,413	155,674	134,226
Ventura	1,679	2,311	2,377	2,406	2,226
Yuba	9,542	24,621	22,232	19,700	15,227
	$972,650	$2,345,066	$3,292,123	$2,760,310	$2,537,324[1]

Table 40 (Continued).

1955	1956	Total	Average	County
$ 41,306	$ 77,188	$ 336,771	$ 48,110	Alpine
17,790	43,783	148,846	21,264	Amador
48,905	72,645	393,720	56,246	Butte
18,327	28,365	148,076	21,154	Calaveras
9,543	12,595	45,829	6,547	Colusa
59,345	303,419	523,098	74,728	Del Norte
119,929	295,620	1,002,824	143,261	El Dorado
124,265	208,652	900,012	128,573	Fresno
27,071	35,664	129,795	18,542	Glenn
32,315	41,218	150,246	21,464	Humboldt
8,845	11,556	75,957	10,851	Inyo
22,551	47,184	144,388	20,627	Kern
35,548	46,832	170,690	24,384	Lake
188,093	224,033	1,389,347	198,478	Lassen
16,020	30,173	80,167	11,452	Los Angeles
47,959	78,410	362,787	51,827	Madera
23,030	36,735	176,539	25,220	Mariposa
24,498	32,335	117,459	16,779	Mendocino
219,933	328,769	1,434,731	204,962	Modoc
11,353	15,775	94,687	13,527	Mono
3,692	1,334	11,252	1,607	Monterey
59,409	75,504	298,972	42,710	Nevada
752	729	4,422	632	Orange
106,589	148,716	572,996	81,857	Placer
462,169	752,819	3,821,015	545,859	Plumas
9,638	13,107	40,595	5,799	Riverside
19,415	27,365	110,474	15,782	San Bernardino
4,165	4,038	20,898	2,985	San Diego
2,196	794	6,694	956	San Luis Obispo
7,370	2,664	22,464	3,209	Santa Barbara
133,723	191,967	916,213	130,888	Shasta
144,118	190,506	782,345	111,764	Sierra
371,434	1,098,230	2,397,707	342,529	Siskiyou
105,122	122,960	657,155	93,879	Tehama
263,806	352,342	1,189,119	169,574	Trinity
54,984	116,511	362,930	51,847	Tulare
123,077	190,516	993,230	141,890	Tuolumne
6,513	2,411	19,923	2,846	Ventura
20,178	30,892	142,392	20,342	Yuba
$ 2,994,976	$ 5,294,356	$20,196,805[1]	$ 2,685,258	

[1] Includes a payment of $40.00 to Santa Clara County on account of receipts by the Felton Forest Station.

Source: Forest Service.

Origin of receipts geographically was decidedly spotty. Four national forests (Plumas, Lassen, Klamath, and Trinity), because of their predominance in timber sales, furnished 44 per cent of the total receipts in 1957. The Modoc National Forest was responsible for 22 per cent of the receipts from grazing, or 2.6 times as much as its nearest competitor (Sequoia). Three forests (Sierra, Tahoe, and Sequoia) provided 77 per cent of the receipts from power, and four forests (San Bernardino, Eldorado, Angeles, and Stanislaus) provided 57 per cent of the receipts from land use.

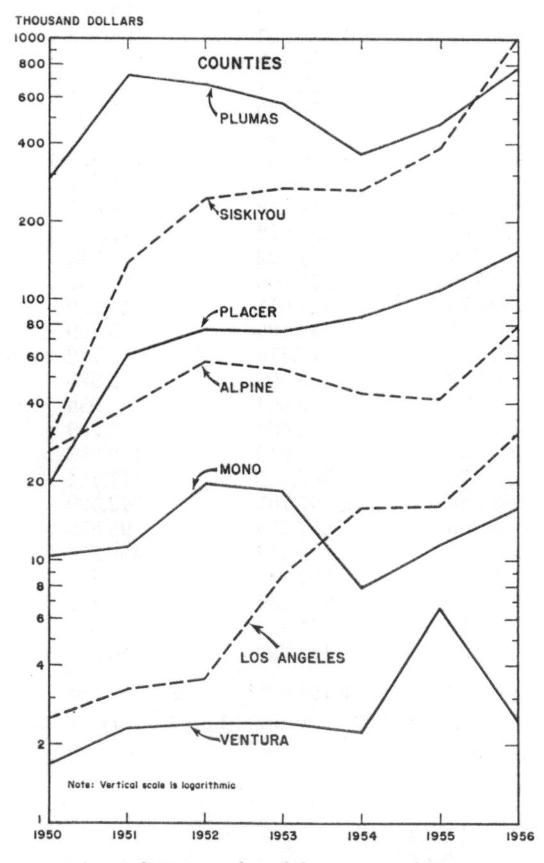

Figure 26. Contributions from national-forest receipts to seven counties in California, 1950-1956.

ROAD AND TRAIL CONSTRUCTION. Expenditures by the federal government for road and trail construction on public lands for 1956, exclusive of federal aid to the state, are shown in Table 41.

Table 41. Federal Expenditures for Road and Trail Construction on National Forests, National Parks, and Indian Reservations, Fiscal Year 1956.

CLASS OF LAND	AMOUNT	
National forests		
10 per cent fund	$ 1,191,444	
Forest development roads and trails	5,050,896	
Forest highways	2,826,384	
		$ 9,068,724
National parks		748,530
Indian reservations		734,000
		$10,551,254

Source: Forest Service, National Park Service, and Bureau of Indian Affairs.

During the last ten years funds for road construction in national parks and Indian reservations have varied from minima of $9,600 and $33,500 in 1947 to their 1956 maxima. In the case of national

Table 42. Expenditures for Road and Trail Construction in National Forests, 1947-1956.

YEAR	10% FUND	FOREST HIGHWAYS	FOREST DEVELOPMENT ROADS	TOTAL
1947	$ 44,612	$ 1,607,047	$ 2,355,805[1]	$ 4,007,464
1948	121,056	932,023	1,899,069[1]	2,952,148
1949	240,313	4,070,900	1,733,253	6,044,466
1950	553,249	3,105,450	1,791,512	5,450,211
1951	365,985	1,746,155	2,464,192	4,576,332
1952	1,678,633	3,108,047	2,038,827	6,825,507
1953	1,592,731	3,823,499	1,386,506	6,802,736
1954	1,460,668	3,979,107	2,584,666	8,022,441
1955	1,030,343	2,699,071	3,593,062	8,322,476
1956	1,191,444	2,826,384	5,050,896	9,068,724
	$ 8,279,034	$27,897,683	$24,897,788	$62,072,505

[1] Includes contributions of $420,958 in 1947 and of $455,387 in 1948 from the National Housing Administration for the building of access roads in order to speed up the production of lumber for housing from national-forest stumpage.

Source: Forest Service.

forests, which accounted for 86 per cent of the 1956 total, annual expenditures during the 10 years from 1947 to 1956 are shown in Table 42.

Access roads built by private owners for the utilization of timber in national forests are in effect paid for by the federal government by a reduction in the appraised value of the stumpage sold by an amount equivalent to the estimated cost of the road construction. This reduction in stumpage price also decreases the amounts received by the counties in the form of 25 per cent of the gross receipts.

FIRE CONTROL. Fire control may be handled either by the federal agency in charge of the lands, as is the case with national forests, with national parks and monuments, and, in small part, with Indian reservations; or by the state under contract with the federal agency, as is the case with unreserved public lands, and, in large part, with Indian reservations. Expenditures for the fiscal year 1956 were approximately as follows:

National forests	$9,401,600
National parks and monuments	160,800
Unreserved public domain	277,000
Indian lands[1]	107,700
	$9,947,100

[1] Does not include expenditures from tribal funds.

For national forests alone, expenditures for the ten-year period from 1947 to 1956 are given in Table 43. Column 1 shows the regular Protection and Maintenance (P&M) funds available for direct fire-control expenditures. It does not include salaries of rangers, supervisor's base staff, or regional office base staff for fire-control direction and planning. Column 2 shows the Fire Fighting (FF) emergency funds spent for emergency guards and fire suppression. Column 3 shows the funds made available by the state to help pay for the cost of protecting state and private lands within national forests in California in Region 5, for the protection of which the Forest Service assumes responsibility. It is a lump-sum payment, not a reimbursement for actual expenditures. Column 4 is the sum of Columns 1 and 2 less Column 3.

Table 43. Federal Expenditures for Fire Control on National Forests in California in Region 5, 1947-1956.

YEAR	FEDERAL FUNDS P & M FUNDS	FF EMERGENCY FUNDS	STATE COOPERATIVE FUNDS	NET FEDERAL FUNDS
1947	$ 1,813,200	$ 1,266,819	$ 231,600	$ 2,848,419
1948	2,041,000	1,962,276	346,100	3,657,176
1949	2,223,900	1,284,412	465,700	3,042,612
1950	2,031,100	2,472,652	499,500	4,004,252
1951	2,069,100	3,882,197	494,600	5,456,697
1952	2,069,100	4,336,086	494,600	5,910,586
1953	2,144,000	1,495,862	765,900	2,873,962
1954	2,128,400	4,699,241	765,900	6,061,741
1955	2,370,600	3,656,514	765,900	5,261,214
1956	2,973,600	7,173,926	756,700	9,390,826
	$21,864,000	$32,229,985	$ 5,586,500	$48,507,485

Source: Forest Service.

The wide variation in emergency expenditures is striking. In spite of the general upward trend in total expenditures for fire control, the Forest Service estimates that the sums now available are only about half of what should be spent for adequate protection.

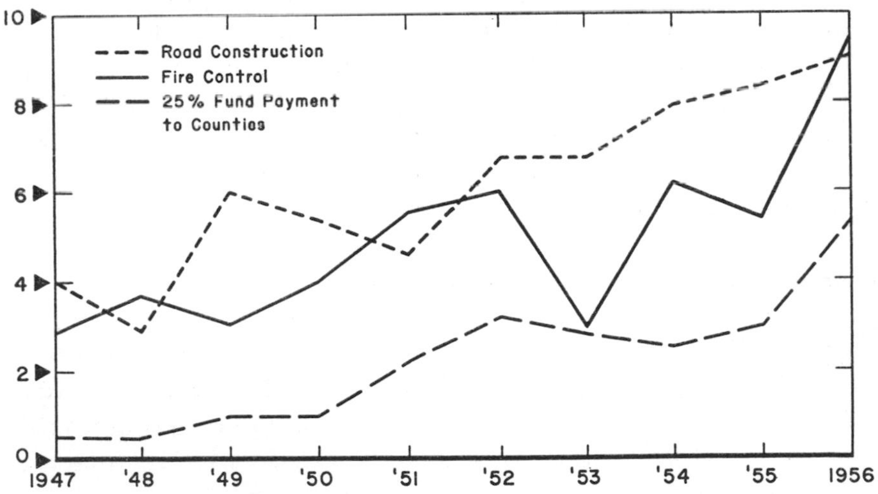

Figure 27. National-forest payments to counties and expenditures for road construction and fire control in California, 1947-1956.

National-forest payments to counties and expenditures for road construction and for fire control in California for the 10 years from 1947 to 1956 are compared graphically in Figure 27.

CONCLUSIONS OF COMMISSION ON INTERGOVERNMENTAL RELATIONS. Probably no subject connected with federal land ownership has received more attention than the real or imaginary burden which it imposes on other governmental units. It has been studied intensively by Congress and the Executive Branch of the federal government, by state legislatures and departments, by counties and other local units of government, and by numerous private organizations and individuals. One of the most recent investigations of the problem (1955) was made by the Study Committee on Payments in Lieu of Taxes and Shared Revenues of the Commission on Intergovernmental Relations ("Kestnbaum Commission").

The committee quoted with approval a statement by the Federal Real Estate Board in 1943 of the goal to be sought: "The cost of national functions and programs should not impose an undue burden on local taxpayers through federal tax exemptions; neither should the federal taxpayer be required to support unjustified subsidies to the localities containing federal lands."

The committee came to the conclusion that the problem of balancing equities between federal and local taxpayers could be solved "only within the framework of considerations germane to the property tax," and that there is "compelling need to maintain robust local government." It recognized two classes of federal properties — those which now do and those which do not share revenues with local communities. With respect to the first of these two classes of property, it recommended that some should make no contribution to local communities, that others should be made subject to nondiscriminatory state and local taxation, and that still others should make payments in lieu of property taxes. Among the properties which it placed in the no-contribution category, and which are of particular interest in the present study, are local irrigation projects and military and naval installations such as forts, camps, armories, observation posts, guard posts, proving grounds, and airfields.

In connection with federal properties now associated with shared revenues, the committee called attention to the fact that in general these properties consist of large tracts of land with few improvements lying in rural areas where the level of governmental services is often considerably lower than in the more populous centers, and that by and large they are a part of the public domain and have never been on local property tax rolls. "The rationale for shared-revenue payments is not altogether clear . . . There is no general agreement concerning the exact philosophy behind revenue-sharing arrangements generally, or behind any particular arrangement. What is clear is that the device of revenue-sharing is generally accepted by local, State, and federal officials as a suitable method for federal payments to states and local governments because of the federal property holdings involved. Furthermore, it is clear that the yardstick most commonly utilized to measure the adequacy of the state or local share of the income receipts is the amount which would be received in property taxes were the land privately owned. This is especially true with respect to lands which are acquired by the Federal Government under circumstances which remove them from state or local property tax rolls . . .

"Under these circumstances the committee has approached the problem of federal payments on these properties from an entirely practical point of view. No attempt has been made to achieve conformity with sophisticated theoretical objectives . . . The committee has, therefore, generally endorsed continuance of the present shared revenue programs and recommended relatively minor modifications . . ." The modifications suggested by the committee may be summarized as follows:

With national forests:

a. The 25-per cent fund should be based upon a centered moving 5-year average of income receipts from the particular national forest.

b. Income receipts should include the value of national-forest timber exchanged for private or state-owned lands.

c. The restriction upon local use of the federal payments to expenditures for roads and schools should be eliminated.

d. For national-forest lands acquired hereafter or within the period of ten years immediately prior to the enactment of authorizing legislation, transitional payments in lieu of taxes should be paid to the states for the benefit of the counties where such lands are located.

The same arrangement as for national forests is recommended for submarginal lands administered by the Forest Service (land utilization projects).

With national parks and monuments:

The following payments should be made to the states for the benefit of the counties in which the lands are located:

a. On lands acquired since September 8, 1939, which were subject to local taxation at the time of acquisition, annual payments in lieu of taxes should be made for the benefit of the local taxing districts involved in the amount which would be assessable against the property if it were taxable.

b. Similar payments in lieu of taxes should be made on improvements such as federally owned lodges and hotels acquired or constructed since September 8, 1939.

c. On lands dedicated to national-park and monument purposes since September 8, 1939, which at the time of such dedication were subject to revenue-sharing arrangements, such as national forests, annual payments should be made for the benefit of the local taxing districts equivalent to the average shared-revenue payments received by such taxing districts from activities on the lands affected during the 10 years immediately preceding the dedication to national-park and monument purposes.

With Taylor Grazing Act public lands (both Section 3 and Section 15):

The present revenue-sharing arrangements should be continued with elimination of the requirement that payments from ceded Indian lands in grazing districts must be used for roads and schools.

With wildlife refuges acquired under the Migatory Bird Conservation Act:

The present revenue-sharing arrangements should be continued, with the following modifications:

a. Payments should be made to the states for the benefit of the counties in which the lands are located, and the restriction upon their use for roads and schools should be eliminated.

b. Payments from mineral-lease receipts should be limited to 25 per cent as at present, but payments from nonmineral receipts should be increased from 25 per cent of the net receipts to 75 per cent of the gross receipts.

c. Payments from both the 25-per cent and 75-per cent funds should be based on a centered moving 5-year average of income receipts.

d. For lands acquired since September 8, 1939, the federal payments should not be less than the taxes which would be assessable if the property were in private ownership.

With mineral leases:

The present arrangements should be continued with elimination of the present restriction on the use of funds for roads and schools.

With sales of public lands and timber, and with Federal Power Commission licenses:

The present arrangements should be continued, with elimination of the requirement that payments on account of sales of public land and timber must be used for roads and schools.

With flood-control lands of the Corps of Engineers:

The present arrangements should be continued, with the following modifications:

a. The annual payments should be based upon a centered moving 5-year average of income receipts.

b. Payments on the basis of receipts from mineral leases should be limited to 25 per cent.

c. For lands acquired since September 8, 1939, federal payments should not be less than the taxes which would be assessable if the land were in private ownership.

No recommendations were made with respect to Indian lands, which the committee regarded as outside its frame of reference.

In summary, for the great bulk of the wildlands in federal ownership, the only important changes in present revenue-sharing arrangements suggested by the committee are to base federal contributions on a 5-year moving average of receipts and to remove the limitation on the use of federal payments for roads and schools. General agreement probably exists as to the desirability of these changes.

Another more radical proposal, which would apply only to a relatively small area, is that payments in lieu of taxes should be substituted for shared revenues, under certain specified conditions, in the case of acquired lands as contrasted with those withdrawn from the public domain. Here again agreement is likely to be fairly general, but with some question as to whether similar payments in lieu of taxes should not be made in the case of lands which have been acquired for military purposes and which have sometimes removed property of considerable value from the tax rolls.

CURRENT PROBLEMS. Many will undoubtedly question whether the committee's basic recommendation — that, with most federal lands, revenues continue to be shared with local communities at approximately the present rates — will actually achieve the objective of securing substantial equity as between federal and local taxpayers. They will feel that further study is distinctly in order in spite of the consideration which the subject has received over a period of many years. For example, Senate Joint Resolution No. 14 which was approved by the 1957 session of the California Legislature called attention to the fact that in 1956 Mono County, with 5.8 per cent (1,150,188 acres) of the total area of national forests in the state, received only 0.3 per cent ($15,775) of the total payments to counties in the form of shared revenues. The resolution memorialized the President and Congress "to take such action as may be required to insure that a thorough study be made to determine the amounts to be apportioned to counties in which exist large areas of federally owned land and which place additional burdens of local governmental services on account of such federal ownership." A similar situation exists in Inyo County, which has 3.9 per cent of the total area of national forests in the state but in 1956 received only 0.2 per cent of the total payments to counties.

Since national-forest receipts come primarily from timber sales, the counties with heavily timbered national forests where cutting is in progress obviously receive the bulk of the shared revenues under the present arrangement. Siskiyou County and Plumas County, for example, in 1956 received respectively 21 per cent and 14 per cent of the total amount distributed. On the other hand, there is little cash revenue to be distributed to counties in which the chief returns from national forests take the form of watershed protection and recreational use, as in the case in southern California and on the east side of the Sierra Nevada. Yet the 400,000 vacationists who visit the Inyo and the Toiyabe National Forests for fishing, hunting, general recreation, and other uses create sanitation, police, and other problems for the local residents and taxpayers of Mono and Inyo Counties.

Hence the question remains as to whether shared revenues really constitute the best method of compensating local communities for the loss of taxes on federal lands. If they do, should the payment to the county be based on the returns in that particular county? Or should the returns from the entire state be distributed among the counties on the basis of (a) the area of national forests in each; (b) the valuation (including "intangible" values) of the national forests in each; (c) the population of the county; (d) the county's financial needs as indicated by its annual budget; or (e) some combination of these and possibly other factors?

Can any reasonably simple share-the-revenue formula be devised that will do substantial justice under the wide variety of relationships that exist between federal lands and local communities? Even if it can be, would the result justify the effort; or is the committee on sound ground in its conclusion that "existing arrangements for federal payments which have been operating to general satisfaction should be left largely undisturbed?" Perhaps the answer depends on how general the satisfaction with existing arrangements really is.

MEASURING THE "BURDEN." Certainly there are many who do not believe that these arrangements attain the objective of turning over to the state or local communities "the amount which would be received in property taxes were the lands privately owned." The subject is an important one which deserves much more study than it has so far received, both in California and elsewhere.

Some interesting light on the existing situation is thrown by a study made by the Forest Service in 1952, in which "estimated taxes" were compared with federal contributions in 135 sample counties out of the 652 counties containing national-forest lands. National-forest land in the sample counties, which were scattered throughout the country, comprised 40 per cent of the total national forest area in the continental United States. In California, the area sampled comprised 8,657,241 acres, or 45 per cent of the total area of national forests in the state. The sample was therefore a substantial one.

Determination of the estimated taxes that would have been paid if the national-forest land had been in private ownership was a difficult matter, but with the cooperation of county assessors was probably accomplished with reasonable accuracy. Contributions from national forests to the local communities included both payments from the 25-per cent fund and contributions in kind. The latter "were limited to those federal expenditures that could reasonably be expected to have been made by state, county, or other local governments in the absence of national forest expenditures . . . National forest expenditures were not included merely because they served a useful purpose or had some public benefit. The test applied was whether the particular expenditures were such that the state or local government would actually have been financially able and willing to spend equivalent funds during the period in question if national forest expenditures had not been made. The specific contributions included in the study represent three types of expenditures — (1) for fire control, (2) for the construction and maintenance of roads, trails, and structures, and (3) for Forest Highways." Contributions in these categories in California have been discussed earlier in this report.

The results of the Forest Service study are summarized in Table 44. The sampling error, taken as one standard error, was 5.7 per cent for the United States as a whole and 11.4 per cent for California.

These figures illustrate clearly the difficulty of attempting to determine the "burden" on local communities imposed by federal ownership on the basis solely of shared revenues. In the case of the national forests, when shared revenues only are taken into account, they fall considerably short of the estimated taxes that would be paid if the land were in private ownership; but when contributions in kind are included, estimated taxes both for the United States as a whole and for California amount to only slightly more than half of all federal contributions (Fig. 28). Doubtless there are many counties in which this situation does not exist. By and large, however, it appears that in all four of the forest regions covered by this particular study the local taxpayer is benefiting financially at the expense of the federal taxpayer because of the existence of national forests. The relative weight that should be attached to 25 per cent fund payments and to contributions in kind in comparisons of this kind is a matter of judgment on which opinions may well differ.

The fact that federal and state lands are exempt from taxation, except in cases where exemption is specifically waived by Congress or the state legislature, is not by itself a strong argument against public ownership. The real test of the relative desirability of public and private ownership is the size of the net return to society, financial and other, contributed by each form of ownership. Basic studies

Table 44. Comparison of Estimated Taxes on National Forest Lands in California with 25 Per Cent Fund Payments and Contributions in Kind, 1952.

	United States		California	
	Million dollars	Cents per acre	Million dollars	Cents per acre
Estimated taxes, calendar year 1952	29.7	18.6	7.5	38.7
25 per cent fund payments, F.Y. 1952	17.4	10.9	3.3	17.0
Contributions in kind, F.Y. 1950-1952, average annual	38.8	24.3	10.5	54.6
Combined 25 per cent fund payments and contributions in kind	56.2	34.2	13.8	71.6

	United States	California
	Per Cent	
Ratio of estimated taxes to 25 per cent fund payments	171	227
Ratio of estimated taxes to combined 25 per cent fund payments and contributions in kind	53	54

Source: Forest Service.

of the sort suggested earlier that will lead to more accurate understanding and evaluation of the different kinds of returns, together with the cost of achieving them, are therefore of major importance. Taxes, shared revenues, and other devices may divide the returns between the owner and the community in whatever proportion seems fair to society; but the amount available for division is governed by the productivity of the land. Who gets the returns may be more significant in the short run to the owners and communities directly affected, but not in the long run to society as a whole.

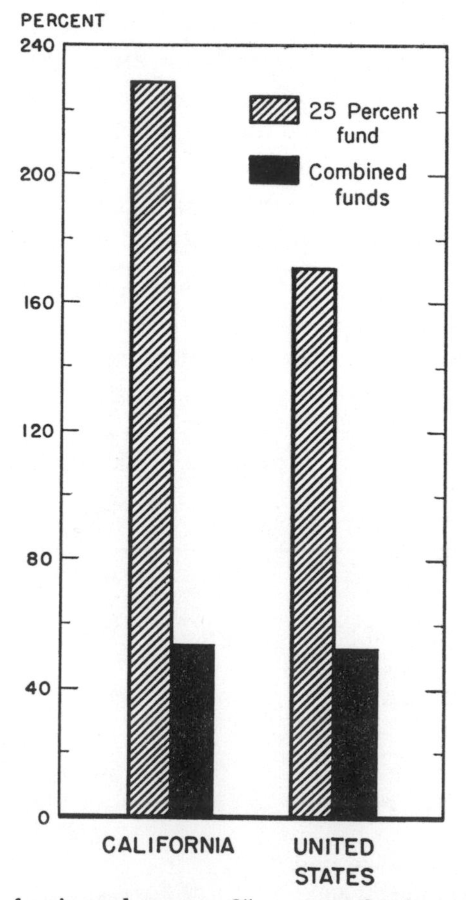

Figure 28. Ratio of estimated taxes to 25 per cent fund payments and to combined 25 per cent fund payments and contributions in kind for California and the United States, 1952.

Legislative Jurisdiction

Federal ownership of land is sometimes criticized on the ground that it subjects the states, local communities, and citizens therein to the control of a distant, almost a "foreign," power. The only substantial basis for this criticism lies in article I, section 8, clause 17 of the Constitution, which gives Congress power "to exercise exclusive Legislation in all Cases whatsoever, over . . . the Seat of Government of the United States, and to exercise like Authority over all Places purchased by the Consent of the Legislature of the State in which the Same shall be, for the Erection of Forts, Magazines, Arsenals, Dock-Yards, and other needful Buildings . . ." In areas where the federal government exercises exclusive legislative jurisdiction, it theoretically removes from the state all of its sovereign authority, executive and judicial as well as legislative, except for the right to serve civil and criminal process in connection with activities which occurred off the area.

The extent to which the federal government has actually exercised exclusive legislative jurisdiction has varied widely from time to time and from state to state. It should be remembered that such jurisdiction can be applied only to acquired lands and with the consent of the state concerned. Both federal legislation authorizing land acquisitions and state legislation consenting to them have resulted in concurrent or partial federal jurisdiction, or even in none at all. A recent study of the subject was made by a federal Interdepartmental Committee for the Study of Jurisdiction over Federal Areas within the States. The committee found that "the extent of jurisdictional control which the Government may have over land can and does vary to an almost infinite number of degrees between exclusive legislative jurisdiction and a proprietorial interest only," and that this whole important field of federal-state relations is "in a confused and chaotic state."

Federal Lands. The problem of federal jurisdiction is not an important one with respect to most of the wildlands in federal ownership, since the United States holds the public domain in a proprietorial status only and has the same rights in the land as does any other landowner. However, according to the committee, "the state may not impose its regulatory power directly upon the Federal Government nor may it tax the Federal land. Neither may the state regulate the action of residents of the land in any way which might directly interfere with the performance of a Federal function . . . Any persons residing on the land remain residents of the State with all the rights, privileges, and obligations which attach to such residence."

So far as acquired lands are concerned, the Weeks Law of 1911 authorizing the purchase of lands for national forests required the consent of the state to such purchases, and applied to the acquired lands the provisions of the act of 1897 relating to national forests created from the public domain: "The jurisdiction, both civil and criminal, over persons within national forests shall not be affected or changed by reason of their existence, except so far as the punishment of offenses against the United States therein is concerned; the intent and meaning of such provision being that the State wherein any such national forest is situated shall not, by reason of the establishment thereof, lose its jurisdiction, nor the inhabitants thereof their rights and privileges as citizens, or be absolved from their duties as citizens of the State."

Similar provisions were incorporated in the Migratory Bird Conservation Act of 1929 authorizing the purchase of wildlife refuges; in the Historic Sites Act of 1935; and in several other acts authorizing federal purchases. The Federal Power Act and the Reclamation Act state that they are not intended to interfere with state laws relating to water. In 1953 Congress transferred to California and certain other states both civil and criminal jurisdiction over Indians in "all Indian country within the State."

WATER RIGHTS. Much confusion, accompanied by considerable heated controversy, exists as to the jurisdiction of the federal and state governments over streams and water rights. The western states claim that by the acts of July 26, 1866, July 9, 1870, and March 3, 1877, the federal government relinquished to the states whatever rights it may have had to the use of the water of non-navigable streams in the West. The federal Department of Justice claims that these acts made no grant to the states, but merely granted to appropriators water rights acquired under state laws. Both sides cite United States Supreme Court decisions in support of their respective positions.

An important aspect of the controversy deals with the scope of the power conferred upon Congress by the Constitution "to regulate commerce with foreign nations, and among the several states." There is general agreement that this provision gives Congress control over the navigable portions of interstate streams, of course with due recognition of existing rights. The contention of states-rights advocates that Congressional control does not extend to non-navigable waters, or to any purpose other than navigation, has not been upheld in several Supreme Court decisions.

For example, in United States v. Appalachian Electric Power Company (311 U. S. 377), the Court in 1940 held that the New River, in Virginia, is a "navigable water" in spite of the fact that obstructions currently prevent navigation, and also that federal control over navigable waters is not limited to navigation but that "flood protection, watershed development, recovery of the cost of improvements through utilization of power are likewise parts of commerce control." A year later, in Oklahoma v. Atkinson Company (313 U. S. 508), the Court went considerably further: "The fact that ends other than flood control will also be served, or that flood control may be relatively of lesser importance, does not invalidate the exercise of the authority conferred on Congress . . . It is clear that Congress may exercise its control over the non-navigable stretches of a river in order to preserve or promote commerce on the navigable portions . . . And we now add that the power of flood control extends to the tributaries of navigable streams . . . There is no constitutional reason why Congress cannot under the commerce power treat the watersheds as a key to flood control on navigable streams and their tributaries."

In 1955, in the Pelton Dam Case (Federal Power Commission v. Oregon et al., 349 U. S. 435), the Supreme Court in a seven to one decision upheld the authority of the Federal Power Commission to grant a license to the Portland General Electric Company to construct, operate, and maintain a hydroelectric plant on a non-navigable portion of the Deschutes River in Oregon, without obtaining the consent of the state. One terminus of the dam would rest on land owned by the United States which had been reserved as a power site since 1910, the other on land in the Warm Springs Indian Reservation which had been reserved for power purposes. The Court held that the government had complete control over the lands in question under the property clause of the Constitution, which gives Congress "power to dispose of and make all needful rules and regulations respecting the territory or other property belonging to the United States." The Federal Power Commission, under enabling legislation, could therefore license use of the lands for the development of hydroelectric power without regard to state law or to the wishes of the state. The Court further held that the acts of 1866, 1870, and 1877 are not germane to the present case since they apply only to unreserved public domain, not to reservations. It consequently declined to rule on whether these acts give the states the control which they claim over water rights on unreserved public lands.

In California, as throughout the West, much concern is felt over the increasing aggressiveness of the federal government, with the apparent support of the nation's highest tribunal, in asserting jurisdiction over water rights which the states have long regarded as belonging to them, and which constitute one of their most cherished possessions. Legislation, which has been pending in Congress for some years without action, seems to offer the only means of definitely confirming the rights which the states claim that they already possess and which they are anxious to retain.

Jurisdiction by Agencies. The character of federal jurisdiction over the lands administered by the agencies with the largest holdings in California is summarized from the report of the Interdepartmental Committee in Table 45.

These figures show that in about 94 per cent of the federal lands in California the United States has a proprietorial interest only; in 3 per cent it exercises exclusive legislative jurisdiction; and in another 3 per cent partial or concurrent legislative jurisdiction.

The Interdepartmental Committee came to the conclusion that it is desirable for the federal government to hold the great bulk of the

Table 45. Character of Jurisdiction Exercised by Various Agencies over Federal Lands in California.

Agency	Exclusive legislative jurisdiction	Partial or concurrent legislative jurisdiction	Proprietorial interest only
	Acres		
Bureau of Land Management	—	—	17,509,575
National Park Service[1]	1,140,361	763,078	2,313,973
Bureau of Reclamation	—	163,885	1,156,616
Bureau of Sport Fisheries and Wildlife[1]	—	156,907	9,031
Forest Service	—	—	19,978,065
Department of the Army	23,244	18,548	1,008,117
Department of the Navy	186,309	136,437	2,114,028
Department of the Air Force	100,792	165,425	155,304
	1,450,706	1,404,280	44,244,709

[1] A small part of this area is in Kansas and Virginia, which were grouped with California in the reports by these bureaus.

Source: Interdepartmental Committee for the Study of Jurisdiction over Federal Areas within the States.

lands which it owns in a proprietorial status only, with legislative jurisdiction remaining in the states. It recognizes, however, the need for exclusive or nearly exclusive legislation jurisdiction by some agencies, notably the Department of Defense, and expresses the belief that concurrent jurisdiction most nearly fits the needs for national parks and for national monuments located in remote areas, and perhaps for some wildlife refuges. No change is suggested in the proprietorial status of national forests and the unreserved public domain.

In line with its general preference for a proprietorial status, and in order to eliminate so far as possible current confusions and conflicts, the committee recommends the passage of federal legislation authorizing the retrocession of unnecessary jurisdiction to the states. At the same time, in many states, legislation or constitutional amendments will be necessary to permit them to accept relinquished federal jurisdiction.

State Land Problems

Lands under departmental jurisdiction have recently come to comprise the largest class of lands in state ownership. Exclusive of highway rights-of-way, they expanded from 56,500 acres in 1930 to 744,500 acres in 1954 – an increase of more than 1,300 per cent in a quarter of a century. Three units of government – the Division of Beaches and Parks, the Division of Forestry, and the Department of Fish and Game – control the great bulk of this area and are of primary importance from the standpoint of land management.

Beaches and Parks

Perhaps the most important problem in connection with beaches and parks has to do with the division of responsibility among state, local, and federal governments for preserving scenic and historic sites and for providing opportunities for wildland recreation. Where do local interests yield to state interests, and state interests to national interests? What criteria determine whether a given area should be a park, and if so under whose jurisdiction?

In this connection, it is worth mentioning that a few units of the state park system preserve scenic values that are definitely of national significance. This is especially true of the larger coast redwood parks along the Redwood Highway, which attract visitors from all over the world. These forests are not represented in the national-park system except at Muir Woods National Monument, which does not compare in quality with the state parks farther north.

When a public activity involves a financial loss, as is commonly the case in the administration of a park system, it is natural for a lower unit of government to favor liberal participation by a higher unit of government with its presumably greater resources. It is not surprising, therefore, that in California the counties should look for help to the State Division of Beaches and Parks, which has received generous support in the form of bonds, appropriations, and the allocation of substantial portions of the tideland oil royalties. Neither is it surprising that the state, whose resources are far from unlimited, should hesitate to acquire and administer lands which it does not regard as meeting state standards or the use of which is likely to be mostly local. The divergence between these points of view suggests the desirability of more widespread use of the legislation authorizing the organization of regional park districts, under which the East Bay Regional Parks have operated so successfully.

One form of state aid consists of buying the parks and then transferring their administration to a local agency, usually the county. Some 37 parks are now being operated in this way under varying arrangements. The advantages and disadvantages of the split between ownership and administration need careful study.

A somewhat similar situation arises when the Division of Beaches and Parks seeks in effect to enlarge the area of a state park by operating a considerable area of surrounding national-forest land under special-use permit. An important difference, however, lies in the fact that such an arrangement limits the use of the national-forest land to a single major activity — recreation. The following statement by the Regional Forester at San Francisco at a joint hearing of two Assembly committees at Los Angeles on January 3, 1957, intimates that a division of responsibility might be made along geographic and topographic lines: "We consider ourselves fortunate in being in a position to provide developed public recreation areas in the high mountains and forests and feel that our program should be coordinated with the efforts of other agencies to furnish companion sites in the valleys, foothills, and along the coast so as to meet the needs of the expanding population."

The official policy of the Forest Service with respect to state and local government recreational developments on national-forest land is stated as follows in an amendment to the National Forest Manual approved in June, 1957:

"As a general practice the Forest Service will plan and develop needed public recreation facilities on national-forest lands, and permit the development of special facilities, such as resorts and ski lifts, by private parties under special-use permit. It is recognized, however, that there will be situations where the public interest might be best served by the development of recreational facilities on certain national-forest lands by state, county, or municipal government agencies, and that if such ventures are successful, they will probably develop into long-term, or in fact permanent arrangements. The following guidelines are established:

"1. Special-use permits authorizing substantial recreation developments on national-forest land by state, county, or municipal agencies will be issued only for: (1) lands which over a very long-term period can in the public interest best be dedicated to that purpose; or (2) lands which could logically be exchanged to state or local government ownership without detriment to national-forest administration or programs. In either case lands eligible for such use must meet at least two of the following criteria:

"a. Be adjacent to exterior national-forest boundaries.

"b. Consist of isolated small tracts of national-forest land — minority ownership situations.

"c. Be adjacent to lands owned by the applicant agency and needed to round out or complete a unit for development as a park or recreation area.

"2. State or local government agencies will not be granted special-use permits to develop parks or recreational areas on national-forest lands which do not qualify under paragraph 1 above, except in unusual circumstances when it is clearly in the public interest to do so. Advance approval of the Chief is required for these exceptions.

"3. Special-use permits should include only the land to be intensively developed. Large buffer strips or large areas for 'wilderness type' parks or recreation areas will not be included.

"4. Ordinarily permits to county and municipal governments will be for areas which will receive primarily local use . . .

"8. The Forest Service will reserve the right to approve over-all development plans for the areas and specifications for facilities to be constructed under these permits.

"9. All such developments on national-forest land should be appropriately signed to indicate that the agency-owned and operated developments are located on national-forest land."

The broad scope of the recreational interests of the state, of which the state parks are an important part, together with the rapidly increasing demand for additional recreational facilities of all types, motivated the 1957 legislature to pass the California Outdoor Recreation Plan Act. This act establishes an ex officio committee of state officials, supplemented by a technical consultant group and an advisory council, whose duty it is to provide the legislature by March, 1960, with a comprehensive plan for recreational developments and facilities throughout the state. The plan is to be based on the anticipated need carefully analyzed and projected through the gathering of all pertinent facts on a scale never before attempted.

So intimate and complicated are the relationships between local, state, and federal levels of government, between public and private agencies, and between recreation and other land uses that the preparation of such a plan will be a difficult task. It is essential for the committee to recognize that there are competing demands for a limited supply of land, and that neither recreation nor any other land use can be considered in a vacuum.

Although the state's present policy of limiting multiple use of state parks to various forms of recreational activity seems thoroughly established, the questions which are occasionally raised concerning its wisdom indicate that it may need further study. The Senate Interim Committee on Recreation, State Beaches and Parks in a 1956 report on "California's State Park Program" expressed its aproval of current policy as follows: "This study finds agreement with the principles of the National Park Service, followed in large measure by the State Park Administration, that parks are for park purposes and that, consequently, commercial activities, such as logging, grazing, and mining should not be permitted within park reservations . . . Adverse uses, such as hunting, should not be permitted."

On the other hand, the Senate Interim Committee on Public Lands, in its 1955 report on "State Land Ownership," commented that the State Park Commission "feels it holds its land in trust and the multiple-use principle is anathema to the 'trust'." Both this committee and other groups have made recommendations concerning tree cutting in parks; opening of certain park areas to hunting, to grazing, or to mining; and reservoir construction. The wide gap between the policy of the Park Commission and proposals such as these suggest lack of full agreement as to state park objectives and the best ways and means of attaining them – a gap which should be narrowed, if not completely closed.

State Forests

The main problem connected with state forests is one of policy with respect to their extent. The California Forestry Study Committee in 1945 recommended a "present goal" of 1,000,000 acres of state forests, with initial purchases of about 200,000 acres. Yet the total area of state forests is now only 70,236 acres, of which 52,042 acres (72 per cent) is in a single forest – the Jackson State Forest in Mendocino County. Of the remaining state forests, only three, with a total area of 17,006 acres, are suitable and available for commercial utilization. The other four, with a total area of 1,188 acres, are used for experimentation, demonstration, and purposes prescribed in the deeds of gift.

Clearly the program visualized by the Forestry Study Committee has not materialized. No public statement has been made by the State Board of Forestry as to why progress has been so slow, or as to its intentions concerning future acquisitions. Presumably the Board believes that the situation has changed sufficiently in the last ten years to justify the radical shift in the original plans that has apparently taken place. Prominent among the changes are improved management by many private owners and increased cost of forest land, which most owners are no longer eager, or even willing, to sell.

Thorough study of the present situation seems to be in order to provide the facts needed for an intelligent decision as to how much farther, if at all, the state should go in acquiring small tracts for demonstration purposes and larger tracts for reforestation and management, as envisioned by the Forestry Study Committee. In view of the fact that multiple uses of all kinds, including mining, are permitted on state forests, consideration might well be given to supplementing the state park system by acquiring for state forests lands with recreational values in which recreation and timber production can be combined.

Wildlife Areas

Although many problems of administration and management exist with wildlife areas, as is true with all classes of state lands, the chief problem from the standpoint of ownership has to do with their adequacy. Study is needed to determine the extent to which additional state acquisition is essential to provide adequate areas for wildlife management and utilization, and to which requirements in this field can be met through cooperative arrangements with private owners and the federal government. Of particular importance is favorable action by the government on the request of the Department of Fish and Game to place a large area of unreserved public domain under its administration.

School Lands

State school lands, with an area of about 850,000 acres, constitute the largest single class of state-owned lands. Past policy has been to sell either the lands themselves or their products (chiefly timber, forage, and minerals) as opportunity offered. Sometimes sales have been contingent on the state's making an exchange which would result in the purchaser's obtaining a desired tract that had previously been in the public domain.

Receipts from sales of school lands from 1948 to 1957 are shown in Table 46. They have averaged $276,499 a year, with large increases during the last two years, when they aggregated 76 per cent of the total receipts during the 10-year period. The substantial increase in 1956 and 1957 is due largely to the fact that sales were made on the basis of the full appraised value of the land, which has been decidedly on the upgrade in recent years.

On June 30, 1957, the corpus of the School Land Fund, derived from the sale of school lands, was $18,826,956, while its total resources were $22,080,458. It seems probable that the corpus of the fund would be considerably larger if the policy of selling lands at

Table 46. Receipts from Sale of School Lands in California, 1948 - 1957.

Fiscal year	Receipts	
	Amount	Per cent
1948	$79,613	3
1949	45,821	2
1950	76,761	3
1951	67,235	2
1952	148,305	5
1953	85,804	3
1954	170,125	6
1955	99,100	4
1956	748,094	27
1957	1,244,128	45
	$2,764,986	100

Source: California State Lands Division.

their appraised value had been adopted much earlier, and if the state had taken more initiative in acquiring desirable lands in the public domain through lieu selections and land exchanges. It is important that from now on all sales of lands and materials should be made at their full value and that advantage be taken of opportunities to increase the value of the state's holdings through the exchange process.

The history and widely scattered character of the school lands increase the difficulty of administering and managing them most effectively. Several methods of dealing with the situation deserve careful consideration:

1. Continuing the present policy of selling the lands in place, or of exchanging them for lands in the public domain desired by a prospective purchaser and then selling the lands acquired by the exchange. This procedure is likely to leave a considerable area of relatively low-value lands, difficult of management and in constant danger of trespass, in the hands of the state for an indefinite period.
2. Blocking up at least a considerable part of the area by ex-

change with other owners, and perhaps by using the proceeds from sales to purchase strategic areas, with the expectation that the land acquired by either method would remain in state ownership. An example of the possibilities in the way of exchange is afforded by the negotiations now in progress between the state and the Forest Service for the exchange of some 16,000 acres of widely scattered school lands for some 4,000 acres in the Sequoia National Forest that would be added to the Mountain Home State Forest. The transaction is the largest exchange that either the state or the Forest Service now has under way and would nearly double the area of the Mountain Home State Forest. The execution of a blocking-up program on any large scale would involve many difficulties but would also have many advantages.

3. Transferring the actual management of the school lands to the State Division of Forestry. This responsibility could readily be assumed by the division in connection with its other activities, and would assure technical competence in the handling of the lands, most of which are primarily valuable for forest, range, or watershed purposes. The State Lands Commission should also seek advice from the Division of Forestry as to whether the sale, or retention and management, of school lands (including lands received in exchange) will be more advantageous from the point of view of the School Trust Fund; in other words, whether the interest on the sale price of the land is likely to be more or less than the net receipts from management.

Tax-deeded Lands

Tax-deeded lands in January, 1956, were down to the relatively low figure of 281,000 acres, or less than 0.3 per cent of the land area of the state. They are badly scattered, usually of low value, and of little public significance from the standpoint of land management. About the only problem which they present is to see that while under state control they are managed as effectively as circumstances permit. With land values and economic prosperity at their present levels, it is unlikely that tax-deeded lands will form the basis of a "new public domain," as has happened at times past in other states.

Contributions in Lieu of Taxes

The problem of what compensation, if any, should be paid to local communities for loss of taxes on state lands is similar to that with federal lands but, of course, on a much smaller scale. At present, compensation is paid only on certain state forest lands and certain wildlife management areas.

The four commercial state forests (Jackson, Latour, Mountain Home, and Boggs Mountain) pay the counties in which they are located an amount equivalent to taxes levied by the county on "similar land similarly situated." Determination of what constitutes similar land similarly situated is made by a committee consisting of the county assessor, a representative of the State Board of Equalization, and a representative of the State Forester. Payments in lieu of taxes, other expenses (exclusive of capital investments), and receipts from 1951 to 1955 for the four forests combined are shown in Figure 29. For 1955 the payment in lieu of taxes amounted

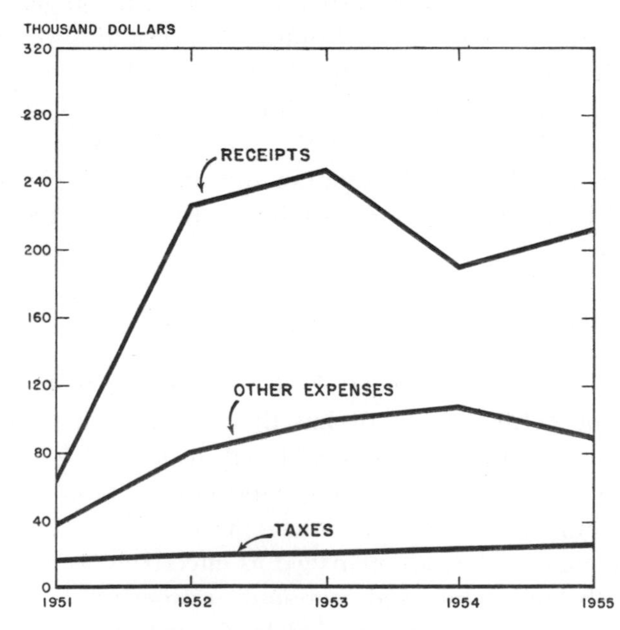

Figure 29. Taxes, other expenses, and receipts from the four commercial state forests, 1951-1955.

to $25,475, or 37 cents per acre. The other four forests (Mount Zion, Las Posadas, Ellen Pickett, and Loghry) were acquired by gift under legislation that does not require any payment in lieu of taxes.

Payment in lieu of taxes is made to the county upon any property used as a wildlife management area from which the state derives income, in an amount equal to the county taxes levied at the time title passed to the state. Payments to counties in lieu of taxes during the fiscal years 1954 to 1957 are shown in Table 47.

Table 47. Payments to Counties in Lieu of Taxes from Wildlife Management Areas, 1954-1957.

COUNTY	1954	1955	1956	1957
Butte	$ 6,519	$ 8,035	$ 8,568	$ 8,568
Fresno	--	--	1,400	1,400
Imperial	2,651	4,200	5,676	8,243
Lassen	1,238	1,238	1,641	1,641
Merced	297	297	297	297
Solano	3,612	3,612	3,612	3,612
Sutter	--	464	464	464
Tehama	674	756	1,966	756
	$14,991	$18,602	$23,624	$24,981

Source: California Department of Fish and Game.

Many county assessors object to the method of determining the amount of the payment as being inequitable because property values have increased materially in the past fifteen years and give every evidence of continuing to rise.

The Senate Interim Committee on Public Lands, in its 1955 report, reached the conclusion that the present situation does not of itself constitute a burden to local communities except in isolated cases, and that a general measure providing for payments in lieu of taxes is not warranted at this time. It further concluded that the present situation does constitute a burden to local communities when considered in relation to the vast holdings of the federal government, and that the state has a moral obligation not to increase such burden. The committee therefore recommended that the legislative and executive branches of both the state and the federal governments make a concerted effort to appraise accurately the present situation and to determine what equitable payments in lieu of taxes should be made by the two governments. Finally, it suggested for consideration by the California Legislature, on completion of these studies, a general tax measure based on the ratio of the assessed value of public lands to the assessed value of all lands in the several counties and the state, and on the relative benefit conferred by the state land on the state as a whole and on the county in which it is located.

Although the federal and the state problems do not necessarily have to be considered together, a joint approach would undoubtedly be desirable. In spite of the relatively small area and value of state-owned properties, their influence on the tax base is often of considerable local importance. Since different classes of land will in all probability require different treatment, the problem is a complicated one which will require intensive study before any satisfactory solution is reached.

County and Other Local Land Problems

Counties and municipalities, both singly and in cooperation, might well give serious thought to the management and acquisition of additional lands. These would probably be used largely for recreation and watershed purposes, but wood and forage might often be worth-while secondary products. With the continuing urbanization of the state there is bound to be a rapidly mounting need for people to have access to adequate recreational areas in public ownership and within easy reach of their homes. Such areas should be acquired promptly, before their occupation for other purposes makes them physically or financially unavailable.

Municipal agencies and public utilities might also advantageously give careful consideration to the possibilities of multiple-use management of lands and waters held primarily for water-supply purposes. Experience is proving that many uses of such areas are more compatible than was once thought to be the case.

Private Land Problems

Although the present study is concerned primarily with lands not in farms, the importance of farms in the land-use picture is clearly recognized. With farm lands comprising 38 per cent of the land area of the state, and with farm products far exceeding in value those from other rural lands, many problems are obviously connected with their ownership and management, of which only two can be mentioned here.

Urban and Highway Encroachment on Farm Lands

In spite of present agricultural surpluses, many people who are thoroughly familiar with the situation foresee difficulty in meeting the needs for agricultural products of an exploding population and an expanding economy. For example, the Soil and Water Conservation Advisory Committee of the U. S. Department of Agriculture, at its meeting on October 8 - 9, 1956, recommended: "That all appropriate measures be taken by the United States Department of Agriculture to inform all the people of the nation that a serious long-time hazard to future agricultural production could result from the continued rapid conversion of highly productive land to urban and other non-agricultural uses." A series of articles in the San Francisco Examiner in May and June, 1955, pointed out that every year since the end of World War II approximately 40,000 acres have been taken over by subdivisions. In a single year subdivisions sprang up at 571 separate locations in 7 counties.

One of the most serious features of this encroachment is that it is largely occurring on the most fertile lands. About half of the land in land capability classes I to IV (discussed earlier in this report) is in areas where 90 per cent of the people of California now live, and where most of the future inhabitants will undoubtedly settle. Industries as well as people are moving into the country until the significance of "city limit" signs is beginning to disappear.

Two attempts to stop or at least to slow down the invasion are worth noting. In Santa Clara County, 15,000 acres had been zoned for agriculture by September, 1956, and a still larger area was in process of being zoned. During 1955 and 1956 Dairy Valley and three other "Dairy" cities in Los Angeles and Orange Counties were incorporated for the purpose of protecting their rural status. The dairymen who were responsible for the action came to the conclusion that, whether they like it or not, they were soon going to be in somebody's town, and preferred to have it their own town in which they could set their own local taxes and resist subdividers.

Local and through roads constitute another threat both to farms and to other rural lands. Super-highways require 50 to 60 acres of land to the mile and ordinary first-class highways 25 acres or more. In addition to taking land out of cultivation, the effect of factories, stores, residences, and the surfaced portions of roads is to virtually put a tin roof over the ground which they occupy. The result is to greatly increase surface runoff and to change the whole hydrologic pattern for the worse.

Estimates by the Soil Conservation Service show that the following areas of land in land capability classes I to IV have been converted to nonagricultural uses:

Period		Acres
Prior to 1942		1,939,928
Since 1942		
1942 - 1946	249,825	
1947 - 1951	263,430	
1952 - 1955	295,923	
Undistributed	10,340	819,518
		2,759,446

Nearly one-sixth of the best land in the state is no longer available for agricultural use, while encroachment by other uses continues at an accelerating rate. In Los Angeles County, which until a few years ago led all counties in the United States in the value of its farm products, 31 per cent of the better land is no longer available for agricultural use. During the last ten years, for the state as a whole, withdrawals for public use show a significant decline and withdrawals for private use a corresponding rise.

Soil Conservation Districts

Soil conservation districts constitute another aspect of land use which is of primary but by no means exclusive interest in connection with farms. In November, 1957, California had 145 soil conservation districts, with an area of about 54,145,000 acres, in which emphasis is placed not only on the control of erosion but on the development and use of improved land-management practices of all kinds (Fig. 30). They are likely to become increasingly useful as cultivation increases in intensity and extends to the rougher and poorer lands. Under the pressure for greater production from a smaller area of first-class land, agriculture will probably encroach on areas now devoted to growing livestock and timber, but it is unlikely that percentagewise the loss to these uses will be serious.

Urbanization and Natural Resources

There is growing recognition of the many problems caused by urban growth, which impinges most directly on agricultural resources but indirectly on all natural resources. The 1956 annual report of Resources for the Future points out that "even in wild areas, hundreds of miles from metropolitan centers, the conflicting demands on land and water for economic production and services, for conservation, and for recreation, are ultimately a reflection of urban growth." In recognition of this situation, Resources for the Future has made a grant of $25,000 to the University of California (1) to study "the land-use aspects of the impact of urbanization on natural resources, particularly as related to the Los Angeles and San Francisco Bay regions, and with special attention to problems of the rural-urban fringe"; and (2) "to analyze spatial structures of metropolitan regions and to identify the causes and the values associated with each."

The first part of the study will include:

"1. an examination of the trends of urban growth and dispersal and their effect upon land and water use in areas affected;

"2. a study of the character and degree of stability or change of urban and nonurban activities — industrial, agricultural, residential,

Figure 30. Approximate location of soil conservation districts, 1957. Courtesy Soil Conservation Service, U. S. Department of Agriculture.

transportation, and recreational — under conditions of a shifting land and water resources base;

"3. an analysis of major problems and areas of conflict in resource use between rural and urban needs and activities;

"4. an analysis of public and private controls, employed or employable, which might promote a more efficient land and water resource-use pattern in rural-urban regions; and

"5. an evaluation of the usefulness of, and gaps in, current knowledge and methods of analysis of the total problem."

This study will help materially to identify and to focus attention upon the many problems in this field which will obviously need further intensive investigation.

Range Lands and Brush Burning

Problems in the management of lands for the production of domestic livestock, both on pastures and on the open range, center chiefly on the rehabilitation of overgrazed areas, the adoption of improved practices, and the conversion of brush to palatable forage. The Forest Service states that "it is certain that the many other uses of our range lands which have increased and replaced much of the grazing use, especially of sheep, are here to stay. We will need to work more with the lands we have now . . . We must find ways to improve and increase the productivity on those areas now in a deteriorated condition, as well as to encourage bringing more of the now marginal lands into production and use."

From the quantitative point of view, the problems are most acute on private lands, where the great bulk of the livestock production is now concentrated. On national forests, for example, the number of sheep spending some part of the year on national-forest land decreased from 15 per cent of the total sheep population in the state in 1909 to 5 per cent in 1954; and during the same period the number of cattle spending part of the year on national forests decreased from 14 per cent to 5 per cent. All federal lands in California contribute less than 5 per cent of the total forage requirement.

Since the conversion of "brush" to useful forage plants constitutes about the only way to increase materially the present area of range land, it is generally regarded by the livestock industry as an opportunity and a challenge of major importance. Although both national forests and unreserved public domain have much larger areas of brush than their managers would like, its chief occurrence is on private lands. The California Forest and Range Experiment Station estimates that outside of areas suitable for growing timber, the Coast Ranges and Sierra-Cascade foothills contain 20 million acres on which woody vegetation introduces a problem in land management. The types included in this "brushland," and the area in each type where brush control may be feasible, can be summarized as follows:

Type	Total area,	Area where brush control may be feasible
	Acres	
Woodland	1,500,000	1,350,000
Woodland-grass	7,500,000	4,720,000
Chaparral, minor conifer, and coastal sagebrush	11,000,000	3,300,000
	20,000,000	9,370,000

Of the somewhat more than 9 million acres on which brush control may be feasible, only about 3 million acres are estimated to be of fair to good quality, and even here the conversion process is likely to be an expensive one. Four steps are involved – selection of a suitable site; removal of the brush by fire, mechanical means, or chemical sprays; establishing a stand of desirable forage plants; and management to control brush sprouts and seedlings and to maintain the productive capacity of the range. Long experience has proved that indiscriminate burning does not give satisfactory results. Much research still remains to be done to place each of the four steps in the conversion process on a sound basis.

Recognizing that "the people of the state have a direct interest in the protection and improvement of public and private lands which are principally used or useful for range or forage purposes for domestic livestock and wildlife," the legislature in 1945 passed two acts providing for controlled burning, clearance, and revegetation of such lands, with the additional objective of promoting fire control, watershed protection, and the prevention of soil erosion. The Division of Forestry in the Department of Natural Resources was authorized (1) to issue permits for the burning of brush on private lands, with adequate precautions to prevent damage to the property of others, and (2) to enter into contracts or cooperative agreements with any person, corporation, or political subdivision of the state owning or controlling brush-covered land within the area where fire protection is primarily a state responsibility, under which the owner can engage in controlled land clearance and revegetation, including brush burning. The burning or clearance must be done under the supervision of the Division of Forestry and in accordance with rules and regulations formulated by the division and approved by the State Board of Forestry. The division is also authorized, both in connection with such contracts and agreements and independently thereof, to conduct experiments and research aimed at determining the best methods of land clearance and revegetation.

No contracts have been negotiated, but during the twelve years from 1945 to 1956, inclusive, 1,337,646 acres were burned under 4,793 permits issued by the Division of Forestry. An additional 124,652 acres were burned by fires that escaped. Seeding after burning was done on 435,204 acres. The peak year in terms of permits used, area burned under permit, and area seeded was 1954. Range technicians employed by the division advise with individual ranchers and groups of ranchers in connection both with controlled burning and other range-management problems.

Results of controlled burning have varied widely. On a sample area of 32,344 acres, or 4.2 per cent of the total area burned between 1946 and 1952, the average grazing capacity was about 15 acres per animal-unit month before treatment and about 6.5 acres per animal-unit month in 1953. These averages, however, have little significance because of the wide variations in grazing capacity both before and after treatment, and because some 60 per cent of the area sampled was still in the lower part of the poor or very poor categories ("poor," 2.5 to 4.0 acres per animal-unit month; "very poor," more than 4.0 acres per animal-unit month). In about 15 per cent of the cases, grazing capacity was essentially zero both when the project was started and in 1953. At the other extreme, represented by nearly 13 per cent of the cases, from 15 to 30 acres were required per animal unit month before the project started and from 1 to 3 acres in 1953.

The Division of Forestry expresses the opinion "that while the average level of success is highly encouraging, the frequency of poor results underscores the need for more basic information, and more intensive application of information which already is known to solution of the problem." Costs are another item of major importance on which much more information is needed. A study of controlled burns in northern California in 1947 and 1948 showed that the combined cost to the permittee and to the state (for standby protection) varied from $3.65 per acre for burns averaging 40 acres in size to $0.60 for those averaging 440 acres, with a rise to $1.20 when the size increased to 640 acres.

Since 1948 the Department of Fish and Game, because of its interest in the relation of controlled brush burning to wildlife management, has been making substantial contributions to research in this field conducted at the University of California. Continued, intensive research by both state and federal agencies on the management of brush lands is of prime importance to both public and private owners, and particularly to the latter. There can be no question as to its urgency.

Another chronic problem that needs continuing study is the occasional conflict between the use of range lands for domestic livestock, wildlife, and recreation. Although the problem is more acute on public lands, where greater emphasis is placed on multiple use, careful consideration needs to be given to ways and means of combining the three uses without serious interference with the private owner's major objective of making a profit out of the production of livestock.

Commercial Forest Lands

Management of commercial forest lands in private ownership is in a period of transition. During the last decade there has been a rapid trend, particularly among the larger owners, away from mere exploitation of the virgin stand toward continuous production of timber crops. This trend is evident in the three comprehensive studies of forest lands which have been made by the Forest Service.

TREND TOWARD BETTER MANAGEMENT. "A National Plan for American Forestry" (1933) concluded that "practically all of the major problems of American forestry center in, or have grown out of, private ownership," and painted a decidedly bleak picture of the future of forestry on private lands. In view of this situation it recommended the acquisition of 90 million acres of forest land by the states and of 134 million acres by the federal government — a program which would have increased the area then in public ownership more than three times.

Two years later a report prepared by the Forest Service for the Land Planning Committee of the National Resources Board proposed a program for the net acquisition by public agencies of 170 million acres as compared with the 224 million acres proposed in 1933. The changes in public ownership of forest land suggested for California were as follows:

OWNERSHIP	PRESENT	PROPOSED	INCREASE
		ACRES	
Federal	18,477,740	29,332,429	10,854,689
State	108,613	18,713	—89,900
County and municipal	167,900	177,000	9,100
	18,754,253	29,528,142	10,773,889

Particularly striking are the proposed increase of 59 per cent in federal ownership and the proposed decrease of 83 per cent in state ownership. It was estimated that the proposed changes would leave 10,366,904 acres of forest land in private ownership.

"A Reappraisal of the Forest Situation in the United States" (1946) classified recently cutover areas by ownership according to the character of the cutting practices used. The results for California are summarized in Table 48.

The report concluded that improved cutting practices are the "focal point of the management job ahead . . . our objective of forest products adequate for future needs will not be attained unless

Table 48. Character of Cutting by Different Classes of Owners in California, 1945.

Class of ownership	Per cent of cutting rated as High order	Good	Fair	Poor	Destructive
All ownerships	1	40	11	46	2
National forests	2	98	—	—	—
Small private holdings	—	2	17	76	5
Medium private holdings	—	3	24	67	6
Large private holdings	—	3	15	81	1

Source: Forest Service.

satisfactory cutting practices are applied by the 4¼ million private forest-land owners." The validity both of the methods used to determine the character of cutting practices and of the results obtained was vigorously questioned by many in industry. The entire study and its interpretation were also viewed with suspicion as an attempt to justify the policy of federal control of cutting on private lands which the Forest Service had been advocating for some years.

This suspicion was strengthened by publication in 1948 of a bulletin entitled "Forests and National Prosperity," which was based on the Reappraisal and in which the Forest Service proposed a three-point program of action including (1) a series of public aids to private forest landowners, especially the small owners; (2) public control of cutting and other forest practices on private land sufficient to stop forest destruction and to keep the land reasonably productive; and (3) expansion and intensified management of national, state, and community forests. The acquisition part of the program was far less extensive than that envisioned in 1933, but the part dealing with public control was much more specific. "The States should continue to have opportunity to enact and administer adequate regulatory laws. However, in order to assure a consistent pattern — Nation-wide and in a reasonable time — a basic Federal law is needed."

The "Timber Resource Review" (published in the form of a preliminary review draft in 1955) adopted a new method for determining the condition of recently cut lands in different ownerships. The report itself states that "unlike the 1945 survey this survey was not concerned with forest management practices. It omitted consideration of intent of ownership, existence of sustained-yield policies, management plans, or planned use of silvicultural systems. Conditions on the ground were appraised as they were found regardless of whether they resulted from accident, a bountiful nature, or purposeful action of the owner." These conditions were expressed in terms of a "productivity index," which was designed to reflect the combined effect of four of the most important elements or factors which affect growth following cutting. These elements include (1) existing stocking; (2) prospects for stocking where present stocking is deficient; (3) species composition; and (4) felling age, or age of the trees or stands at the time the cutting occurred.

The productivity index scale of 0 to 100 was divided into the three broad classes of low (0-39), medium (40-69), and high (70-100). The condition of the land was finally expressed by showing the proportion of the total operating area that fell in each of these classes. "Thus, a statement that 65 per cent of the operating area of the country was in the high-productivity class means that 65 per cent (area wise) of the forest types on which there was recent cutting in the individual ownerships examined had a productivity index rating between 70 and 100 per cent of what is considered reasonably attainable under current conditions."

The estimated productivity by combined productivity class for different classes of ownership in California is shown in Table 49.

Private ownerships, and particularly the medium and large ownerships, make a much better showing in the Timber Resource Review than in the Reappraisal. To what extent the change is due to the difference in method and to actual improvement in cutting practices is not clear, but the latter undoubtedly had much influence. Considerable question has been raised as to the soundness of the new method for determining productivity; and there are some in industry who still suspect that any attempt to measure productivity may have federal control in view as an ultimate objective, even though the subject of public control (federal or state) is not mentioned anywhere in the Timber Resource Review.

Additional evidence of the improvement in forest practice by

Table 49. Productivity of Recently Cut Commercial Forest Lands in California by Ownership and Combined Productivity Class, 1953.

CLASS OF OWNERSHIP	— — PRODUCTIVITY CLASS — —		
	HIGH	MEDIUM	LOW
	— — — — PER CENT — — — —		
Public ownerships			
Douglas fir	78	22	—
Redwood	100	—	—
Ponderosa pine	71	29	—
Western white pine	72	28	—
Fir-spruce	80	20	—
Small private ownerships			
Douglas fir	75	24	1
Redwood	75	25	—
Ponderosa pine	41	36	23
Fir-spruce	—	100	—
Medium and large private ownerships			
Douglas fir	81	19	—
Redwood	90	10	—
Ponderosa pine	85	15	—
Western white pine	90	10	—
Fir-spruce	100	—	—

Source: Forest Service.

private owners is furnished by the number and area of registered tree farms in the state. At the close of 1956 there were 185 tree farms with 1,680,281 acres in the pine region, and 43 tree farms with 330,792 acres in the redwood region. By December 1, 1957, the total number of tree farms had increased to 252 and the area to 2,228,048 acres. In addition, there is a large area which is not registered as tree farms but which is receiving comparable treatment. This progress, however, does not mean that all of the problems relating to private ownership of forest land have been solved. Some of these will be discussed first as they apply to all classes of owners, and later as they apply more specifically to small, medium, and large ownerships.

TAXATION. A perennial problem is to discover, and apply, a method of taxation that will encourage the practice of forestry without relieving the forest owner of his obligation to contribute his fair share to the support of community activities. Since timber, unlike minerals, is above ground where it may be seen and readily measured, its appraisal for the purpose of applying the ad valorem property tax is easy. When that tax is applied year after year, particularly if the appraisal approaches the full value of the timber, it tends to discourage the holding of cutover land, and to encourage the premature cutting of the timber, as a means of relief from the tax burden, or from fear of that burden.

In order to remedy this situation the people of California in 1926 amended Section 12¾ of Article XIII of the State Constitution to read: ". . .All immature forest trees . . . planted or of natural growth, on lands from which the merchantable original growth timber stand to the extent of 70 per cent of all trees over 16 inches in diameter has been removed, shall be exempt from taxation, and nothing in this article shall be construed as subjecting such . . . forest trees to taxation provided, that forest trees or timber shall be considered mature for the purpose of this act at such time, after 40 years from the time of planting, or removal of the original timber as above provided, as a board consisting of a representative from the State Board of Forestry, a representative from the State Board of Equalization and the county assessor of the county in which the timber is located, shall by a majority thereof so determine."

Two rather serious difficulties have developed under this provision. The demand of the people for more and more services, coupled with increased costs, has forced tax assessors to seek additional sources of revenue, including timber. As a result, in some counties, the assessors have concluded that the 30 per cent or less of the trees over 16 inches in diameter left after cutting is taxable, and that second-growth timber over 40 years old which is merchantable is "mature" for tax purposes. These interpretations of the constitution tend to encourage both clear cutting of older timber and premature cutting of younger timber which may be merchantable but which has not yet reached either silvicultural or financial maturity. It should be recognized, however, that the assessor is placed in a difficult position when he is forced to tax the owner who is demonstrating value through cutting his timber, if he fails to tax, on an equal basis, the timber owner who is not conducting cutting operations, even though the latter may be practicing better forestry.

The situation is particularly acute for those owners whose timber stands have, until quite recently, been considered marginal or submarginal, with the assessed value approaching quite closely that of recently cutover land. Now, when cutting operations in the same general locality demonstrate that the timber has a cash value, the assessment is raised immediately, irrespective of the plans of the owner or of the probable effect of such an increase on his practice of forestry. The practice of assessing values in line with stumpage sales in the vicinity has grown rapidly in the last five years, and has been known to increase the assessment of individual properties as much as ten times.

Interest in tax laws and practices is keen on the part of assessors, timber owners, and other property owners, whose taxes are governed in part by the taxes levied on timberlands. The State Board of Forestry and the State Board of Equalization are giving the entire matter serious consideration, and in 1957 began a joint study in Mendocino County to determine how the provisions of Section 12¾ of the Constitution are working out in actual practice.

There is a growing feeling that this section may have outlived its usefulness and that a reconsideration of the whole problem of forest taxation is in order. That the present situation is not satisfactory is clear. It may be noted in passing that the California law has no counterpart in any other state, and that it might be interpreted so as to exempt all timber from taxation after the original cutting. Some believe that this is a desirable arrangement, but that the land tax should be based on the full productive capacity of the land. There are also many other alternatives, such as the deferred timber tax and various combinations of the land and the yield tax, some of which have been tried elsewhere and some of which have not. The entire subject of forest taxation is a difficult and complicated one which is in urgent need of thorough research.

Public Control. Action on the controversial issue of public control of cutting on privately owned forest lands was taken by the legislature in 1945 through passage of the Forest Practice Act. This act followed the general policy recommended by the Forestry Study Committee: "That some regulation is desirable and necessary is admitted, but we believe it can and should be imposed and administered by the State and that it is a State responsibility and function. We believe further that state regulation should be self imposed as nearly as is possible. We do not believe that force is the most effective way to achieve desirable results. On the other hand we feel that the State is obliged to see to it that forest land is kept productive and that the few who may be recalcitrant must be made to conform with the desirable practices adopted by the more progressive ones . . . The committee therefore strikes out boldly and confidently on the principle of self regulation under State guidance and surveillance, and we recommend a forest cutting practices law embodying this principle."

The act establishes four forest districts and authorizes the creation in each of a forest practice committee "whose duty shall be to formulate and adopt forest practice rules, and approve forest management plans for final approval of the State Board of Forestry," after their prior approval by two-thirds of the private timber ownership in the district. The forest practice rules may be superseded by forest management plans submitted by the owner and approved by the forest practice committee and the State Board of Forestry. Forest practice rules and forest management plans approved by the Board have the force of law, but the original act contained no penalty for noncompliance. An amendment adopted by the 1957 legislature provides that every timber operator must obtain a permit to operate from the State Forester; that engaging in timber operations without a valid permit constitutes a misdemeanor; and that a permit may be suspended or revoked by the Director of the Department of Natural Resources for failure or refusal to comply with the forest practice rules or applicable forest management plan, for material misrepresentation or false statement, or for refusal to allow inspection by the State Forester.

Much difference of opinion exists as to the effectiveness of the Forest Practice Act. Some feel that it has amounted to little more than a well-intentioned gesture. Others believe that it has proved to be an educational tool of considerable value and that it has resulted in many cases in distinct, if not spectacular, improvement in forest practice. In the long run its success will depend on two major factors.

First and foremost is the character of the rules of forest practice formulated by the district committees and approved by two-thirds of the timberland owners and by the State Board of Forestry. The original standards were purposely not set at too high a level, with the expectation that they would gradually be strengthened as timberland owners generally become familiar with the program and as silvicultural knowledge and economic conditions permit. Both the district committees and the State Board of Forestry have a responsibility to see that this is done.

Of almost equal importance, is the use which the Department of Natural Resources makes of its new power to suspend or revoke operators' permits for failure to comply with the act. Self-regulation can hardly attain its objectives, especially as minimum standards of satisfactory practice are raised, without the backing of the police power of the state.

Continuing research is needed to determine the effectiveness both of the standards themselves and of their enforcement. The success of self-regulation, "imposed and administered by the State," like that of any other regulatory program, will be measured by the extent to which it actually improves cutting practices in the woods.

Public Aid. The State of California assumes the primary financial responsibility for the prevention and suppression of fires on all state and private lands having "state-wide interest values" of forest, watershed, and range resources as determined by the State Board of Forestry. The area requiring state protection is divided into "Zone I" and "Zone II" lands. Zone I consists of forest and primary watershed lands which qualify for a federal grant-in-aid under the Clarke-McNary Act ("CM-2"). Zone II consists of secondary watershed and range lands which do not qualify for federal aid. Lands within these two zones in the national forests are protected by the Forest Service, and lands within six "outside" counties (Los Angeles, Kern, Marin, San Mateo, Santa Barbara, and Ventura) which have elected to provide their own protection are protected by the counties — in each case with partial reimbursement by the state. "Zone III" comprises an additional area not having "state-wide interest values," nearly 10 million acres of which are protected by the Division of Forestry under reimbursement contract with 25 counties. These areas may be summarized as follows for 1957:

		Acres
Zones I and II		
Protected by Division of Forestry	19,692,168	
Protected by Forest Service	5,245,649	
Protected by 6 contract ("outside") counties	2,901,703	
		27,839,520
Zone III		9,740,000
		37,579,520

These areas include both state and private lands, but the great bulk are in private ownership. During the last ten years the federal grant-in-aid has decreased from nearly 50 per cent to about 20 per cent of the expenditures by the state for the protection of lands in Zone I. An additional area of nearly 2 million acres in the unreserved public domain is protected by the state under contract with the Bureau of Land Management.

The state also cooperates, financially and otherwise, with the federal government and private owners in the control of insects and diseases on state and private forest lands, mainly the latter. Federal contributions are not on a matching basis and have averaged somewhat less than expenditures by the state, while private contributions have averaged about 3 per cent of the total cost.

In addition to providing material for its own use, the state sells planting stock from its forest tree nurseries to private owners at a "nominal cost" for use in windbreaks, soil-erosion control, watershed protection, and the reforestation of cutover lands. Federal grants-in-aid under the Clarke-McNary Act ("CM-4") are also received for the support of this activity, which is conducted on a relatively small scale as compared with similar programs in other states.

Further aid to private owners is furnished by the state through service foresters who give technical advice and "in the woods" assistance to small forest landowners on the protection and management of forest lands and on the harvesting and marketing of forest products therefrom. The program includes advice on such matters as planting, thinning, pruning, preparation of simple management plans, selection of trees to be cut, estimating timber values, sale of timber, and primary processing of forest products. The Division of Forestry handled 1,250 requests for such services in 1956. A federal grant-in-aid, which during the last five years has averaged about 20 per cent of the amount spent by the state, is received under the Cooperative Forest Management Act of 1950.

Still another state aid to private owners is rendered by the Extension Service of the University of California. Here emphasis is placed on education rather than on specific service. From 1952 to 1955 a federal grant-in-aid averaging 10 per cent of the state's expenditure was received from the federal government under the Clarke-McNary Act ("CM-5"). The grant was discontinued as a separate item in 1956 and added to the general Smith-Lever fund for extension work.

State and federal expenditures in these various fields in the fiscal year 1956-1957 are shown in Table 50. With the exception of fire, insect, and disease control on the small area of state land, the purpose of the programs is to protect and to promote better management on lands in private ownership. It should be noted that in every case the federal grants-in-aid are made to and spent by the state, which is in charge of the administration of the programs. Combined state and federal expenditures in several of the programs for the 10 years from 1947 to 1956 are shown in Figure 31.

Table 50. State and Federal Expenditures in Various Cooperative Activities, Fiscal Year 1957.

	State	Federal	Total
Fire Control – Zone I	$ 8,151,776	$1,308,378	$ 9,460,154
Fire Control – Zones I and II	13,282,428	1,308,378	14,590,806
Insect and Disease Control	119,714	115,194	234,908
Distribution of Nursery Stock	41,283	29,406	70,689
Cooperative Forest Management	54,250	17,009	71,259
Extension Program	19,500	– –	19,500

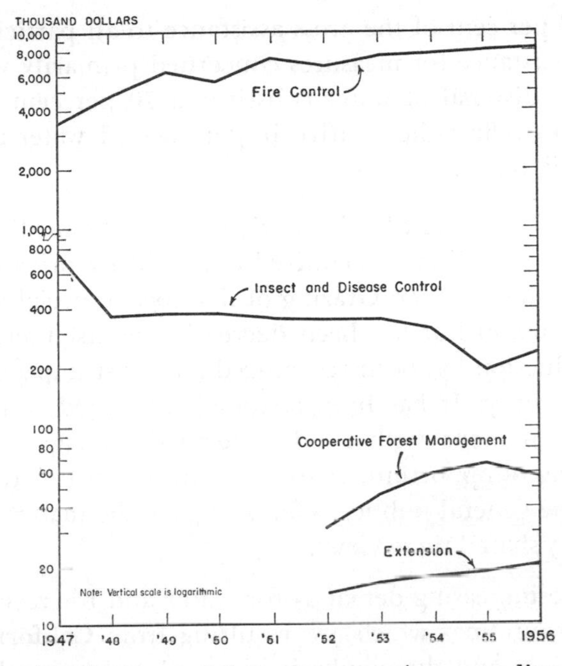

Figure 31. Combined state and federal cooperative expenditures for various activities in California, 1947-1956.

All of these programs seem to meet with general approval, and the California fire-protection system is regarded as one of the best in the country. Study is needed to appraise the results actually being obtained by the other programs and to determine ways and means of making them more effective. Research to increase the success of forest planting under the difficult conditions prevailing in many parts of California is a prerequisite to any material enlargement of the planting program on the part of either the state or private owners.

Direct federal assistance in large amounts is furnished to farmers through the Agricultural Conservation Program, but is of minor importance so far as forestry is concerned. In California, during the period from 1936 to 1955, inclusive, tree planting was done on 2,159 acres under the program, and forest stand improvement was conducted on 1,518 acres. In 1955, 86 acres were planted and 435 acres were improved. Payments to owners on account of these activities totaled 0.33 per cent of the gross assistance to all participants in the program. Assistance for measures concerned primarily with the conservation or disposal of water constituted 70 per cent of the total. These figures reflect the relative importance of water and of wood on California farms.

MULTIPLE USE. Forest lands, particularly in the medium and large ownerships, are ordinarily acquired and held by private owners for the production of timber. Grazing of livestock, especially on ranches, has been common but has been decreasing as its interference with timber production has been recognized and as stumpage values have increased steadily. It has been assumed that good timber management is synonymous with good watershed management and that the providing of opportunities for recreation is a function of public agencies. The general public, so far as it gave the matter any thought at all, largely shared these views.

Today the increasing demands for water and for recreation in attractive surroundings which are resulting from California's exploding population, and the emphasis being placed on multiple use by the Forest Service and others, are changing that situation. Without being too sure just what "multiple use" means in practice, the man on the street, the newspaper editor, the legislator, and even the timberland owner — in short, most of us — have accepted the theory as sound. There is rather general agreement that multiple use, if not a panacea, is at least an important element in sound land management. It is therefore essential to know much more than we now do about its potentialities and limitations on private land, from the standpoint of both the owner and the public.

Since water is universally recognized as California's primary natural resource, consideration of multiple use may well start with the subject of watershed management. For the state as a whole, the total supply of water is apparently adequate to meet the needs of a much larger population for domestic, industrial, and municipal use, for the disposal of sewage and industrial waste, for power, and for irrigation for a long time to come; and the engineering and economic difficulties in the way of transporting water from the northern part of the state, where water is relatively abundant and population relatively scarce, to the southern part of the state, where the situation is reversed, are apparently not insuperable. The Assembly Interim Committee on Government Organization in its 1956 report quoted David L. Grove of the Bank of America that "ultimate development would allow for the irrigation of nearly 20 million acres of land instead of the 7.3 million presently watered. It would provide for a population of 40 million persons heavily concentrated in the three major metropolitan areas." This conclusion, of course, is predicated on careful management of the water resource and especially on the existence of engineering works for impounding water during years of excess to provide for years of deficiency.

Land management has received far less attention than engineering as a major aspect of the water problem. The Senate Interim Committee on Public Lands in its 1953 report commented that "large areas of public domain and forest land are set aside for power site developments or other uses related to water supply, yet nothing is done with relation to watershed management." The committee quoted E. N. Munns, formerly in charge of the Division of Watershed Management Research in the Forest Service, as follows: "To my knowledge, there is no announced forest policy for this State as to the manner in which its forest lands should be treated in relation to the water resource . . . No land managing agency, public or private, has yet shown any marked appreciation or need for research in the Central Valley on the relation of the timber areas to water production. No research agency or institution in the State has seriously undertaken projects that would determine quantitatively how greatly the production and quality of water can be increased or decreased by the type of forest or species favored or discouraged in forest managment, or by the size or character of the trees, by the density or openness of the stand, or by the practices used in harvesting the forest crop, by the growth or use of ground cover by domestic or wild animals, or by any other kind of forest practice."

The problems of water with reference to private timberlands lie in three areas — watershed management, impounding reservoirs, and possible loss of water for industrial uses, such as manufacture of pulp and paper, through export to areas of deficiency. As Munns has pointed out, we know relatively little of the effect of different species, types, and methods of management on the water supply. Some preliminary studies, however, indicate that there will be better water yields if the snow can be intercepted in small openings in the stand created by clear cutting. This, however, may not be the best silvicultural practice for the species involved. Under this kind of management, even if there were no serious conflict with the silvicultural requirements of the species, there still would be losses in timber production. If water requirements are so acute as to demand this or any other form of forest management that materially reduces the potential production of timber, a formidable problem may be imposed on the private timberland owner, especially an owner with an expensive processing plant.

Large reservoirs for the impounding of water may react unfavorably on individual private timberland owners. They may have a serious effect on management plans and on the investment in processing facilities, particularly in the case of a pulp plant, which does not have the same flexibility as a sawmill in adjusting its daily production to shrinking supplies of raw materials. In addition to the loss of timberland by flooding, there is almost bound to be an accompanying loss to recreational use of lands surrounding the reservoirs because of the limited number of small lakes in California.

Northern California, which now produces a large surplus of water in relation to its needs, is also the area of greatest timber production. If populous southern California is to break out of limitations imposed by the acute shortage of water production in its own region, it must import large quantities from northern California. This situation produces strong sectional feelings. The northern counties are inclined to look with suspicion on any large diversion of water to southern California in the absence of well-authenticated data as to possible future needs within the northern area. Calculations by well-informed individuals and groups, however, do not indicate any serious difficulties in this respect, particularly with reference to industrial uses, including pulp and paper production.

The Coordinating Group of the Cooperative Pulp and Paper Study, which is sponsored by several governmental departments of the state, has estimated that the amounts of chippable mill and woods material shown in Table 51 would support a daily production of about 6,000 tons of pulp, chiefly in the redwood region. The figures assume conversion factors of 80 cubic feet of solid wood per cord, two cords of wood per ton of pulp, and 350 operating days per year. They also assume that with good forest management this amount of pulp can be produced without reducing the state-wide production of lumber by the sawmill industry below its present level. Undoubtedly woods waste, sawmill waste, and lower value logs will increasingly go into pulp, particle boards, and other non-lumber products.

Table 51. Material Required for the Production of 6,000 Tons of Pulp per Day.

Class of material	Million cu. ft. per day	Million cords per day	Tons of pulp per day
Unused coarse mill residues	121.7	1.52	2,170
Diversion of coarse mill residues now used for fuel	30.8	0.38	540
Logging residues	83.4	1.04	1,490
Logs, largely low grade	105.6	1.32	1,880
	341.5	4.26	6,080

Source: Coordinating Group of the Cooperative Pulp and Paper Study.

The Coordinating Group estimates the water requirements for the production of 6,000 tons of pulp per day as follows:

	Million gallons per day	Total requirement, acre-feet per year	Net consumptive use, acre-feet per year
Minimum water requirement (hardboard)	30.1	33,600	12,900
Maximum water requirement (Kraft process)	464.3	521,000	200,600

These figures assume that pulp mills situated in close proximity to the ocean will empty their effluent into a bay or the ocean without any treatment. Mills located on rivers or other inland streams will so treat the effluent that 90 per cent of the water can be utilized for other purposes downstream from the mill. The column headed "Net consumptive use" is based on these assumptions. The maximum net consumptive use of 200,600 acre-feet per year is a small fraction of the estimated natural runoff of 29,110,000 acre-feet per year from streams of the North Coastal Area and of 22,720,000 acre-feet from the Sacramento River Basin. There would therefore seem to be no difficulty in meeting the water requirements for a pulp industry of the size envisioned by the Coordinating Group without injustice to other uses or to other parts of the state.

Hunting and fishing are forms of multiple use with which most forest owners are more or less familiar, but which few care to make a major objective of management. They recognize that a certain amount of game production will take place without any special effort on their part, that hunters and fishermen will wish to use the lands during the appropriate seasons, and that it will be difficult to keep them off. Such use presents problems in the form of increased fire hazard, injury to soft roads by motor vehicles, litterbugism, vandalism, danger to woods workers from shooting, and danger to the visitors from travel on logging roads in active use. Although problems of this sort are irritating and sometimes serious, owners are learning to solve them by the application of foresight and the development of good public relations. Cooperation by most hunters and fishermen in complying with reasonable regulations can be expected if they feel that so long as they behave themselves they are welcome guests, and that so far as practicable the owner is avoiding methods of management likely to eliminate or materially reduce the game and fish populations.

Other forms of recreation such as picnicking and camping are impinging more and more heavily on private lands as the swelling hordes of tourists find the facilities on public lands inadequate to meet their needs. Free picnicking and camping on forest land is almost as much a part of the American tradition as free hunting and fishing. "No trespass" signs are resented and commonly ignored. The situation is particularly difficult when the private land is contiguous to or surrounded by national-forest land. Here the recreationist is unaware of the boundary line, or, if he is aware of it, sees no reason for a difference in management objectives — a difficulty which the Forest Service might make more effort to remedy.

Private owners are increasingly recognizing that the situation differs little from that created by hunters and fishermen. Rather than attempting the almost impossible task of keeping recreationists completely off their lands, they are turning to the more practical alternative of making them welcome but at the same time keeping them under control. Experience seems to be proving that setting aside some desirable sites for public use, under reasonable restrictions, and equipping them with the facilities needed for health and safety, will go far toward accomplishing both objectives. Whether or not a charge is made for the use of such sites and facilities, the program should more than pay its way in the reduction of trespass and the creation of good will.

Only a few private owners have made grazing an important part of the multiple-use management of their forest lands. Cut-out-and-get-out operators sometimes did allow grazing on their lands as a source of added income. Also, many of the redwood owner-operators, who for a long time were dependent on ship transportation of lumber and return shipment of supplies, went into the raising of beef cattle as a means of safeguarding their meat supply. Imports were unsatisfactory because of the lack of refrigeration on cargo vessels and because shipments were sometimes seriously delayed by rough weather.

As more and more effort is made to get maximum yields of timber from forest lands, it is inevitable that less forage will be available for grazing. Then, too, the more intensive management of other lands for the production of forage, e.g., irrigated pastures, will cause less competition between grazing and timber for the use of commercial forest lands. Most of the large operators believe that grazing should not continue as a part of their total operation.

Much research will be needed to determine what combinations of uses are both feasible and desirable. Particularly urgent are studies in the field of water relations under the widely differing conditions of climate, topography, soil, and cover that occur throughout the state. Should research prove conclusively that the public interest requires the use by private owners of methods of watershed management or recreation management that interfere materially with timber production, consideration will have to be given to means of securing such management and also for compensating the owner for such financial losses as it may entail. In special cases it may be necessary to convert private lands to public ownership by purchase in order to attain the desired objectives.

RELATION TO NATIONAL FOREST TIMBER. The fact that 52 per cent of the commercial forest area of 17,317,000 acres in California is under federal ownership or trusteeship, with 50 per cent in the national forests, raises problems for private timberland owners and operators. Since a large part of the timber utilized by the wood-using industries in the state must come from the national forests, the timber-sale policy of the Forest Service is a matter of major importance. That policy was described as follows by the Chief on February 21, 1956, in a statement to a subcommittee of the U. S. Senate Committee on Interior and Insular Affairs: "The general policy of the Forest Service is to offer sales of a size and duration to best serve the needs of dependent industry and to provide purchase opportunity to large and small industry alike."

More specifically, he stated that in the Northwest small sales (less than 5 million board feet) have increased greatly in recent years and now contribute from 25 to 30 per cent of the annual cut; that medium-size sales (5 to 25 million board feet) contribute from 40 to 45 per cent of the cut; that large sales of 25 to 50 million board feet contribute from 20 to 25 per cent of the cut; and that still larger sales of more than 50 million feet contribute about 10 per cent of the cut. The size-of-sale pattern has changed considerably in recent years and further changes will occur as better access is developed. Future trends as he sees them will be somewhat as follows:

"A material expansion in the very small sales of around 100,000 board feet or less is highly desirable to increase salvage and improvement cuttings. Increases in this sale class will much more adequately than heretofore take care of the smallest class of operation. Increases in the volume sold in sales of 5 million feet and less to better meet the needs of other small operations will also be desirable.

"Medium-size sales of 5 to 25 million board feet are the dominant class by volume of timber sold and should continue as such. They generally are suited to all classes of operations except the very small.

They afford an opportunity for the small operator to purchase up to three years' supply of timber in one transaction and thus facilitate his planning and stabilize his operation. They allow the larger operator a chance to supply his needs by making several purchases instead of one. Large sales, those ranging from 25 to 50 million board feet, probably should not be eliminated entirely, at least for a considerable time.

"In respect to duration of sales, practically all of the small and medium sales, and many of the large sales, can be for a period not exceeding three years. Few large sales will need to exceed five or six year periods. Longer periods will be for exceptional cases with unusual need for plant or road amortization."

The policy of favoring small and medium-size sales of relatively short duration means that the owner of a processing plant has no assurance of being able to meet his needs by continuing purchases of national-forest timber. This situation may be particularly serious for owners of processing plants involving a heavy capital investment. The emphasis on small and medium-size sales may also decrease the likelihood of complete utilization of raw materials which is more characteristic of large-scale, integrated production.

This facet of the problem needs to be considered in connection with sustained yield and the mill capacity of the state. The 1957 sawmill directory of California published by "The Lumberman" indicates an approximate annual mill capacity of 5 billion board feet on a one-shift basis. An exact figure is difficult to determine because of varying lengths of operating seasons. The estimated capacity approximately equals the 5 billion board feet cut in 1956, but because of the high degree of flexibility possible through extending the season of operation and using additional shifts the potential capacity is considerably greater. Even modest figures of the mill capacity for the state as a whole may well obscure serious excess mill capacity for the "logsheds" of certain communities. The potential cut can be at least 6 billion board feet. This fact is highly significant in view of the estimated sustained-yield production of the state of 3½ to 4 billion board feet. The discrepancy between the two figures emphasizes the need for as complete utilization as possible of the raw material from stump to finished product.

The situation involves questions both of fact and philosophy. Is it true that the present timber-sale policy of the Forest Service fails to assure processors, and particularly the larger processors, of the supplies necessary for the continued operation of their plants, and that it tends to perpetuate the uneconomic processing of raw materials with consequent physical waste and higher cost of the finished product? Or are these effects negligible, at least in comparison with the advantages of maintaining small operations, often conducted by non-landowners, which must rely largely on national-forest timber, particularly in view of the trend toward concentration of private land holdings in the larger ownerships? Is the perpetuation of small business in itself a desirable social objective? These are questions that have an important bearing on the ownership and management of both private and public lands and that deserve careful study.

Access roads constitute an aspect of national-forest timber-sale policy which is of considerable interest to private owners and concerning which there is much difference of opinion. In 1952 the Forest Service proposed the following division of responsibility for the construction of access roads in the entire country:

	Miles	Cost
Federal government	5,532	$112,472,000
Timber purchasers	9,888	109,292,000
Local road authorities and private interests	1,287	34,038,000
	16,707	$255,802,000

In 1956 the Chief of the Forest Service told a Senate committee that a new look is needed, with special consideration of these items:

1. The size of the road program which should be financed with federal appropriations in order to permit reduction in the number of large, long-term sales and an increase in the number of small and moderate-sized short-term sales.

2. The additional roads needed to apply light salvage cutting to all portions of each working circle in order to achieve full-scale salvage of endemic mortality.

3. The additional roads needed for a suitably distributed hauling system for a current cut of 7.6 billion feet and an expected cut of 9.5 billion feet in 1960 in all national forests.

The lumber industry is inclined to be critical of the large share of access-road construction assigned to the federal government. It feels that federal construction will proceed more slowly, will be more costly, and will increase the number of what it regards as uneconomic small sales. It also suspects that the location and quality of the roads will be determined in part by their probable future use for recreational purposes, as well by the needs for current timber harvesting, which is desirable or not depending on one's point of view. Main roads are generally conceded to be the responsibility of the Forest Service, and differences of opinion exist chiefly with respect to secondary and tertiary spur roads.

Rights of way over privately owned lands for the removal of national-forest timber and for other purposes constitute a more serious problem. The situation is particularly acute where there is considerable intermingling of private and government ownerships, and constitutes an argument for readjustment of boundaries. The basic attitude of the Forest Service with respect to rights of way, as stated by the Chief to a Senate committee in 1956, is as follows:

"The general, and basic, policy is that the United States must have permanent rights of way to all of its lands. Adequate rights of way are needed to permit the government to protect, administer, and utilize all the resources of the national forests. For adequate access, rights of way over private lands must generally be free of conditions or limitations on their full use, including use by the general public, when such use is compatible with public safety and protection of the roads and forest resources.

"Another basic policy is that national forest timber will not be advertised for sale until permanent easements for hauling it to market over an economically feasible route are obtained. This insures a bidding opportunity to every operator."

The desire of the Forest Service to have permanent access to all parts of the national forests is based on a sound policy of forest management. With a complete network of roads, the forest manager not only has access to all parts of the forest for fire control, but he also has a high degree of flexibility in the manipulation of the stand and in the use of the land for recreational purposes. He can select trees with a current high marketability and salvage wind-thrown, bug-killed, or diseased portions of the forest. Even in a virgin stand a complete road system permits the selection of high-risk trees and the bypassing of stands of relatively immature timber which is still capable of putting on considerable growth in value.

The private owner, on the other hand, is strongly averse to losing control over at least a portion of the road system in which he may have a sizeable investment. In the cases in dispute, the private owner has not opposed the right of egress for national-forest timber, even when that timber may be sold to another operator, provided he is compensated for the use of the road at a specified rate per thousand board feet per mile. He does object strenuously to a permanent right of way which involves public use for resources other than timber. The Forest Service, in turn, does not object to imposition of a fee for use of the road during the first cutting cycle only; and it insists that the road be available for general public use. This insistence ties in closely with the Forest Service emphasis on multiple use.

Owners of private land within national forests created from the public domain have the right to cross them under the Act of June 4, 1897, providing for the administration of national forests. The Forest Service believes that Congress should authorize the Secretary of Agriculture to require a reciprocal exchange of rights of way with neighboring timberland owners in connection with the issuance of easements to them. This authority is now exercised by the Secretary of the Interior, but doubt exists as to whether it is possessed by the Secretary of Agriculture. The problem should receive such study and action as may be necessary to break the present impasse.

Small Ownerships. Each class of ownership has problems which are more or less peculiar to it. With the small owner, his objectives govern in no small degree the character of management which his lands receive. When an owner receives his main income from a ranch and has an intense interest in good land management, the degree of forest management may well be the highest possible. On the other hand, an absentee owner who has inherited the land, which may originally have been homesteaded by a grandfather, may be more interested in converting the timber to cash without thought of the future of the land.

A timber operator familiar with the situation in Humboldt County stated that a common pattern for that area was for an uninformed owner to sell first to a "gyppo" logger who would take off the larger material. The property might then be sold to a re-logger who would remove much of the remaining live stand. The final sale would be to a salvage logger for removal of chunks, old windfalls, and any other material, dead or alive, still on the tract. This is the extreme situation that leads to tax delinquency and sometimes to reversion of the land to public ownership. Unfortunately little information is available as to the magnitude of these extreme practices or, for that matter, of other practices being followed on small ownerships where cutting operations are now being conducted. The service foresters of the State Division of Forestry believe that there is a significantly high percentage of such operations which do not comply with the forest-practice rules of the forest district in which they are located.

The small owner who is really interested in timber production is confronted by a number of problems. Among these are taxation, which has already been discussed, trespass, dependence on the logging contractor or timber buyer, and financial needs. During the last ten years stumpage prices have risen far above their previous levels. This rise has been due chiefly to competition among prospective buyers, including an influx of "gyppo" loggers from Oregon and Washington, but also in part to the publicity which has surrounded the high prices bid for national-forest stumpage. One result of this situation has been an increase in timber trespass, to which the small ownership is particularly exposed. Premeditated trespass, which amounts to outright stealing, is difficult to combat unless the trespasser can be apprehended in the process of cutting and has down timber or lumber on the area against which a lien can be placed.

In many cases the small owner is not as well informed on current stumpage values as are trespassers and legitimate buyers. Unless he obtains advice from a consulting forester, a state service forester, or other competent and disinterested person, he is likely to sell the timber for much less than its actual worth. Even when he is informed as to values, he may be uninformed as to the volumes in his stand. He may have a cruise of the timber made many years ago and still be ignorant of the ingrowth during the intervening years. Finally, the small owner is pretty much at the mercy of the logging contractor for the complete utilization of the timber felled, for the amount of damage to the residual stand, and for general application of forestry practice, including compliance with the rather simple forest-practice rules for the forest district in which the timber is located. In general, the rancher-owner is in the best position to get a fair price for his timber and to enforce good forest practice.

The attitude of the small owner with reference to management of timberland for continuous production is intimately related to his desires as to total income. If those desires are completely satisfied from another source such as a ranch, business, or profession, he may be interested in maintaining a forest property of almost any size, however small. If he wishes or needs to maintain himself solely from the returns from his forest property, the acceptable minimum size depends on his desires or needs. For example, let us assume a property of 2,500 acres which is in such shape that it will yield 200 board feet per acre annually in perpetuity. With a stumpage value of $20 per M board feet, the gross annual income is $10,000. If taxes, protection, and other costs total $2,000 a year, the owner will net $8,000; if they total $4,000, he will net $6,000. Under these conditions, the minimum sized property, above or below 2,500 acres, that would be completely sustaining would depend on the needs or desires of the owner. If he had an abiding interest in good land management, he might find additional, compensating satisfaction in so manipulating the stand as to markedly increase the annual yield. Such an owner might conceivably practice an intensity of management, on a relatively small area, considerably above that practiced by any other type of owner.

MEDIUM-SIZED OWNERSHIPS. Land management of the medium-sized ownerships varies from poor to excellent. Since the Timber Resource Review, in appraising the condition of recently cut-over lands by use of the productivity index, unfortunately combined the medium-sized and the large ownerships, there is no way of distinguishing between them. Observation, however, indicates that as a group the medium-sized ownerships are being managed considerably better than the small ownerships but not as well as the large ownerships. This is probably due in considerable part to the fact that the larger owners commonly possess processing plants, which provide an incentive to practice sustained-yield forestry in order to increase the assurance of a continuous supply of raw material for their operation.

Both the intensity and stability of forest management depend on the intent of the owners or managers. Corporate owners, who are well represented in this class, are on the whole more likely to take the long look ahead, and therefore to be more interested in stability, than are the small owners, although there are many exceptions to this generalization. Continuity of policy and of good forest practice is more likely if the ownership is represented by management responsible to a continuing body of stockholders than if it is in the hands of a single individual. Even if the current owner is keenly interested in intensive management, he is likely to be succeeded, perhaps by inheritance, by someone who has quite a different attitude and who has in no sense built himself into the property.

Although taxation is an important problem for this class of owners, it is considerably less pressing than for the small owners. This may be due in part to the fact that the county assessor recognizes a greater degree of stability in the medium-sized ownerships. Even so, the burden will increase as supplies of virgin timber diminish, especially in counties where timberlands constitute a rather large part of the tax base. In general, the relatively small, individual owner in this size class is likely to feel the pressure of taxation more than the larger, corporate owner, especially one who also has a processing plant.

Another problem confronting the medium-sized owner concerns the logging and processing of his timber. If the ownership is of such a size that logging can be done by an owner who has a real interest in forest management, cutting practices are likely to be of a higher order than if the work is done under contract. This does not imply that highly responsible logging contractors are not available, but rather that the owner is inclined to give greater attention to the land management aspects of the operation if he has more direct responsibility for them.

Processing of the timber constitutes an even greater problem. With the present lively competition for stumpage, the owner of timberland can realize good returns from sale of the stumpage alone; but if he wishes to realize the larger returns usually associated with at least partial manufacture of the logs, he must decide on the degree of refinement in manufacture and utilization that he is capable of financing and that is justified by the size of his ownership. Among other things, he must choose from among circular saw, single bandsaw, and multiple bandsaw mills, and perhaps also such adjunctive equipment as resaws, gangsaws, planers, log barkers, chippers, and dry kilns. Under proper conditions, each right choice can increase the intensity of utilization and add to the magnitude of the returns, which are often reduced by inefficient equipment.

Closely related to the processing equipment is the matter of markets and marketing. The latter is of major importance because of the difficulty that may exist in taking full advantage of the highly active market for lumber that has prevailed during the past decade. If his processing plant is a circular sawmill merely turning out rough lumber, the owner may be forced to sell his output to a concentration yard which assumes responsibility for further refinement and sales. Even with considerable refinement beyond the stage of rough lumber, the owner may find it advantageous to handle his output through a sales organization. However, without direct contact with the market, an owner finds it more difficult to keep production in line with market demands. This frequently creates a problem in financing to tide the owner over slack, or "soft," periods in the lumber market. In all phases of marketing, the larger operator is in a somewhat more advantageous position.

LARGE OWNERSHIPS. This class of owners is fully cognizant of the value of timberland so managed as to be in a productive condition.

As a consequence, 15 of the 19 large ownerships have stated a policy of continuous production. Three others which have no clearly stated policy may nevertheless be said to be working toward this objective. One ownership is unable to state just what the future management policy will be. In general, the land in the large ownership class will undoubtedly continue to receive better management than the other two classes. The fact that a significant percentage of the total area in this class is connected directly with processing plants will help to keep the objectives of the owners in line with good long-run management. Furthermore, the trend in the use of forest lands is such that even owners without processing plants are apt to develop strong management policies. The land held by the one ownership whose plans are still uncertain will almost certainly eventually fall into the category of good forest management, if for no other reason than the competition for ownership of this sort of land by processing companies committed to a policy of expanding their holdings with long-term forest management in view.

The past few years have witnessed a significant number of mergers among this group of owners. Some consolidations have taken place by absorption of timberlands previously in the medium-size class. While this may indicate a temporary instability of ownership, there is no indication that instability of land management will result. In a few cases the opportunity for integrated processing plants created by grouping of capital and ownership can lead to increased stability of land management.

Taxation continues to be a problem for this class of ownership as well as for the other two classes because of the mad scramble of taxing agencies to find sources of revenue. The large ownerships are, however, in a better financial position to combat inequities so far as the individual ownerships are concerned, and they can also make important contributions to the solution of the taxation problem inherent in the ownership of forest land through their ability to employ specialists in this field. Annual taxation of young crops is, however, almost certain to be a deterring factor in the consideration of plans for extensive planting, either following current cutting or for the rehabilitation of nonstocked and partially stocked lands.

The processing members of this class of ownership are generally in a position to engage in direct marketing of lumber, but they do have problems of changing markets. For example, the competition of the fiber box has taken away a large market for the low-grade lumber which formerly went into wooden boxes. In general, a situation of this sort must be met by new ways of processing the lumber to make it salable for other uses. The extent to which this can be done depends both on technology and on adequate capital to finance the investment usually required by new processing methods.

The large owners of timberland in California who are also owners of processing plants have an historical background of sawmilling. Most of them do not have experience in the manufacture of plywood, particle boards, and pulp products. The capital required for the installation of equipment for the production of these commodities adds to the lag inherent in long-continued familiarity and experience with one type of product. Integrated production however, permits more complete utilization of the raw material and, if efficiently handled, should yield greater returns to invested capital. The degree of integration possible has a definite relationship both to the size of the ownership and the amount of capital available. Even larger consolidations than have already taken place may result from the desire to obtain the highest practicable degree of integrated production.

Size of Ownership and Returns. Comprehensive and accurate information is conspicuously lacking as to the number, area, location, character, and condition of forest properties of less than 50,000 acres in private ownership, and as to the objectives and management practices of their owners and the returns received by them. This situation holds particularly for ownerships of less than 5,000 acres. Much more information is needed concerning these two classes of ownership, which include 62 per cent of the total area in private ownership. The information must also be kept up to date because of the constant shifts in ownership, with resulting changes in size classes, management practices, and problems.

Data by timber types are needed on possible monetary returns from properties of various sizes and qualities to enable the owner to decide whether to retain and possibly to enlarge his property, and if so what kind and intensity of management to apply to it. In this connection, it is pertinent to emphasize the importance of the quality as well as the size of the property in question. Size alone is no more a measure of the productivity of forest land than it is of agricultural land. Determination of site quality is therefore indispensable in estimating probable rates of growth and future yields in volume from an area of any given size.

Accurate and comprehensive information concerning all of the major factors that will control returns is especially needed by the small and medium-sized owners, who commonly are not in a position to obtain it for themselves. It should be kept current so as to reflect changes in markets and in forest practices. Information on present and prospective markets is particularly important because of the changes that are constantly taking place in wood-conversion processes and in the demand for various products.

Up to a certain point, increased intensity of management usually results in increased net returns. Owners of properties too small to justify the permanent employment of a forester may be able to utilize the services of consulting foresters. They can also obtain a limited amount of professional advice on cutting practices, utilization, and marketing from service foresters of the State Division of Forestry, from the University of California, and from the lumber trade associations. It is possible, too, that some of the large processors will furnish advice on management in return for the privilege of buying the timber, as is the case in the southern pine region. The formation of cooperatives may also help to promote better management and marketing.

The most complete use of the standing tree compatible with sound economics is highly desirable from the point of view of the owner, the manufacturer, and the general public; so too is the use of each part of the tree or log for the purpose to which it is best suited. These objectives are best attained through integrated production, which may or may not be concentrated in a single plant or series of plants under the control of the same owner. Unified control of all the processes involved in complete utilization has certain obvious advantages, but it requires so heavy a capital investment as to be beyond the means of most manufacturers. Fortunately integrated production can be achieved, at least in large part, by marketing arrangements which provide for the pooling of material from several plants. Thus, a sawmill or a veneer plant or a partially integrated plant producing lumber and hardboard can send their residuals to a common pulp plant. Research to determine the best ways and means of promoting integrated production which will make the best and fullest possible use of the large amount of raw material now improperly used or wasted is much needed.

Zoning

The basic principle of multiple use is now generally accepted by private owners, or at least by the larger owners, as applicable to private as well as to public lands. But accepting the principle and applying it to specific pieces of property are quite different matters — irrespective of ownership. What single use or what combination of uses of this acre, this 40 acres, this 640 acres, or this 100,000 acres is both feasible and most desirable from the combined standpoint of the owner and the public is one of the most difficult problems in the entire field of land management. Some of its ramifications and complications have previously been discussed.

The extent to which zoning might be applied to control the use or combination of uses to which wildland is put has received less consideration in California than in several other states. City zoning is of course well known and widely applied, but rural zoning is another matter. As an example of the latter, Santa Clara County has zoned some 15,000 acres for the exclusive use of agriculture under the "greenbelt law" of 1955. The incorporation of the four "dairy" cities in Los Angeles County and Orange County in order to protect themselves against invasion by subdivisions is in effect a form of zoning. Might not the principle be applied on a wider scale and to different types of land?

Just as Santa Clara County has zoned certain lands for agriculture, some other counties with wholly different conditions might wish to zone certain lands against agriculture and for timber production and recreation. Unusual circumstances might make zoning for recreation only, or for timber production only, a logical procedure, perhaps for a limited period. For example, it is quite possible that intial forest management in the pine region will call for a cutting cycle of 25 years, and that for periods of 5 years logging will be going on in different parts of the watershed included in the cutting cycle. The areas being logged might be zoned against recreational use during the period of the operation – a measure that would contribute fully as much to the safety of the public as to the convenience of the owner. Still another situation in which safety is a matter of paramount importance is in the brush-covered foothills which occur in many parts of the state. Areas where the hazard of conflagration is high and means of quick exit lacking might be zoned against human habitation, at least during periods of major fire danger.

Zoning of wildlands would be based on the obvious but often overlooked fact that their use for all purposes, at all times, and in all places is neither possible nor desirable. Multiple use, like all other good things, has its limitations. Decision as to what use or combination of uses is best under any given set of circumstances will be greatly facilitated if owners whose primary interest is in the production of timber or forage will recognize that the public has a legitimate interest in the water that comes from the land and in the recreational opportunities which it affords; and if the public in its turn will develop a respect for land, a genuine concern in its wise management, and a recognition of the rights as well as the responsibilities of its owner.

These "ifs" involve so much human nature as to make it fairly certain that intervention by a governmental agency will occasionally be necessary to assure a form of use that is reasonably satisfactory to all concerned. Here is where zoning comes in as one means of effectuating an over-all plan of land management. If and when it results in substantial loss to the owner, consideration must obviously be given to some form of compensation or to public ownership. Equally obviously, zoning or any other form of community guidance or restriction must be based on well-considered facts determined by research, and not on snap judgments or on pressures exerted by special-interest groups.

A different kind of "zoning," which requires no enabling legislation and no administrative action by state, county, or municipal authorities, has been undertaken by the Forest Service in recent years as a step toward more effective management of the national forests of California. For this purpose the California region has been divided into several subregions, for each of which a comprehensive plan of management is embodied in a "management direction." Each subregion in turn is divided into "management zones."

For example, the Northeast Plateau Subregion includes parts of seven national forests (Tahoe, Plumas, Lassen, Modoc, Shasta-Trinity, and Klamath) and six counties (Sierra, Plumas, Lassen, Modoc, Shasta, and Siskiyou), divided into the following zones:

Eastside Intermediate — those parts of the subregion where climate and soil are generally suited for the production of timber crops.

Basin Plateau — the drier parts of the subregion characterized in the natural state by the sagebrush-bitterbrush-juniper association.

Waterfront — scattered areas suitable for intensive recreational use around lakes and along certain streams.

Roadside — strips of varying width along the more important highways and roads.

Streamside — relatively narrow strips along stream channels.

Special—of particular public significance, such as wilderness areas.

"To reconcile competing demands in multiple use of the land, the directives assign each zone primary and secondary priorities for management. Noncompeting uses will be permitted, but competing uses will be adjusted in favor of the primary and secondary uses." The plan is expected to exercise control over management activities until 1970, with provision for minor reviews in 1960 and 1965.

The entire program is, in substance, a form of regional planning for the management of the extensive and widely divergent properties under the control of a single administrative agency — the Forest Service. It suggests an approach that might well be given serious consideration should California at any time embark on a program of state or regional planning. Such planning might aim to control land use by legal zoning under state legislation, or merely to encourage wise land use through land classification and educational measures. In either case, recognition and practical application of the fact that the state (or a region) has been divided by nature into "zones" with different characteristics and different optimum uses, would seem to have much merit.

PART V

SUMMARY AND CONCLUSIONS

California's exploding population is putting an increasingly severe strain on its rich but limited natural resources. How these resources are managed will determine what water, wood, forage, wildlife, minerals, and opportunities for recreation will be available to meet the needs and desires of its own and other citizens. That management in turn will be governed largely by the pattern of land ownership, by the objectives and abilities of the owners, and by the guidance, cooperation, and control furnished by state and federal agencies.

Pattern of Land Ownership

Within a century the pattern of land ownership in California has changed from one of relative simplicity to one of great complexity. When California became a state in 1850, title to its entire land area rested in the United States with the exception of some 8,850,000 acres in Spanish and Mexican grants that were later confirmed by the federal government. Today the nation owns some 47 per cent of the state's land area; the state, counties, and other local governmental units own some 3 per cent; and the remaining 50 per cent is in private ownership.

The great reduction in original federal ownership was effected by grants to the state for the construction of permanent improvements, for the reclamation of swamp and overflowed lands, for the promotion of education, and for state parks; by grants to corporations to aid in railroad construction; and by sales and grants to individuals primarily to promote settlement and to encourage mining. No land was marked for permanent retention until 1890, when Congress created the Yosemite, General Grant, and Sequoia National Parks, and 1892, when President Harrison established the San Gabriel Forest Reserve. These actions marked the beginning of a reversal of the federal policy from one of extensive land disposal to one of reservation, and later of acquisition, of land for national parks, national forests, wildlife refuges, reclamation and flood-control works, grazing districts, oil reserves, and military installations. The new policy reached its climax in 1934 and 1935, when President Franklin D. Roosevelt withdrew all of the remaining public domain from entry except under the mining laws – unless and until it should be classified and opened for entry by the Secretary of the Interior.

The state followed the example of the federal government in selling as rapidly as possible the lands granted to it by the latter. By the turn of the century it had succeeded in disposing of most of its holdings except for a fairly sizeable area of scattered and largely unsurveyed school sections. Then came a shift in policy, as a result of which thc state has acquired several hundred thousand acres for parks, wildlife refuges and management areas, and state forests.

With the exception of a small area of military reservations and of administrative sites, the area now in federal and state ownership consists almost entirely of "wildlands," while the area in private ownership is much more diverse in character. The Spanish and Mexican grants were chiefly valuable for farms and ranches, with relatively small areas of forest land; but they also included sites that were later to become important metropolitan centers, such as San Francisco, Sacramento, Monterey, Santa Barbara, Los Angeles, and San Diego. Grants and sales by the federal and state governments transferred to private ownership most of the remaining area that was suitable for cultivation and for town sites, together with a considerable area of forest, range, and mineral land.

Farms and ranches now comprise about three-fourths of the area in private ownership. Only about 30 per cent of the land in farms and ranches is used for the production of harvested crops (including fallow), while about two-thirds is pastured (including woodland pasture). Outside of farms and ranches, somewhat more than half of the area in private ownership consists of commercial forest land. The remainder is made up of urban, suburban, and other residential sites, and of noncommercial forest, range, and mineral lands.

California's wildlands, with which this study is chiefly concerned, are thus owned and managed by numerous federal and state agencies in several different departments and by tens of thousands of individuals and corporations. (The estimate that there are more than 10,000 private owners of commercial forest land alone is generally believed to be ultra-conservative.) These lands vary greatly in character and occur in parcels of all sizes, with the area under a single ownership sometimes well concentrated but often widely scattered. The intermingling of holdings under different ownerships (both private and public) and the diversity of policies followed by different owners (both private and public) complicate administration and management for all classes of owners. A striking, but not unique, example of this situation is the checkerboard pattern of alternate sections in private and public ownership resulting from the railroad grants.

Objectives and Problems

Theory and Practice

Agreement is general (1) that land ownership and management should be such as will most effectively promote the "public interest," and (2) that this goal can be approached either through private ownership, where financial profit is properly a dominant motive, or through public ownership, where other forms of "profit" may be more important. Opinions vary widely, however, as to how to define, how to measure, and how to attain the "public interest." Theory, in other words, is not easy to put into practice.

The interest of individuals, of local communities, of the state, and of the nation are not always identical. What seems best for the present may not be best for the future. When conflicts exist, where does the "public interest" lie? What patterns and programs of ownership and management will contribute most effectively to its realization? What changes in the present setup do the answers to such questions as these suggest?

Two tools are now being widely acclaimed as providing the key to wildland management in the "public interest." If all owners would only practice multiple use and sustained yield, many believe that utopia would be in sight. Widespread and intelligent application of these practices would certainly enhance the hope that land can be made to yield — and to yield permanently — all the goods and services that we desire or need; but their successful use is unfortunately beset with many difficulties.

A first prerequisite for the really effective employment of multiple use on a state-wide or national basis is that we know just what we want to produce, and in what proportions. Next, what is the responsibility of different classes of owners for achieving that production? Should private owners concentrate on the production of tangible goods such as wood and forage, and public owners on the production of less tangible services such as protection of the water supply, control of erosion, and provision of recreational areas; or should all owners place equal weight on the production of all kinds of goods and services; or is some middle ground between these two extremes desirable?

Thirdly, the techniques of intensive multiple-use management still remain to be perfected. Many uses are competitive, and all land has a limit to the kind and amount of products and services it can yield. Maximum yields of wood, forage, recreation, and other products cannot be obtained from the same area, whether it is one acre or a hundred thousand acres in size, and the technical problem of producing whatever combination of goods and services may be sought is a difficult one.

Equally difficult is a valid answer to the question usually asked to test the desirability of any activity: "Does it pay? — are returns greater than costs?" In the case of multiple use, both returns and costs vary not only in amount but in kind. They may be tangible or intangible, personal or social, present or future. Some can be measured in dollars and cents, others cannot.

In the absence of any adequate measuring stick for comparing the various costs and returns associated with different forms of land management, the decision as to which to adopt must be based on judgment, after careful consideration of all the factors involved. Current decisions will be made by owners, managers, administrators, and legislators, but they will be influenced (and in the long run controlled) by the voters, as is the case with education and other activities whose profitability cannot be gauged wholly in monetary terms. Surveys to determine public opinion with respect to the relative values at stake are therefore needed both to guide those responsible for the formulation and execution of land-management policies, and to steer educational efforts along lines that will result in a better informed citizenry with heightened ability to exercise sound judgment, especially as to the fundamental values of the several uses and resources of wildlands.

Sustained yield denotes a continuing equality between production and use. Wood, forage, and wildlife will be harvested in the same amounts year after year, or period after period; opportunities for recreation will be maintained in perpetuity. This concept is sound but does not go far enough. Production needs not only to be sustained, but sustained at a high level of quantity and quality, which usually necessitates building up production to equal anticipated demand. The increasing pressure on natural resources being exerted by a swelling population and an expanding economy makes it imperative to utilize more and more effectively the productive capacity of the land.

This task, which is really one aspect of multiple use, raises problems of technique in acute form, since the difficulties of management increase rapidly as the level of production is stepped up. It also raises the problem of determining what intensity of management can be practiced without passing the point of diminishing returns. Much research in these fields will be necessary before sustained yield can play the role of which it is capable in assuring not only continuing but adequate supplies.

In brief, there is need to clarify the concept of "public interest" as a major objective of land ownership and management, and to decide what measures are most likely to promote its attainment.

Where do we want to go, and how can we get there? Among the subjects that must be considered in finding an answer are appraisal of the relative weights that should be attached to personal, local, state, and national points of view; identification, and so far as practicable measurement, of costs and returns of all kinds (tangible and intangible, personal and social, present and future); the potentialities and limitations of multiple use and sustained yield, including the techniques involved in their successful application; and the efficiency of different classes of owners in furthering progress toward the desired goal.

Clear thinking and intensive research along these lines will progressively indicate what changes in land ownership and in land management policies and practices appear to be desirable, and will facilitate their application. "Hasten slowly" is often good advice, and drastic changes would be unwise unless and until thorough and impartial analysis shows that they promise definite improvement, There are, however, many important adjustments that could be made on the basis of existing knowledge or relatively short-time studies.

Federal Lands

Of the total area in California under the jurisdiction of the federal government (including Indian lands), nearly 49 per cent is administered by the Department of the Interior, about 42 per cent by the Department of Agriculture, nearly 9 per cent by the Department of Defense, and less than 0.5 per cent by other agencies. Federal holdings occur in every county in the state, but the great bulk of the area is in the desert and mountainous portions. Four-fifths of the area is used for the production of wood, domestic livestock, and wildlife.

Department of the Interior. Nearly three-fourths of the area administered by the Department of the Interior consists of unreserved public domain. Since 1935 these lands have been withdrawn from all forms of entry except mineral entry. They may, however, be opened to entry under existing legislation by the Secretary of the Interior if classification shows them to be suitable for the purpose desired by the applicant. Nearly a fourth of the area is in grazing districts, and much of the remainder is used for the production of forage and wood.

Classification of the unreserved public domain, which has now been in a state of "temporary" withdrawal for nearly a quarter of a century, should be speeded up to determine what lands can properly be opened to entry and what lands should be retained. Decision on this point is particularly important with respect to the grazing districts — the reserves that are not reserves — and the still larger area that is primarily of value for grazing. A decision should also be reached as to the future of the 324,000 acres of commercial forest land, which are widely scattered, subject to frequent trespass, and difficult of administration. Should these lands be sold to private owners, added to adjacent national forests, retained and blocked up by exchange and purchase for permanent administration as a new type of reserve, or handled by some combination of these methods?

Careful scrutiny of the Small Tract Act and its administration is very much in order. Many people, including the board of supervisors and the planning commission of San Bernardino County, where four-fifths of the entries in California have been located, mostly in the last few years, feel that it has too often created rural slums, led to undesirable speculation, and greatly complicated life for the local planning and administrative bodies. Prompt action is needed to determine what changes in the law or in its administration, or in both, should be made before the situation gets any further out of hand.

The most important problems connected with national parks and monuments have to do with their adequacy, administration, and management. To what extent are either minor or major adjustments necessary to achieve the objectives for which these reserves exist? This question bears most directly on the relationship between national parks, national monuments, and national forests, which are often adjacent and whose physical and biological features commonly bear a striking resemblance to each other. It also raises the broader question as to the wisdom of establishing numerous types of reserves by legislative action, as compared with the handling of all federal lands under a policy of multiple use which would devote every area to the purpose that would contribute most to the "public interest."

The swelling flood of visitors is making it increasingly difficult to achieve the ideal stated by Secretary of the Interior Franklin K.

Lane in 1918 that "the national parks should be maintained in absolutely unimpaired form." Continued study is needed to devise means of approximating this ideal as closely as possible while at the same time making the parks available for the enjoyment of the mounting millions of people who wish to visit them. Consideration of the formal establishment of "wilderness areas" within the parks deserves consideration in this connection.

Reclamation projects (and flood-control and navigation projects under the control of the Army Corps of Engineers) involve the problems of locating reservoirs so as to interfere as little as practicable with other uses such as timber production and recreation, and of providing adequate opportunities for recreation in the immediate vicinity of the reservoirs. The interference may be particularly serious in wilderness areas, where the preservation of natural conditions and the exclusion of roads are prime objectives.

The present policy of delegating administration of recreational activities at reservoirs to local, state, or other federal agencies seems to be sound and to be working out well. Careful consideration should, however, be given to the desirability of liberalizing the current policy of land acquisition so as to permit the acquisition of lands adjacent to reservoirs for the specific purpose of making them available for recreational purposes.

Federal migratory bird refuges are located chiefly on reclamation projects. They furnish an excellent example of multiple use and of cooperation between two federal agencies.

The main problems connected with the management of Indian lands arise from the prospect that Congress may carry out its announced intention of terminating federal supervision over them. Both the human and natural-resource problems that will have to be faced in such an eventuality are receiving careful study by the Senate Interim Committee on California Indian Affairs.

DEPARTMENT OF AGRICULTURE. National forests comprise practically the entire area in California under the jurisdiction of the Department of Agriculture. Most of them were created hastily and without adequate field examination during Theodore Roosevelt's administration. Since then, both exterior and interior boundaries have been subject to continuing adjustments, which have included extensive eliminations and substantial additions by exchange and purchase. Studies should be continued, in cooperation with other agencies and owners, to determine what further eliminations, additions, or exchanges will develop a more logical pattern of ownership and facilitate administration and management by both public and private owners.

Enlargement of the national forests by the exchange of timber for land ("stumpage for stumps") has been subject to vigorous criticism and has been virtually stopped since 1953. Acquisition by purchase has not only ceased, but in 1957 the Southern Redwood Purchase Unit was abolished and the Northern Redwood Purchase Unit greatly reduced in size. On the other hand, there have been no large recent eliminations. The tendency has thus been to maintain the status quo, with relatively minor adjustments by the exchange of land for land and by the modification of exterior boundaries.

Question may well be raised as to whether this is a desirable situation. Is it true that substantial additions to or subtractions from the area now in federal ownership would be unwise – both in general and for national forests in particular? The answer of course depends on whether they would be in the "public interest." This is a matter on which opinions will always differ, but on which agreement will become increasingly possible as research permits more accurate evaluation of the many factors involved. The point is that the end is more important than the means. There is nothing intrinsically objectionable about effecting changes by Congressional enactment, by Presidential proclamation, by exchange (either of land for land or of timber for land), or by purchase and sale, provided the objective is sound.

Drastic changes in national-forest boundaries, in either direction, would be unwise until they can be more clearly justified than is now the case. There is, however, need for more rapid progress in effecting relatively minor but nevertheless important adjustments than is now being made. For example, little if any question exists as to the desirability of blocking up holdings in areas of intermingled ownerships, particularly where checkerboarding exists, or of eliminating areas that make no substantial contribution to the purpose for which national forests are established. There seems to be general agreement that legislation should be enacted to authorize the sale of town sites within national forests, and of isolated and projecting strips of national forest land. Should such legislation include more general authority to sell, and perhaps to buy, land within national forests? Does the ability to make exchanges go far enough in permitting desirable adjustments? Do public agencies lack the ability or the reliability to be permitted to engage in transactions which are a matter of course in private enterprise?

A thorny problem of national-forest administration is involved in the establishment and management of wilderness areas. How much is enough, from the national as well as the state point of view? What are the minimum requirements in the way of protection from fire, insects, and disease, the provision of campgrounds and sanitary facilities, the maintenance of forage for pack animals, and protection from overuse? While these questions are being debated, as they doubtless will be for a long while, action should be taken to acquire private properties within wilderness areas, to prohibit mining operations not needed to meet a national emergency, and to permit only essential water development.

Other problems in the recreational field have to do with the relationship between national forests, national parks, and state parks. It involves the difficult question as to the relative weight that should be placed on recreation as an increasingly important form of land use. A recent statement of Forest Service policy will help to clarify the conditions under which it will make national-forest land available for administration by the State Division of Beaches and Parks under special-use permit.

The perennial problem of what contributions tax-exempt federal lands should make to state and local governments assumes particular importance in the case of the national forests, from which comes 60 per cent of all federal contributions in lieu of taxes. Most of the remaining 40 per cent comes from mineral sales and leases. In addition to the contribution of 25 per cent of the gross receipts from national forests to counties for school and road purposes, the federal government makes even larger expenditures for fire control and for the construction of roads and trails (contributions in kind), which would have to be made by the state or the counties if the land were in private ownership. Both the theoretical and the practical advantages and disadvantages of these methods of compensation for the loss of direct taxes need much more thorough analysis and impartial study than they have so far received. Does federal ownership under present conditions impose a burden on someone? If so, is the burden carried by the local taxpayer or by the national taxpayer, or in part by both? Do some counties obtain more in the form of federal contributions of all kinds than they would if the land were privately owned, and do some counties obtain less? And how much more or less? Most important of all, what changes in the present system would result in greater equity?

National-forest policies on timber sales, stumpage appraisals, access roads, and rights of way have an important influence on private enterprise which deserves constant study. So, too, does the efficiency of national-forest administration. To what extent, if at all, is the Forest Service handicapped by inadequate appropriations and salary scales, or by alleged bureaucratic inefficiency in making the most of what it has? If such handicaps exist, how can they be removed?

DEPARTMENT OF DEFENSE. World War II and the ensuing "cold war" have resulted in the marked expansion of military holdings in California. These holdings now amount to nearly 4 million acres, of which about 61 per cent is under the jurisdiction of the Navy; 27 per cent, the Army (excluding the Corps of Engineers); and 12 per cent, the Air Force. Outside of urban centers and airfields, most of the land is brushy, desert, or mountainous. Single-purpose management for military purposes naturally prevails, but there is some use for grazing, hunting, and fishing.

The occasional charge that withdrawals and acquisitions of land for military purposes have been excessive is countered by the claim that many of the installations are too small to meet the needs of atomic warfare. The moral of the argument is that the various units in the Department of Defense should continue, and perhaps expand, the present policy of full consultation with other agencies — federal, state, and local — to make sure that the size and location of prospective enlargements of the system are such as to interfere as little as practicable with other uses.

Military installations make no contributions in lieu of taxes to local communities. This fact is of little significance in the case of the lands of low value, with little or no revenue, which comprise the great bulk of the military holdings. It is, however, of considerable significance in the case of the 250,000 acres, more or less, of high-value urban lands. There seems to be no strong sentiment in favor of changing the present situation, but its equity is at least open to argument.

Air-space reservations by the Department of Defense over non-military lands may substantially affect their use and management. Such reservations are particularly extensive in Nevada, but the problems which they create may also deserve study and attention in California.

State Lands

Of the 2¼ million acres of state-owned lands, more than two-fifths are "proprietary" lands under the jurisdiction of the various departments, more than a third are school lands under the jurisdiction of the State Lands Commission, and the remainder are in the category of tax-deeded lands. Some 200,000 acres under the control of the Department of Public Works raise few questions in land management other than the best means of making state highways safe and attractive and of establishing and maintaining roadside rest areas.

The state system of beaches and parks has grown in fifty years from practically nothing to well over half a million acres. Ambitious plans for further expansion have been prepared and appear to meet with legislative approval. A major problem concerns the division of responsibility among the state, the counties, and other local agencies for the provision of park facilities and their administration. Integration of recreation on state lands and national forests will need further study if the new Forest Service policy with respect to special-use permits does not work out as satisfactorily as is hoped. Occasional criticism of the restrictions placed on multiple use in state parks suggests consideration of the advisability of permitting more uses than is now the case on certain areas where the primary emphasis is still on recreation — whether these areas are known as parks, recreation areas, forests, or by some other name.

In 1945 the California Forestry Study Committee recommended, and the legislature approved in principle, the acquisition of from 200,000 to 1,000,000 acres for state forests. Purchases and gifts brought the total area of state forests to about 71,000 acres by 1953. Since that date no additions have been made and none appear to be contemplated. This situation raises the question whether the entire program for state forests should not be reconsidered and a definite decision reached with respect to future policy. Has the need for state forests for restocking and demonstration purposes which was stressed in 1945 actually disappeared? If so, is there perhaps a new need for the acquisition of state lands on which timber production and recreation can be combined in a way that is not possible on either state parks or private lands?

Wildlife management, like every other field of land management, involves many unsolved technical, economic, and social problems. With respect to ownership, the 104,000 acres of wildlife refuges and management areas which have been acquired by the Department of Fish and Game appear to be reasonably adequate, provided the federal government grants the request of the state to place under its administration for wildlife purposes more than half a million acres primarily valuable for those purposes.

Somewhat more than 800,000 acres still remain in state ownership of the approximately 5,534,000 acres in Sections 16 and 36 in each township which were granted by the federal government to the state for common-school purposes. Whatever may have been the wisdom of the past policy of selling as rapidly as possible school lands, or lieu lands obtained by exchange with the federal government, the desirability of continuing that policy deserves careful scrutiny. A possible alternative would be to retain at least a considerable part of the lands in state ownership, to block up desirable holdings so far as practicable by exchange or otherwise, and to place their management in the Division of Forestry. The decision as to whether sale, or retention and management, is preferable would naturally depend on which choice is likely to result in the larger income for school purposes – a question on which the advice of the Division of Forestry would be helpful.

A problem common to all state lands is whether they should make any contributions in lieu of taxes to local communities. Such contributions are now made in the case of certain state forests and certain wildlife management areas, but no others. It is less urgent than with the national forests and other federal lands because of the much smaller area involved, but nevertheless merits attention.

Private Lands

Commercial forest lands in private ownership, according to the Timber Resource Review of the Forest Service, comprise 8 million acres. This area is about a million acres less than the area of commercial forest land in federal ownership in the state and about half a million acres less than that in national forests. Of the privately owned area, 38 per cent is in the form of large holdings (50,000 acres or more), and 32 per cent in small holdings (less than 5,000 acres). Only 20 per cent of the commercial forest area in private ownership is in farms, as compared with 34 per cent in the West and 46 per cent in the continental United States. Outside of farms, the present trend is toward the consolidation of private holdings into larger units and toward more intensive management, particularly on the part of the larger owners.

Much more information than is now available is needed concerning the number, size, and management of properties in different classes of ownership. This is particularly true for the smaller ownerships, which include nearly a third of the area in this category. The relationship between size of ownership, character of the land, and potential returns should be more definitely established. Possibilities for wider application of the principle of multiple use of private forest lands, with emphasis on water and recreation as important secondary products, should be thoroughly investigated, particularly by the larger owners.

The prospect of stimulating improved management through the blocking up of small and scattered ownerships deserves careful study. Striking examples of the unfavorable effect of a "scrambled" ownership pattern are plentiful in northern California in the redwood, Douglas fir, and pine belts. Here, lands are often still held in the relatively small tracts in which they were originally acquired from the federal government, or with a very minor degree of consolidation. Separate sales have been made by the individual owners to numerous contract loggers, with no thought of their effect on intermingled tracts (both private and public) or on future yields. The results, in the form of depleted lands which can be restored to productivity only at great cost, point to the need either for a new pattern of ownership or for cooperative action by the present owners. Experience shows that sustained yield at a high level, with economical and integrated utilization of the product, is most likely to be attained under unified control of a reasonably well-blocked area of sufficient size to make such management and utilization technically and financially feasible.

Mention has already been made of the need for further knowledge of the effect on private forest management of national-forest policies with respect to the size and duration of timber sales, the appraisal of stumpage values, access roads, and rights of way. Opinions differ widely as to the influence of these policies on the stability of management and processing operations of private owners, and on the likelihood of obtaining full use of the raw material in national-forest stumpage through integrated production. The latter item is important not only because unnecessary waste is always deplorable, but also because existing mill capacity is in excess of the estimated sustained-yield production of the state.

Thorough study is needed of the Forest Practice Act, as amended by the 1957 legislature, to determine how effective it has been and is likely to be in attaining its objectives. The levels of forest practice set by the rules established by the regional committees and the State Board of Forestry, together with legislative and administrative action to assure compliance with them, deserve special attention. Study should also be made of the effectiveness of state and federal aid to private owners in the fields of forest protection. reforestation, forest management, and forest utilization and marketing.

Although taxation is a problem to which there will never be an answer satisfactory to all concerned, improvements are always possible. Intensive research is therefore needed on the effectiveness of Section 12 3/4 of Article XIII of the Constitution from the standpoint of timberland owner, tax assessor, and the general public. Other methods of taxing both land and timber should also be given careful consideration.

What to do with California's extensive brush fields constitutes a problem of major importance for both private and public owners, and particularly for the former. Continued research on the possibilities of converting these areas to palatable forage or to stands of coniferous trees, and on ways and means of effecting the conversion most effectively and economically, is urgently needed. The possible effect of such conversion on watershed values should also be an important part of the research program.

Zoning

Zoning is a well-known and widely used tool for controlling the utilization and development of urban lands. Experiments are now being made in applying it to agricultural lands in California, but not to wildlands, except so far as the Forest Service is using the principle on a purely voluntary basis in the management of the national forests.

Careful study should be made of the possible advantages of providing legislative authority for the zoning of non-urban and non-agricultural lands by state and local officials. Such authority, if wisely exercised, might provide an effective means of implementing land-use plans and of encouraging the use of all lands for the purposes for which they are best suited. Zoning for watershed protection, timber production, forage production, or recreation, or for specified combinations of these purposes — permanently, periodically, or seasonally — might constitute a major step toward intelligent multiple land use. It must be recognized, however, that the tool is a dangerous as well as a useful one, and that sound judgment based on thorough knowledge of the biological, economic, and social implications of zoning is essential for its successful application. If zones are established, they should be reconsidered periodically, perhaps at intervals of ten years.

RESEARCH AND ACTION

Any reader who thinks that this report recommends "endless research" is quite right. Research is the key to progress in every field of human activity. The need to know more about the world we live in, including individuals and communities as a part of that world, grows more urgent as more and more people demand higher and higher standards of living. How to achieve this goal with finite resources may not be an unsolvable problem, but it is certainly a difficult one.

The task will require expanded and coordinated effort on the part of all research agencies with competence in the field of natural-resource management. "Muddling through" will never support the kind of economy to which 40 million prospective Californians will aspire. Fortunately the state has already made a good, albeit inadequate, start at two major research centers — the University of California and the California Forest and Range Experiment Station of the Forest Service, located at the University of California in Berkeley. Other resources can be mobilized as a comprehensive research program is developed.

The University of California is well equipped with many strong units which have a direct or indirect interest in natural-resource problems. Among these are the Agricultural Experiment Station, the School of Forestry, the Forest Products Laboratory, the Kearney Foundation, the Giannini Foundation (all of which are affiliated with the Agricultural Experiment Station), the Bureau of Business and Economic Research, the Bureau of Public Administration, and departments covering all the biological, physical, and social sciences. Several of these units have had a long and sustained interest in research relating to wildland problems, including specifically that of ownership. The volume of this research has been substantial and numerous publications have resulted from it.

The common tendency of university departments and other units to prefer a relatively autonomous existence means that special effort must be made to assure coordination in any research program requiring teamwork. The need is emphasized by the great diversity of available talent and by the strong individualities possessed by most investigators of high calibre. The existing unit in the strongest position to effect such coordination is the Agricultural Experiment Station, which already has interdepartmental research committees and a large Committee on Water, Forest, Range, and Natural Resource Conservation. With greater emphasis on this field its interest could be sharpened, its organization strengthened, and its budget increased.

Another alternative would be the creation at the University of an autonomous California Wildland Research Institute. Such an institute, in addition to taking the leadership in cordinating the activities of other units, would have a staff of its own whose full time would be devoted to wildland research. The necessity of building a new organization from the ground up would be a handicap. So, too, would lack of experience and contacts with other units in the University, and some difficulty might exist in capitalizing on the research capacity now and potentially available in the Agricultural Experiment Station. On the other hand, its autonomous position and its concentration on the single but enormous field of wildland research could give that field greater recognition and more adequate financial support than would be likely in an experiment station the bulk of whose activities is almost certain to continue to deal with more orthodox "agricultural" research. These and other advantages and disadvantages deserve careful consideration.

The California Forest and Range Experiment Station is a successor of the Feather River Forest Experiment Station, which was established in 1911. Like the University of California, it has a long record of substantial accomplishment in the field of wildland research. Its activities include investigations in forest and range management, forest protection, forest resources, forest products, and pest-control detection and appraisal. Its budget for the fiscal year 1958 is $920,165, plus additional cooperative funds and allotments from the Regional Office of the Forest Service. Although it cooperates closely with the latter office, it is administratively wholly independent. It has both the strengths and the weaknesses of a "monolithic" organization. It has the experience, the prestige, and the staff to continue to play a leading part in research in the wildland field. Its program of activities, which is formulated with the assistance of a representative advisory committee, should of course be integrated with that of the University and other research agencies.

The action of the 1957 Legislature in appropriating $100,000 a year for research by the Division of Forestry in the State Department of Natural Resources, beginning wtih the fiscal year 1958 - 1959, will enable that division to expand materially its present limited activities in that field. To what extent the funds at its disposal should be spent by the division itself and through cooperative agreements with other agencies, such as the University of California, the California Forest and Range Experiment Station, and other qualified research agencies, is a subject for continuing study. Other units in the state government, such as the Department of Fish and Game, the Department of Agriculture, and the Department of Water Resources, might advantageously participate to an increasing extent in the broad field of wildland research.

Many other agencies, notably educational institutions, have latent resources for research in this field. Private owners can, and should, increase their activities. The services of management consultants can sometimes be used to advantage on specific problems. An essential but formidable task is to mobilize all available resources in a unified program of research in which each agency will assume the responsibility for which it is best fitted.

This report makes no attempt to list the various problems to which it calls attention in any order of priority. This is a matter to be decided after further study of their relative urgency and of available facilities. It is, however, appropriate to call attention to the advisability of conducting simultaneously investigations likely to be of indefinite duration, such as the identification and measurement of intangible, personal, and social values, and those likely to yield at least partial answers in a relatively short time, such as the adjustment of national-forest boundaries, the blocking up of public and private holdings, and the adoption of a policy with respect to further acquisition of state forests. It must also be remembered that new problems will constantly arise and that priorities will change.

Emphasis should be placed on the fact that advocacy of more and better research does not even remotely imply that action should be postponed until the results of research are forthcoming. Policies must be adopted, administration must be conducted, lands must be managed in the light of the best information currently available. Caution may be in order when the wisdom of any specific policy or practice is seriously in doubt, but when circumstances demand action, it must be taken. The function of research is not to stop action, but to make possible more intelligent action by increasing our fund of knowledge.

Knowledge alone, however, is not enough to bring about effective land management. It must be put to work, not here and there, but everywhere. It is an indictment of our vaunted practicality that this goal is achieved so slowly, if at all. In nearly every field of endeavor, and particularly perhaps in land management, we fail to apply the knowledge we already have. What causes the delay in making practical use of the results of research, and how it can be shortened or abolished, would itself be a fruitful subject for study.

Next Steps

This exploratory study has made it clear that there is no one problem of land ownership in California. Rather, there is a multitude of problems, all of them interrelated, and many of them of national as well as state significance. Management of any one resource (water, wood, forage, wildlife, minerals, or recreation), which is controlled primarily by its ownership, affects directly or indirectly every other resource. Nor can wildlands be considered wholly independently of farm and urban lands. An exploding population, wherever it is located, puts a steadily mounting pressure on wildlands to produce ever more goods and services, and at the same time provides a market for their products.

These facts point unmistakably to the need for some arrangement that will assure continuing joint consideration of the land problems of the state by representatives of all interested agencies, owners, and the general public. Its overall purpose would be (1) to identify and stimulate a coordinated attack upon the problems urgently in need of study, and (2) to promote cooperation in the development and application of policies and programs of common interest. No means of attaining these objectives now exists. There is, of course, more or less constant communication among agencies within the state government and among agencies within the federal government. Moreover, the state and federal agencies often communicate with each other, with county and other local officials, and with private owners and users of wildlands. But these communications are for the most part haphazard and intermittent. They seldom bring together all of the agencies and groups interested in the particular problem under consideration.

Natural Resources Council

The urgent need for some device that will assure continuity and coordination in the consideration of wildland problems is more clear than the precise form which it should take. The authors and the committee believe that the most promising approach is the creation by the Legislature of a non-salaried Natural Resources Council, to be appointed by the Governor, with the advice and consent of the Senate. Such a Council might well consist of twelve members, with staggered three-year terms, of whom three would be chosen from the general public and one from each of the following groups: state government, federal government, county governments, timberland owners and forest products industries, livestock industry, farm interests, water interests, recreation interests (including hunting and fishing), and mineral interests. Its duties would be:

1) To identify, stimulate, and coordinate studies of current problems connected with the ownership and management of natural resources;

2) To advise the Legislature, the Governor, and the various agencies and interests represented in its membership with respect to natural-resource policies, administration, and management; and

3) To facilitate contacts and to promote cooperation among the groups and interests represented in its membership.

The Council would have no administrative or policy-making functions. It would need an executive secretary and perhaps a small staff, but would rely primarily on other agencies, organizations, and individuals to supply the information essential for its deliberations. To that end it should be authorized to call on any branch of the state government for needed assistance, and funds for the purpose should be provided by the Legislature either through the Council or by direct appropriation to the units concerned. While the state is without authority to commandeer help from other than its own agencies, it is assumed that those represented on the Council would voluntarily cooperate to the best of their ability in supplying desired information.

One important responsibility of the Council would be the development of a unified program of research in which each agency plays the part for which it is best fitted. Another major aspect of its activities would be to make sure that they take full cognizance of the national picture. Every state's internal policies are influenced by national policy, and they in turn influence that policy. Some of California's land problems are unique, but most of them it shares to a greater or less degree with other states. The Council cannot therefore discharge its responsibilities most effectively without keeping in close touch with developments elsewhere, particularly at the national level. In doing this, it will be materially assisted by having in its membership a representative of the federal government who can serve in a liaison capacity with other federal agencies.

The proposed Natural Resources Council would fill a serious gap. It would supplement and help to coordinate the activities of existing agencies — state, federal, and private — without duplicating or taking over any of their responsibilities. It has some resemblance to the state natural resource advisory councils suggested by the Study Committee on Natural Resources and Conservation of the Commission on Intergovernmental Relations. That committee stressed the need for "promoting better understanding and facilitating cooperation among Federal and State agencies of government," and added that "the councils will also prove helpful to the States in promoting the more efficient handling of their own natural-resource problems and activities." Its comment that "the appointment of highly qualified members is of paramount importance" applies equally well to the Council proposed herein. The chairman, in particular, must be a strong man, with breadth of view, vision, courage, and leadership of a high order.

Other Alternatives

Other possibilities of course suggest themselves. One would be to create a Natural Resources Council consisting of one representative from each of the existing boards and commissions dealing with natural resources. These include the Board of Forestry, Park Commission, Soil Conservation Commission, Mining Board, Fish and Game Commission, Wildlife Conservation Board, State Lands Commission, Recreation Commission, Board of Agriculture, Water Resources Board, Water Pollution Control Board, Public Works Board, and Board of Public Health. Members might be appointed by the Governor or selected by the body they represent.

Such a council would have the advantage of being composed of persons who are already familiar with the appropriate departments of the state government and who have a voice in the conduct of their activities. This intimate relationship might also prove a disadvantage if it resulted in a one-sided approach to problems that ought to be considered from the broadest possible point of view. Another, more serious disadvantage would be the failure to include in the council any representative of the agency which owns and administers nearly half of the land in the state – the federal government. It may well be that there is room both for an ex officio council of this sort, which would deal only with activities within the framework of the state government, and a council with independent representation and much broader scope.

Another possibility would be for the Governor or the Director of the Department of Natural Resources, without legislative action, to appoint a committee with such composition as seems to him desirable to perform so far as practicable the functions outlined for the Natural Resources Council. An additional function might well be to prepare a plan for a more formal, more permanent, and more authoritative organization for consideration and action by the Legislature. A committee with similar objectives but with no governmental connections might also be set up on their own initiative by a group of interested and public-spirited citizens. Either of these approaches would have the advantage of getting prompt action, but they would have the decided disadvantage that any committee established in this way would lack the prestige and influence of a council created by the Legislature. At best it would hardly be more than a stopgap, although perhaps a fairly effective one.

". . . And New Eras in Their Brains"

California is accustomed to new eras. Gold mining, extensive ranches with countless sheep and cattle, vast fields of grain, huge vineyards and citrus orchards, intensive irrigation, giant water developments, large-scale logging and milling operations, tourists and immigrants by the million, mammoth industrialization — all have successively molded its economy and influenced its way of life. Today it faces still another new era, in which far more intensive management of its natural resources than has previously been practiced, or even contemplated, will be necessary to meet the increasing pressure that is being placed on them by an apparently unlimited potential population, with an insatiable appetite for the goods and services that only the land can supply. The task is one to challenge the traditional capacity of Californians to do big things in a big way.

Time is of the essence in starting action that will assure continuous and coordinated consideration of California's land problems by all interested agencies. Even under the most favorable conditions there is bound to be a time lag in the initiation of adequate research and the achievement of usable results, and a still greater lag in their practical application.

"It is later than you think."

APPENDIX I

CHRONOLOGICAL SUMMARY OF SELECTED FEDERAL AND STATE LEGISLATION RELATING TO WILDLAND OWNERSHIP IN CALIFORNIA

The purpose of the following summary is to trace the evolution of federal and state policies with respect to wildland ownership as indicated by legislative enactments. Acts that have little or no bearing on policy, including those that go into administration in considerable detail, are not included. The summary shows only by inference, and even then only incompletely, the status of legislation now in force. This information can be obtained from the appropriate federal and state codes.

Federal

1820. Act of April 24 (3 Stat. 566[1]) provided that public lands should thereafter be offered at public sale to the highest bidder in half-quarter sections (80 acres) at a minimum price of $1.25 per acre, with full cash payment at the time of sale. Private sale at not less than the minimum price of lands unsold at public auction was authorized.

1831. Act of March 2 (4 Stat. 472) provided penalties for unlawfully cutting or removing any live oak, red cedar, or other timber from lands reserved or purchased for the use of the Navy, and also for cutting or removing any live oak, red cedar, or other timber from any other lands of the United States without written authorization, or with intent to export it or use it for any other purpose than for the Navy of the United States.

1841. Act of September 4 (5 Stat. 453) granted 500,000 acres for purposes of internal improvement to each of the nine existing public-land states and to such new states as might later be admitted to the Union. It also permitted preemptors to settle upon and purchase at the minimum price of $1.25 per acre not more than 160 acres of surveyed, nonmineral, unoccupied, and unreserved public lands. Preemptors must inhabit and improve the land and must swear that it was being taken up for their own exclusive use and benefit.

1844. Act of May 23 (5 Stat. 657) provided for the disposal of town sites on the public lands in tracts not exceeding 320 acres.

1846. Act of August 3 (9 Stat. 51) authorized the Commissioner of the General Land Office to sell isolated or disconnected tracts of unoffered lands.

1848. Treaty of February 2 with Mexico (9 Stat. 922) added some 335 million acres to the public domain, including California.

1850. Act of September 9 (9 Stat. 452) admitted California to the Union, with the proviso that the state should never interfere with the primary disposal of the public lands within its

[1] Page numbers refer to the first page of the statute cited, and not necessarily to the page on which the provision referred to appears.

limits or lay any tax upon them.

1850. Act of September 28 (9 Stat. 519) authorized the President to appoint not more than three agents for the Indian tribes in California.

1850. Act of September 28 (9 Stat. 519) granted to California and eleven other states all of the swamp and overflowed lands within their borders, with the proviso that the proceeds should be used exclusively, as far as necessary, for the construction of levees and drains.

1851. Act of March 3 (9 Stat. 631) created a commission to determine the validity of the private land claims in California, subject to review by the courts.

1852. Act of August 30 (10 Stat. 41) appropriated $100,000 for the preservation of peace with the Indians who had been dispossessed of their lands in California until permanent arrangements could be made for their future settlement.

1853. Act of March 3 (10 Stat. 244) provided for the survey of the public lands in California and extended the Preemption Act of September 4, 1841, to the state. The act also granted to California (1) Sections 16 and 36 for purposes of public schools in each township; (2) 72 sections for the use of a seminary of learning; and (3) 10 sections for the purpose of erecting the public buildings of the state. Mineral lands were specifically excluded from the latter two grants, and the Supreme Court later ruled that they were excluded by implication from the grant of Sections 16 and 36.

1854. Graduation Act of August 4 (10 Stat. 574) reduced the price of public land according to the time it had been on the market, with a minimum of 12.5 cents per acre after 30 years.

1855. Act of March 3 (10 Stat. 701) liberalized military bounties so as to grant 160 acres to all participants in all wars from the Revolution to date.

1859. Act of March 3 (11 Stat. 408) forbade the unlawful cutting of timber on lands of the United States reserved or purchased for military or other purposes.

1862. Homestead Act of May 20 (12 Stat. 392) granted 160 acres of unappropriated public land subject to preemption and sale at a minimum price of $1.25 per acre to persons who would reside on and cultivate it for five years. Commutation, or purchase of the land at its regular price, was possible at any time after six months from the date of filing.

1862. Act of June 2 (12 Stat. 413) extended the Preemption Act to unsurveyed lands in all the states and territories and repealed the graduation Act of 1854.

1862. Act of July 1 (12 Stat. 489) granted the Union Pacific and the Central Pacific Railroads alternate, odd-numbered sections of public land for 10 miles on each side of the road. This distance was increased to 20 miles in 1864 (13 Stat. 356). Mineral lands were not included, but the amendatory act of 1864 excluded coal and iron lands from this category. Three years after completion of the roads any lands remaining were to be subject to preemption by settlers and sold to them for not more than $1.25 per acre. The price of sections retained by the government was not increased.

1862. Morrill Act of July 2 (12 Stat. 503) granted to each state 30,000 acres of nonmineral public land (with minimum price of $1.25 per acre) for each senator and representative to which it was entitled under the census of 1860, for the establishment of colleges of agriculture and the mechanic arts. States without public lands were given an equivalent amount of scrip, purchasers of which were not to take up more than a million acres in any one state.

1864. Act of June 30 (13 Stat. 325) granted the Yosemite Valley and the Mariposa Big Tree Grove to California to be held forever "for public use, resort, and recreation."

1864. Act of July 1 (13 Stat. 332) required the surveyor-general of California to survey all confirmed private land claims when requested by the claimant.

1864. Act of July 1 (13 Stat. 343) repealed the act of May 23, 1844, relating to town sites and provided for the sale at auction of town sites established on public lands at not less than $10 per lot (not to exceed 4,200 square feet in size).

1864. Act of July 1 (13 Stat. 343) provided for the sale of coal lands in the public domain at auction at a minimum price of $20 per acre.

1865. Act of March 3 (13 Stat. 504) confirmed the assignment by the Central Pacific Railroad Company to the Western Pacific Railroad Company of the right to construct a railroad from San Jose to Sacramento, "with all the privileges and benefits of the several acts of Congress relating thereto, and subject to all the conditions thereof."

1866. Act of July 13 (14 Stat. 94) granted the Placerville and Sacramento Valley Railroad Company 10 alternate, odd-numbered, nonmineral, and unappropriated sections per mile on each side of the road to aid in the construction of a railroad from Folsom to Placerville.

1866. Act of July 23 (14 Stat. 218) provided in considerable detail for the quieting of land titles in California.

1866. Act of July 25 (14 Stat. 239) granted the California and Oregon Railroad 10 alternate, odd-numbered, and nonmineral sections per mile on each side of the road to aid in building a railroad from some point on the Central Pacific Railroad in the Sacramento Valley to the Oregon line.

1866. Act of July 26 (14 Stat. 251) authorized the exploration and occupation of mineral lands in the public domain, both surveyed and unsurveyed, and provided for the purchase of lode mines at $5 per acre if the claimant had occupied them according to local mining rules and had expended as much as $1,000 in labor and improvements.

1866. Act of July 27 (14 Stat. 292) granted the Atlantic and Pacific Railroad Company (now the Atchison, Topeka, and Santa Fe Railway) and the Southern Pacific Railroad 10 alternate, odd-numbered sections per mile on each side of the road in the states and twice that amount in the territories traversed. The Atlantic and Pacific was to build a railroad from Springfield, Missouri, to the Pacific Ocean, and the Southern Pacific from the junction with that road to San Francisco. The price of the alternate sections retained by the government was raised to $2.50 per acre. Five years after completion of the roads, the railroads were required to sell all unmortgaged lands still in their possession for not more than $2.50 per acre.

1867. Act of March 2 (14 Stat. 548) granted the Stockton and Copperopolis Railroad Company 5 alternate, odd-numbered sections per mile on each side of the road to aid in building a road between the two towns.

1870. Act of July 9 (16 Stat. 217) provided for the sale of placer mines at $2.50 per acres in tracts not exceeding 160 acres.

1871. Act of March 3 (16 Stat. 573) granted the Texas Pacific Railroad Company 10 alternate, odd-numbered sections per mile on each side of the road in California, and 20 sections per mile in New Mexico and Arizona, to aid in the construction of a railroad from Marshall, Texas, to San Diego, California.

1872. Act of May 10 (17 Stat. 91) constituted mineral lands a distinct class and provided for their survey and sale at $2.50 per acre for placer mines and $5.00 per acre for lode mines.

1873. Timber Culture Act of March 3 (17 Stat. 605) offered to donate 160 acres of public land to any one who would plant a specified portion of it to trees. Claimants must meet certain requirements, which reached their final form in 1878.

1877. Desert Land Act of March 3 (19 Stat. 377) provided for the sale in eleven western states and territories of 640 acres of nontimbered, nonmineral land unfit for cultivation without irrigation to any settler who would irrigate it within three years after filing. A payment of $0.25 per acre was to be made at the time of filing and $1 per acre at time of final proof.

1878. Timber and Stone Act of June 3 (20 Stat. 89) provided for the sale in Washington, Oregon, California, and Nevada of 160 acres of surveyed, nonmineral land, chiefly valuable for timber or stone and unfit for cultivation, which had not been offered at public sale, for not less than $2.50 per acre. The purchaser had to swear that the land was being acquired solely for his own use and benefit.

1880. Act of June 15 (21 Stat. 237) relieved timber trespassers on the public domain prior to March 1, 1879, from both civil and criminal prosecution on payment of $1.25 per acre.

1885. Act of February 25 (23 Stat. 321) forbade the making of enclosures on the public domain and authorized the destruction of unauthorized enclosures.

1886. Act of July 6 (24 Stat. 123) forfeited the lands granted to the Atlantic and Pacific Railroad Company adjacent to the uncompleted portion of the road and restored them to the public domain. The forfeiture included all of the lands in California.

1888. Act of June 4 (25 Stat. 166) amended the act of March 3, 1859, to include timberlands in Indian reservations.

1888. Act of August 1 (25 Stat. 357) provided that whenever the Secretary of the Treasury or any other officer of the government is authorized to procure real estate for public buildings or other public uses, he is authorized to acquire the property by condemnation if in his judgment it is advantageous to the government to do so.

1888. Act of October 1 (25 Stat. 498) authorized the Secretary of War to detail three officers from the Army Corps of Engineers to act as a commission to investigate the mining debris problem in California, with special reference to the conflict between the mining and the farming sections of the state.

1889. Act of February 16 (25 Stat. 673) authorized the President to permit Indians to cut and sell dead timber on Indian reservations, provided the timber had not been intentionally killed.

1890. Second Morrill Act of August 30 (26 Stat. 417) provided for additional assistance to land-grant colleges out of proceeds from the sale of public lands.

1890. Act of September 25 (26 Stat. 478) set apart the Sequoia National Park as a public park, or pleasure ground.

1890. Act of September 29 (26 Stat. 496) forfeited and restored to the public domain all land in grants adjacent to the uncompleted sections of railroads to which grants had been made.

1890. Act of October 1 (26 Stat. 650) set apart the Yosemite National Park and the General Grant National Park as "forest reservations."

1891. Act of March 3 (26 Stat. 1095) repealed the Timber Culture Act of 1873 (as amended) and the Preemption Act of 1841; put a stop to auction sales of public lands except isolated tracts and abandoned military and other reservations; tightened up the requirements for improvement and cultivation under the Desert Land Act of 1877; did not allow commutation under the Homestead Act of 1862 until 14 months after filing; limited the time within which suit to annul patent might be brought; restricted withdrawals for reservoir sites to the area actually needed for that purpose; authorized rights of way for irrigation canals and drainage ditches through public lands and reservations; and empowered the President to set aside as forest reserves public lands covered with timber or undergrowth, whether of commercial value or not.

1893. Act of March 1 (27 Stat. 507) created the California Debris Commission, consisting of three officers of the Army Corps of Engineers, to prepare plans for the regulation of hydraulic mining in the territory drained by the Sacramento and San Joaquin Rivers and for such other action as might be needed to improve the navigability of those rivers.

1894. Section 4 (Carey Act) of the Sundry Civil Appropriations Act of August 18 (28 Stat. 372) authorized the donation to states having desert lands (or to their assigns) of not more than 1 million acres each which they should cause to be settled, irrigated, and in part cultivated within 10 years. Not more than 160 acres was to be sold or disposed of to any one person.

1895. Act of February 26 (28 Stat. 687) amended the act of August 3, 1846, to authorize the sale at public auction of isolated tracts containing not more than 160 acres at not less than $1.25 per acre.

1897. Act of February 11 (29 Stat. 526) made oil lands subject to the laws relating to placer mineral claims.

1897. Act of February 24 (29 Stat. 594) provided penalties for setting fire to any timber, underbrush, or grass on the public domain, or for failing to totally extinguish any campfire or other fire in or near any forest, timber, or other inflammable material.

1897. Sundry Civil Appropriations Act of June 4 (30 Stat. 11) specified the purposes for which forest reserves might be established and provided for their protection and administration.

1899. Act of February 28 (30 Stat. 908) authorized the Secretary of the Interior to lease ground near or adjacent to mineral, medicinal, or other springs in forest reserves for the erection of sanitariums or hotels, under such regulations as he might prescribe.

1900. Sundry Civil Appropriations Act of June 6 (31 Stat. 588) limited lieu selections for lands in forest reserves under the act of June 4, 1897, to vacant, nonmineral, surveyed public lands subject to homestead entry.

1901. Act of February 15 (31 Stat. 790) authorized the Secretary of the Interior to grant rights of way through forest reserves for canals and ditches, dams and reservoirs, electrical lines, and other purposes, revocable at the discretion of the Secretary or his successor.

1901. Act of March 3 (31 Stat. 1436) extended to California, Oregon, and Washington the provisions of the Free Timber Act of June 30, 1878 (20 Stat. 88), as amended, authorizing the free use of timber on public lands, subject to regulations prescribed by the Secretary of the Interior.

1902. Newlands Act of June 17 (32 Stat. 388) created the "reclamation fund" out of receipts from the sale and disposal of public lands in certain states west of the Mississippi River; authorized the Secretary of the Interior to construct irrigation works and to withdraw irrigable public lands from entry; and provided for the homesteading of irrigated lands and their sale at a price estimated to return to the reclamation fund the cost of construction.

1905. Act of February 1 (33 Stat. 628) transferred the administration of the forest reserves from the Secretary of the Interior to the Secretary of Agriculture; covered all receipts from the forest reserves for a period of 5 years into a special fund for the protection, administration, improvement, and extension of the reserves; and granted rights of way for dams, ditches, and flumes across the reserves under regulations prescribed by the Secretary of the Interior and subject to state laws.

1905. Act of February 6 (33 Stat. 700) authorized the arrest by any officer of the United States, without process, of any person taken in the act of violating the regulations relating to forest reserves and national parks.

1905. Act of March 3 (33 Stat. 861) changed the name of the Bureau of Forestry to Forest Service, effective July 1.

1905. Act of March 3 (33 Stat. 1264) repealed the lieu-land provision of the act of June 4, 1897, but permitted the perfecting of valid selections already made.

1906. Act of April 16 (34 Stat. 116) authorized the Secretary of the Interior to lease for a period of not more than 10 years any surplus power developed in connection with an irrigation project, giving preference to municipal purposes.

1906. American Antiquities Act of June 8 (34 Stat. 225) forbade any one, without proper authority, to appropriate, excavate, injure, or destroy any historic or prehistoric ruin or monument or any object of antiquity on lands owned or controlled by the government of the United States. It also authorized the President to establish by proclamation national monuments for the preservation of features of historic, prehistoric, and scientific interest, under administration of the department already having jurisdiction over the land in question. The area reserved must be as small as compatible with the proper care and management of the objects to be preserved.

1906. Forest Homestead Act of June 11 (34 Stat. 233) authorized the Secretary of Agriculture to open for entry forest-reserve lands chiefly valuable for agriculture which were not needed for public purposes and which in his judgment might be occupied without injury to the forest. Each tract was to be surveyed by metes and bounds and must not exceed 160 acres in area or 1 mile in length. Commutation was not allowed.

1906. Joint Resolution of June 11 (34 Stat. 831) accepted recession by California of the lands in the Yosemite Valley and the Mariposa Big Tree Grove granted to it in 1864 for use as a state park.

1906. Agricultural Appropriations Act of June 30 (34 Stat. 669) provided that 10 per cent of all money received from the forest reserves during any fiscal year, including 1906, was to be turned over to the states or territories for the benefit of the public schools and roads of the counties in which the reserves were located, but not to the extent of more than 40 per cent of their income from other sources. It also forbade unrestricted spending after June 30, 1908, from the special fund set up in 1905.

1907. Act of March 4 (34 Stat. 1256) changed "forest reserves" to "national forests"; forbade the further creation or enlargement of national forests except by act of Congress in Washington, Oregon, Montana, Idaho, Wyoming, and Colorado; abolished the special fund established in 1905 but increased Forest Service Appropriations by $1,000,000; and required the Forest Service to submit to Congress annually a classified and detailed report of receipts and estimate of expenditures.

1908. Agricultural Appropriations Act of May 23 (35 Stat. 251) directed such officials of the Forest Service as might be designated by the Secretary of Agriculture to aid in the enforcement of state laws relating to stock, forest-fire control, and fish and game protection, and to aid other federal bureaus in the performance of their duties. The act also increased the payment to the states for the benefit of county schools and roads to 25 per cent of the gross receipts from national forests, eliminated the 40 per cent limitation, and made the legislation permanent.

1909. Act of February 18 (35 Stat. 626) authorized the Secretary of Agriculture to acquire by exchange certain specified lands in Tuolumne County (379 acres) to be known as the Calaveras Big Tree National Forest.

1909. Act of March 3 (35 Stat. 781) authorized the Commissioner of Indian Affairs to manage the timber on Indian reservations.

1910. Act of June 22 (36 Stat. 583) authorized entry of coal lands under the agricultural land laws but with retention of mineral rights by the government.

1910. Act of June 25 (36 Stat. 847) authorized the President to temporarily withdraw public lands from entry and reserve them for specified purposes, such withdrawals or reservations to remain in force until revoked by him or by Congress. It also provided that all withdrawn lands shall be open to exploration, occupation, and purchase for all minerals other than coal, oil, gas, and phosphates.

1910. Act of June 25 (36 Stat. 855) extended to Indian reservations the penalties provided by the act of February 24, 1897, for failing to extinguish fires built in or near any forest, timber, or other inflammable material upon the public domain. It also provided for the sale and management of timber on Indian reservations (except in Minnesota and Wisconsin) and on certain Indian allotments, for the benefit of the Indians, under regulations prescribed by the Secretary of the Interior.

1911. Act of February 21 (36 Stat. 925) authorized the sale of surplus water from an irrigation project for use on lands outside the project.

1911. Weeks Law of March 1 (36 Stat. 961): (1) authorized the enactment of interstate compacts for the conservation of forests and the water supply; (2) appropriated $200,000 to enable the Secretary of Agriculture to cooperate with any state which had provided by law for a system of forest-fire protection; and (3) appropriated 11 million dollars for the examination, survey, and acquisition by the government of lands located on the headwaters of navigable streams. It also created a National Forest Reservation Commission to pass upon lands approved for purchase and to fix the price at which purchases shall be made, and provided for the protection and administration of acquired lands.

1911. Act of March 4 (36 Stat. 1235) authorized the head of the department having jurisdiction over public lands, national forests, and reservations of the United States to grant rights of way for transmission, telephone, and telegraph lines for a period not exceeding 50 years.

1912. Act of March 28 (37 Stat. 77) authorized the Commissioner of the General Land Office, on application of adjoining owners, to sell at public auction at not less than $1.25 per acre tracts containing not more than 160 acres of public land which is mountainous or too rough for cultivation, whether isolated or not.

1912. Act of April 30 (37 Stat. 105) opened coal lands for selection by the states and for sale in isolated tracts, with reservation to the United States of the coal in such tracts.

1912. Act of June 6 (37 Stat. 123) reduced to 3 years the length of residence necessary to obtain patent under the Homestead Act and set up certain minimum cultivation requirements. Commutation was allowed after 14 months of actual residence.

1912. Act of June 13 (37 Stat. 132) added California to the list of states covered by the Enlarged Homestead Act of February 18, 1909 (35 Stat.

639), permitting homesteaders to acquire up to 320 acres of public land.

1912. Agricultural Appropriations Act of August 10 (37 Stat. 269): (1) directed the Secretary of Agriculture to select, classify, and segregate all lands that may be opened to settlement and entry under the homestead laws applicable to national forests; (2) authorized and directed the Secretary to sell timber at actual cost to homestead settlers and farmers for their domestic use; and (3) made 10 per cent of the gross receipts from national forests available for expenditure by the Secretary of Agriculture for the construction of roads and trails within national forests. The latter provision was made permanent by the act of March 4, 1913 (37 Stat. 828).

1912. Act of August 24 (37 Stat. 497) provided that all lands withdrawn from entry by the President under the act of June 25, 1910, should at all times be open to exploration, discovery, occupation, and purchase under the mining laws of the United States so far as these applied to metalliferous minerals. It also added California to the list of states named in the act of March 4, 1907, within which national forests can be created or enlarged only by act of Congress.

1913. Agricultural Appropriations Act of March 4 (37 Stat. 828) permitted timber cut on any national forest to be exported from the state or territory in which cut. It also authorized the National Forest Reservation Commission to acquire lands subject to rights of way, easements, and reservations which the Secretary of Agriculture believes will not interfere with the use of the lands so encumbered.

1913. Act of March 4 (37 Stat. 1015) authorized the Secretary of the Interior to sell any timber on public lands outside of national forests which had been killed or seriously damaged by fire prior to passage of the act.

1913. Act of September 30 (38 Stat. 113) authorized the President to prescribe the methods of opening to entry public lands thereafter excluded from national forests or released from withdrawals.

1913. Act of December 19 (38 Stat. 242) gave San Francisco the right to construct a reservoir in the Hetch Hetchy Valley in the Yosemite National Park to supply the city with water.

1914. Act of April 16 (38 Stat. 345) authorized the Secretary of the Interior and the Secretary of Agriculture to exchange timber or timber and land within the Yosemite National Park and the Sierra and Stanislaus National Forests for private land for the purpose of eliminating private holdings within the park.

1914. Act of May 13 (38 Stat. 376) authorized the exchange of certain specified lands in the Sierra National Forest and the Yosemite National Park for private lands within the forest and the park.

1914. Agricultural Appropriations Act of June 30 (38 Stat. 415) increased from 5 to 25 per cent the payment to states of the gross receipts from lands acquired under the Weeks Act of March 1, 1911.

1914. Act of July 17 (38 Stat. 509) authorized the entry and patenting, under the nonmineral laws, of lands withdrawn, classified, or valuable for phosphate, nitrate, potash, oil, gas, or asphaltic minerals, with reservation to the United States of the mineral deposits.

1915. Agricultural Appropriations Act of March 4 (38 Stat. 1086) authorized the Secretary of Agriculture to grant permits for summer homes, hotels, stores, or other structures needed for recreation or public convenience in national forests in tracts of not more than 5 acres and for periods of not more than 30 years.

1916. Act of July 11 (39 Stat. 355)

appropriated 11 million dollars a year for 10 years for the construction of roads and trails within or partly within national forests when necessary for the use and development of their resources. Additional appropriations of 3 million dollars a year for the same purposes were made for the fiscal years 1919, 1920, and 1921.

1916. Act of August 9 (39 Stat. 442) established the Lassen Volcanic National Park, with the provisos that the Reclamation Service might utilize for flowage or other purposes any area within the park which may be necessary for the development of a government reclamation project, and that the Secretary of the Interior may sell and permit the removal of such matured or dead or down timber as he may deem necessary or advisable for the protection or improvement of the park.

1916. Act of August 11 (39 Stat. 446) authorized the President to establish refuges for the protection of game animals, birds, or fish on any lands purchased under the Weeks Act of March 1, 1911.

1916. Act of August 25 (39 Stat. 535) created the National Park Service in the Department of the Interior, defined the purposes for which national parks may be established, and authorized the Secretary of the Interior to make rules and regulations for their proper use and management. Grazing was authorized when in the judgment of the Secretary it will not be detrimental to the primary purpose for which the park, monument, or other reservation was established.

1916. Stockraising Homestead Act of December 29 (39 Stat. 862) authorized the Secretary of the Interior to open for entry under the homestead laws not more than 640 acres per person of public lands the surface of which is chiefly valuable for grazing and raising forage crops, do not contain merchantable timber, are not susceptible of irrigation from any known source of water supply, and are of such a character that 640 acres are reasonably required for the support of a family. Instead of cultivation, the entryman must make permanent improvements to the extent of $1.25 per acre. Commutation was not allowed. All minerals were reserved to the United States and made subject to disposal under the coal and mineral-land laws.

1917. Act of October 2 (40 Stat. 297) authorized the Secretary of the Interior to lease public lands containing potash.

1919. Act of March 3 (40 Stat. 1316) authorized the addition of certain specified lands to the Modoc National Forest.

1920. Act of February 25 (41 Stat. 437) provided for the leasing of deposits of coal, phosphate, sodium, oil, oil shale, or gas, and authorized the Secretary of the Interior to reserve the right to sell, lease, or otherwise dispose of the surface of lands embraced in such leases if not necessary for the use of the lessee. The act did not apply to national forests acquired under the Weeks Act of 1911, to national parks, to game refuges, or to military or naval reservations.

1920. Act of June 5 (41 Stat. 980) authorized the exchange of national forest land or timber for private land in the Sierra National Forest on an equal value basis.

1920. Act of June 10 (41 Stat. 1063) created the Federal Power Commission and authorized it to issue leases for a period not exceeding 50 years "for the development and improvement of navigation, and for the development, transmission, and utilization of power across, along, from or in any part of the navigable waters of the United States, or upon any part of the public lands and reservations of the United States (including the Territories), or for the purpose of utilizing the surplus water or water power from any Government dam."

1921. Act of August 19 (42 Stat. 171) authorized the states of Arizona, California, Colorado, Nevada, New Mexico, Utah, and Wyoming to enter into a compact for the disposition and apportionment of the waters of the Colorado River.

1921. Federal Highway Act of November 9 (42 Stat. 212) started the practice of appropriating funds specifically for the construction of "forest-development roads" and "forest highways" in national forests.

1922. General Exchange Act of March 20 (42 Stat. 465) authorized the Secretary of Agriculture to exchange surveyed, nonmineral land or timber in national forests established from the public domain for privately owned or state land of equal value within national forests in the same state.

1922. Agricultural Appropriations Act of May 11 (42 Stat. 507) made the first appropriation ($10,000) for the improvement of public campgrounds in national forests, with special reference to protection of the public health and prevention of forest fires.

1922. Act of September 20 (42 Stat. 857) authorized the Secretary of the Interior to protect timber on lands under his jurisdiction from fire, disease, and insects, either directly or in cooperation with other departments, states, or private owners.

1923. Act of March 4 (42 Stat. 1445) extended the provisions of the Enlarged Homestead Act of 1909 to homestead entries in national forests under certain conditions.

1924. Clarke-McNary Act of June 7 (43 Stat. 653) authorized appropriations to enable the Secretary of Agriculture to cooperate in forest-fire control with states meeting prescribed standards, in the growing and distribution of planting stock to farmers, and in promoting the efficient management of farm woodlots and shelterbelts; authorized the purchase of lands anywhere on the watersheds of navigable streams and for timber production as well as streamflow protection; authorized the acceptance of gifts to be added to the national forests; authorized the Secretary of Agriculture to report to Congress such unreserved public timberlands as in his judgment should be added to the national forests; and authorized the creation of military and naval reserves as national forests, without interference with their use for military and naval purposes.

1925. Act of February 20 (43 Stat. 952) authorized the acquisition by exchange of certain specified lands and their addition to the Plumas, Eldorado, Stanislaus, Shasta, and Tahoe National Forests.

1925. Act of February 24 (43 Stat. 969) authorized the Secretary of Agriculture, upon application by the board of supervisors of Los Angeles County, to issue a free permit for the use of not more than 5,000 acres in the Angeles National Forest by the county for "free public camp grounds under conditions which will allow the fullest use of the lands for recreational purposes without interfering with the objects for which the national forest was established." Lands so designated and segregated are not subject to the mining laws of the United States.

1925. Act of February 28 (43 Stat. 1090) amended the General Exchange Act of 1922 to permit either party to an exchange to make reservations of timber, minerals, or easements, the values of which shall be considered in determining the values of the exchanged lands, provided that such reservations shall be subject to the tax laws of the states concerned.

1925. Act of March 3 (43 Stat. 1127) included watersheds from which water is secured for domestic use or irrigation among the lands on which the federal government can cooperate with states in control of forest fires under Section 2 of the Clarke-McNary Act of 1924.

1925. Act of March 3 (43 Stat. 1132) authorized the acceptance of contributions to constitute a special fund for the reforestation, administration, or protection of lands within or near national forests.

1925. Act of March 3 (43 Stat. 1132) authorized the Secretary of Agriculture to purchase land for national forest headquarters or ranger stations when no suitable government land is available for the purpose, and to accept donations of land for any national-forest purpose.

1925. Act of March 3 (43 Stat. 1215) authorized the exchange of land or timber for land within the exterior boundaries of national forests acquired under the Weeks Act of 1911 or the Clarke-McNary Act of 1924, on an equal-value basis.

1926. Act of May 25 (44 Stat. 636) limited to 160 acres the area in single ownership that might receive water in an irrigation project.

1926. Act of June 14 (44 Stat. 741) authorized the Secretary of the Interior to make available to states, counties, or municipalities, by exchange, sale, or lease, unreserved, nonmineral public lands classified by him as chiefly valuable for recreational purposes.

1926. Act of July 3 (44 Stat. 890) amended the act of March 4, 1913, to permit the sale of fire-killed timber on the public lands irrespective of the date of its destruction.

1927. Act of January 25 (44 Stat. 1026) granted to the states all school sections that are mineral in character, with the proviso that in disposing of such lands title to all the coal and other minerals must be retained by the state. The act did not apply to lands within existing reservations or subject to any valid claim, or to indemnity or lieu selections.

1927. Act of February 7 (44 Stat. 1057) authorized the Secretary of the Interior to lease public lands containing potash under the general provisions of the Mineral Leasing Act of February 25, 1920, and repealed the prior act of October 2, 1917.

1928. Act of March 9 (45 Stat. 253) increased to 320 acres the size of isolated tracts that might be sold at public auction at not less than $1.25 per acre, but left at 160 acres the size of mountainous tracts that might be sold on application of adjoining owners.

1928. Act of May 18 (45 Stat. 602) authorized the Attorney General of California to bring suit in the Court of Claims on behalf of the Indians of California for compensation for lands of which they had been dispossessed by the United States, and declared "that the loss to the said Indians on account of their failure to secure the lands and compensation provided for in the eighteen unratified treaties is sufficient ground for equitable relief." The amount of any judgment (less reimbursement to California for court costs) was to be placed in the Treasury of the United States to the credit of the Indians of California, to draw 4 per cent interest, and to be subject to appropriation by Congress for the benefit of the Indians but not in the form of per capita payments.

1928. McSweeney-McNary Act of May 22 (45 Stat. 699) authorized a comprehensive 10-year program of research in all phases of forestry and range management, including a timber survey, with an annual appropriation amounting to $3,625,000 by the end of the period, and thereafter such amounts as needed to carry out the provisions of the act.

1928. Boulder Canyon Project Act of December 21 (45 Stat. 1057) provided for the construction of works for the protection and development of the Colorado River Basin and authorized the states concerned to enter into supplemental compacts for the development of the Colorado River.

1929. Migratory Bird Conservation Act (Norbeck-Andresen Act) of February 18 (45 Stat. 1222) established the Migratory Bird Conservation Commission and authorized a continuing program for the acquisition of migratory-bird reservations, subject to the consent of the state concerned.

1930. Act of April 10 (46 Stat. 153) authorized an appropriation of $50,000 to enable the President to appoint a commission to study and report on the conservation and administration of the public domain.

1930. Knutson-Vandenberg Act of June 9 (46 Stat. 527) authorized appropriation of not to exceed $400,000 a year by the fiscal year 1934 for reforestation activities on the national forests, and provided that additional charges could be made in timber sales to provide a special fund for reforestation or silvicultural improvement of the cutover area included in the timber sale.

1931. Act of February 14 (46 Stat. 1115) provided that land in the San Bernardino and Cleveland National Forests covered by special-use permits, for other than pasture purposes, in tracts of no more than 160 acres, shall not be subject to entry or adverse occupancy unless the permit is discontinued or revoked.

1933. Act of March 3 (47 Stat. 1487) granted to California certain public lands for state park purposes (now the Anza Desert and Borrego State Parks), with reservation to the United States of all mineral rights and with a proviso that title should revert to the United States upon a finding by the Secretary of the Interior that the land had not been used by the state for park purposes for a period of more than one year.

1933. Act of March 4 (47 Stat. 1563) extended the General Exchange Act of March 20, 1922, so as to permit the addition of certain specified lands to the Modoc National Forest.

1933. Emergency Conservation Work Act of March 31 (48 Stat. 22) appropriated funds for the dual purpose of relieving unemployment and promoting conservation of natural resources. In addition to other activities it authorized use of the funds for forest research and for acquisition of land by purchase, donation, condemnation, or otherwise.

1933. President Roosevelt by Executive Order, under authority of the Reorganization Act of March 3, 1933, placed all national monuments, the National Capital parks, and national military parks under the administration of the Department of the Interior.

1934. Act of March 10 (48 Stat. 400) authorized the President, upon recommendation of the Secretary of Agriculture or the Secretary of Commerce and with the approval of the legislatures of the states concerned, to establish fish and game sanctuaries or refuges in national forests.

1934. Coordination Act of March 10 (48 Stat. 401) authorized the Secretary of Agriculture and the Secretary of Commerce to cooperate with federal, state, and other agencies in developing a nationwide program of wildlife conservation and rehabilitation; to study the effect of water pollution on wildlife and to recommend remedial measures; and to prepare plans for the maintenance of an adequate supply of wildlife on public lands, Indian reservations, and unallotted Indian lands. It also provided for use for wildlife purposes of water impounded by the Bureau of Reclamation or otherwise, and for facilitating the migration of fish in connection with the construction of any future dam by the federal government or under federal permit.

1934. Migratory Bird Hunting Stamp Act of March 16 (48 Stat. 451) required takers of migratory waterfowl to buy a federal hunting stamp, and made the proceeds available for the acquisition and management of migratory waterfowl refuges and the conduct of research.

1934. Act of June 18 (48 Stat. 984) directed the Secretary of the Interior to make rules and regulations for managing Indian forestry units on the principle of sustained yield; for restricting the number of livestock grazed on Indian range units to their estimated carrying capacity; and for protecting the range from deterioration, preventing soil erosion, and assuring full utilization of the range.

1934. Taylor Grazing Act of June 28 (48 Stat. 1269) authorized the Secretary of the Interior to establish not more than 80 million acres of grazing districts in the unreserved public domain (exclusive of Alaska) and to make rules and regulations for their occupancy and use. It also increased to 760 acres the size of isolated tracts that could be offered for sale and authorized the Secretary of the Interior to sell not more than 160 acres of land that is mountainous or too rough for cultivation, whether isolated or not, to adjoining owners.

1935. Soil Conservation Act of April 27 (49 Stat. 163) declared it to be the policy of Congress to provide permanently for the control and prevention of soil erosion, delegated all activities relating to soil erosion to the Secretary of Agriculture, and established the Soil Conservation Service in the Department of Agriculture.

1935. Act of June 15 (49 Stat. 378) authorized the addition to wildlife refuges of land acquired by exchange of (1) land, timber, or other materials in wildlife refuges, or (2) of unreserved non-mineral public lands, in both cases on an equal-value basis.

1935. Act of August 21 (49 Stat. 666) authorized the Secretary of the Interior to acquire and administer historic sites and buildings, and established an Advisory Board on National Parks, Historic Sites, Buildings, and Monuments.

1935. Fulmer Act of August 29 (49 Stat. 963) authorized an appropriation of 5 million dollars for the purchase by the federal government of lands to be administered as state forests under plans of management satisfactory to the Secretary of Agriculture.

1936. Soil Conservation and Domestic Allotment Act of February 29 (49 Stat. 1148) authorized the Secretary of Agriculture to make benefit payments to farmers as a soil-conservation measure.

1936. Flood Control Act of June 22 (49 Stat. 1570) recognized the fact that flood control on navigable waters or their tributaries is a proper activity of the federal government, in cooperation with the states and their political subdivisions; divided responsibility in the field between the War Department and the Department of Agriculture; authorized interstate flood-control compacts; and authorized a long list of projects for prosecution by the Army Corps of Engineers.

1936. Act of June 23 (49 Stat. 1892) authorized the City of Los Angeles to purchase public lands in Mono County at $1.25 per acre "which may be necessary" for certain specified purposes in connection with the development and utilization of the water supplies of the city. Mineral rights were reserved by the United States.

1936. Act of June 23 (49 Stat. 1894) authorized and directed the National Park Service to make a comprehensive study, other than on lands under the jurisdiction of the Department of Agriculture, of the public park, parkway, and recreational-area programs of the United States and of the several states and political subdivisions thereof, and of the lands chiefly valuable as such areas, and to cooperate with the states and their political subdivisions in planning such areas. It also authorized the states to enter into interstate compacts for the establishment and development of park, parkway, and recreational areas, subject to the approval of the state legislatures and of Congress.

1936. Act of June 26 (49 Stat. 1976) increased the maximum allowable area of grazing districts to 142 million acres, and authorized land exchanges with states on either an equal-value or equal-area basis.

1937. Cooperative Farm Forestry Act (Norris-Doxey Act) of May 18 (50 Stat. 188) authorized an annual appropriation of $2,500,000 for the promotion of farm forestry in cooperation with the states.

1937. Act of June 28 (50 Stat. 319) established the Civilian Conservation Corps as the official successor to the Emergency Conservation Work, and provided in detail for its administration.

1937. Act of July 9 (50 Stat. 485) authorized the Secretary of the Interior to purchase certain specified lands for addition to the Yosemite National Park.

1937. Bankhead-Jones Farm Tenant Act of July 22 (50 Stat. 522) provided for loans to farm tenants, for rehabilitation loans, and for the retirement and rehabilitation of submarginal agricultural lands. It also authorized the Secretary of Agriculture to cooperate with federal, state, and other public agencies in developing plans for a program of land conservation and land utilization.

1937. Water Facilities Act of August 28 (50 Stat. 869) provided for the development by the Secretary of Agriculture of facilities for water storage and utilization in the arid and semiarid regions.

1937. Wildlife Restoration Act (Pittman-Robertson Act) of September 2 (50 Stat. 917) provided for federal financial and technical cooperation with the states in approved wildlife restoration projects.

1938. Small Tract Act of June 1 (52 Stat. 609) authorized the Secretary of the Interior to sell or lease not more than 5 acres of certain public lands, outside of Alaska, which he may classify as chiefly valuable as home, cabin, health, convalescent, recreational, or business sites, subject to a reservation to the United States of all oil, gas, and other mineral deposits.

1938. Act of June 15 (52 Stat. 699) authorized the appropriation of receipts from the San Bernardino and Cleveland National Forests for the purchase of lands within those forests in Riverside County.

1938. Act of June 22 (52 Stat. 835) extended the boundaries of the Modoc, Shasta, and Lassen National Forests.

1938. Act of June 22 (52 Stat. 836) extended the boundaries of the Shasta and Klamath National Forests.

1938. Act of June 22 (52 Stat. 838) extended the boundaries of the Plumas, Tahoe, and Lassen National Forests.

1938. Pierce Act of June 23 (52 Stat. 1033) authorized the Secretary of the Interior to lease any state, county, or private land chiefly valuable for grazing within the exterior boundaries of a grazing district.

1939. Act of July 14 (53 Stat. 1002) provided for the establishment within each grazing district of an advisory board of 5 to 12 local stockmen elected by the users of the range but appointed by the Secretary of the Interior, who may also on his own initiative appoint one wildlife member on each board.

1939. Act of August 11 (53 Stat. 1418) authorized the Secretary of the Interior to construct water conservation and utilization projects in the Great Plains and arid and semiarid regions of the United States in cooperation with the Department of Agriculture.

1940. Act of March 4 (54 Stat. 41) created the Kings Canyon National Park, to be administered "for public recreational purposes," with the proviso that no grazing permits in effect on January 15, 1939, for whose renewal an application is made before the date of expiration, shall be affected by the act, except that they shall be subject to such terms and conditions as are prescribed by the Secretary of the Interior. The act abolished the General Grant National Park and made it the General Grant section of the Kings Canyon National Park.

1940. Lea Act of April 26 (54 Stat. 168) authorized federal cooperation in the protection of forest lands from white pine blister rust, irrespective of ownership, provided that on state or private lands federal expenditures must be at least matched by state or local authorities or by individuals or organizations.

1940. Act of May 28 (54 Stat. 224) authorized the President, on the basis of a cooperative agreement between the Secretary of Agriculture and the municipality concerned, to withdraw national-forest lands from which a municipality obtains its water supply from all forms of entry. The Secretary of Agriculture may prescribe such rules and regulations as he considers necessary for adequate protection of the watershed.

1940. Act of June 11 (54 Stat. 297) authorized the appropriation of receipts from the Cleveland National Forest for the purchase of lands within that forest in San Diego County.

1940. Act of June 11 (54 Stat. 299) authorized the appropriation of receipts from the Angeles National Forest for the purchase of lands within that forest.

1940. Act of June 17 (54 Stat. 402) authorized the appropriation of receipts from the Sequoia National Forest for the purchase of lands within that forest.

1940. Transportation Act of September 18 (54 Stat. 898), with certain specified exceptions, authorized the payment of full commercial tariff rates for the transportation of persons or property for the United States to land-grant railroads which within one year would waive all further claims under their grants. Lands already patented, certified for patent, or sold to innocent purchasers were not affected.

1941. Act of November 15 (55 Stat. 763) extended to all lands owned by, leased by, or under the jurisdiction of the United States, including Indian lands and lands in process of acquisition, the penalties (somewhat modified) for setting and for failing to extinguish fires in or near any timber, underbrush, grass, or other inflammable material.

1942. Executive Order of April 12 delegated to the Secretary of the Interior authority to make withdrawals and restorations of public lands.

1943. Act of July 12 (57 Stat. 392) appropriated funds for "the investigation and establishment of water rights, including the purchase thereof or of lands or interests in lands or rights-of-way for use and protection of water rights necessary or beneficial in connection with the administration and public use of the national forests."

1944. Treaty of February 3 between the United States and Mexico (59 Stat. 1219) established the International Boundary and Water Commission and provided for the allocation of the flow of the Rio Grande River and Colorado River, the construction of dams, and other purposes.

1944. Sustained-Yield Forest Management Act of March 29 (58 Stat. 132) authorized the Secretary of Agriculture and/or the Secretary of the Interior to establish cooperative sustained-yield units consisting of federal forest land and private forest land, or federal sustained-yield units consisting only of federal forest land, when in their judgment the maintenance of stable communities is primarily dependent upon federal stumpage and when such maintenance cannot be secured through usual timber-sale procedures. Provision was made for the sale of federal stumpage to cooperating landowners or to responsible purchasers within communities dependent on federal stumpage, without competitive bidding at prices not less than the appraised value of the timber.

1944. Act of May 5 (58 Stat. 216) amended the Clarke-McNary Act of 1924 by authorizing annual increases in the appropriation for cooperative forest-fire protection with the states up to a maximum of 9 million dollars for the fiscal year 1948 and thereafter.

1944. Act of September 27 (58 Stat. 745) authorized the Secretary of the Interior to dispose of sand, stone, gravel, vegetation, and timber or other forest products on unreserved public lands during the period of hostilities.

1946. Act of August 13 (60 Stat. 1049) created an Indian Claims Commission of three members to pass upon claims against the United States of any tribe, band, or other identifiable group of American Indians. All claims must be submitted within 5 years from the date of the act. Decisions of the Commission are final, subject to appeal to the Court of Claims, which is also given jurisdiction over claims arising subsequent to the date of approval of the act.

1946. Act of August 14 (60 Stat. 1080) strengthened the Coordination Act of 1934 by authorizing the Secretary of the Interior, through the Fish and Wildlife Service, to provide assistance to, and cooperate with, federal, state, and public or private agencies and organizations in the development, protection, and rehabilitation of the wildlife resources of the United States.

1947. Forest Pest Control Act of June 25 (61 Stat. 177) declared it to be the policy of the government to protect all forest lands irrespective of ownership from destructive forest insect pests and diseases. It authorized the Secretary of Agriculture, either directly or in cooperation with other federal agencies, state and local agencies, and private concerns and individuals, to conduct surveys to detect infestations and to determine and carry out control measures against incipient, potential, or emergency outbreaks.

1947. Act of July 30 (61 Stat. 630) increased the size of isolated tracts that might be offered for sale to 1,520 acres and of mountainous tracts to 760 acres.

1947. Materials Disposal Act of July 31 (61 Stat. 681) authorized the Secretary of the Interior to dispose of sand, stone, gravel, clay, timber, and other materials on public lands exclusive of national forests, national parks, national monuments, and Indian lands.

1947. Act of August 4 (61 Stat. 739) extended the boundaries of the Modoc National Forest.

1947. Interior Department Appropriations Act of August 6 (61 Stat. 790) amended the Taylor Grazing Act of 1934 to authorize the Secretary of the Interior, in fixing fees for the grazing of livestock in grazing districts, to "take into account the extent to which such districts yield public benefits over and above those accruing to the users of the forage for livestock purposes. It also divided fees into a grazing fee and a range improvement fee, and provided for their disposition.

1947. Mineral Leasing Act for Acquired Lands of August 7 (61 Stat. 913) authorized the Secretary of the Interior to lease acquired lands containing deposits of coal, phosphate, oil, oil shale, gas, sodium, potassium, and sulfur under the provisions of the mineral leasing laws, with the consent of the head of the department having jurisdiction over the lands and subject to such conditions as he may prescribe.

1948. Act of February 10 (62 Stat. 19) provided that whoever, without lawful authority or permission, shall go upon any national-forest land while it is closed to the public by a regulation of the Secretary of Agriculture made pursuant to law, shall be subject to fine and imprisonment.

1948. Act of March 19 (62 Stat. 83) added certain lands surrounding the Shasta Reservoir to the Shasta National Forest "for the purpose of protecting, improving, and utilizing their forests, watershed, recreational, and other resources."

1948. Act of May 19 (62 Stat. 240) authorized transfer of certain real property controlled but no longer needed by federal agencies (1) to the states for wildlife-conservation purposes other than for migratory birds, or (2) to the Secretary of the Interior if the property has particular value in carrying out the national migratory-bird management program.

1948. Water Pollution Control Act (Taft-Barkley Act) of June 30 (62 Stat. 1155) provided for technical and financial cooperation by the federal government with states and municipalities in the formulation and execution of programs for the abatement of stream pollution.

1949. Anderson-Mansfield Reforestation and Revegetation Act of October 11 (63 Stat. 762) authorized a schedule of appropriations for the reforestation and revegetation of the forest and range lands of the national forests.

1949. Act of October 26 (63 Stat. 909) amended the Clarke-McNary Act of 1924 by authorizing increases in the appropriations for cooperation with the states in forest-fire protection and in the production of planting stock, and for cooperation with the land-grant colleges or other suitable state agencies in educating farmers in the management of forest lands and in harvesting, utilizing, and marketing the products thereof.

1950. Granger-Thye Act of April 24 (64 Stat. 82) contained many important administrative provisions "to facilitate and simplify the work of the Forest Service."

1950. Act of June 15 (64 Stat. 216) authorized the Secretary of Agriculture to convey to Plumas County 145 acres of land known as the Chester Airport in exchange for 21 acres to be added to the Lassen National Forest.

1950. Fish Restoration and Management Act (Dingell-Johnson Act) of August 9 (64 Stat. 430) provided for federal financial and technical cooperation with the states in fish restoration and management projects.

1950. Cooperative Forest Management Act of August 25 (64 Stat. 473) authorized an annual appropriation of $2,500,000 to enable the Secretary of Agriculture to cooperate with state foresters in providing technical service to private forest landowners and operators and to processors of primary forest products. The Cooperative Farm Forestry Act of 1937 was repealed.

1953. Submerged Lands Act of May 22 (67 Stat. 29) confirmed and established the titles of the states to lands beneath navigable waters within state boundaries and to the natural resources within such lands and waters; provided for the use and control of such lands and resources; and confirmed the jurisdiction and control of the United States over the natural resources of the sea bed of the continental shelf seaward of state boundaries.

1953. Agricultural Appropriations Act of July 28 (67 Stat. 205) appropriated 5 million dollars to conduct studies and carry out preventive measures for the protection of watersheds under the provisions of the Soil Conservation Act of 1935.

1953. Act of August 7 (67 Stat. 462) provided for the jurisdiction of the United States over the submerged lands of the outer continental shelf and authorized the Secretary of the Interior to lease such lands for certain purposes.

1953. Act of August 15 (67 Stat. 613) amended the Federal Reserve Act to authorize national banks to make loans secured by first liens up to 40 per cent of their appraised value "upon forest tracts which are properly managed in all respects."

1954. Act of May 28 (68 Stat. 151) removed the limitation of 142 million acres on the total area that might be included in grazing districts.

1954. Act of June 8 (68 Stat. 239) amended the Small Tract Act of 1938 to permit the sale or lease of small tracts chiefly valuable for residence, recreation, business, or community site purposes, to individuals, associations, corporations, states, municipalities, or other governmental subdivisions, if such sale or lease will not unreasonably interfere with the use of water for grazing purposes or unduly impair the protection of watershed areas.

1954. Watershed Protection and Flood Prevention Act of August 4 (68 Stat. 666) authorized the Secretary of Agriculture, under specified conditions, to cooperate with states and local organizations for the purpose of preventing erosion, floodwater, and sediment damages and of furthering the conservation, development, utilization, and disposal of water.

1954. Internal Revenue Code of August 16 (68A Stat. 67) authorized farmers in computing income taxes to deduct expenditures for soil or water conservation or for the prevention of erosion, up to 25 per cent of gross income.

1954. Act of September 3 (68 Stat. 1146) authorized the issuance by federal agencies of permits, leases, or easements to states or local governmental bodies, for periods not to exceed 30 years, on lands within their respective jurisdictions. The act applied to "public lands and national forests, except national parks and monuments."

1955. Act of July 23 (69 Stat. 367) amended the Materials Disposal Act of July 31, 1947, by adding common pumice, pumicite, and cinders to the materials specified in that act, and authorized the disposal of all such materials on both unreserved and reserved public lands except national parks, national monuments, and Indian lands by the secretary of the department having jurisdiction over the lands in question. It also provided that on unpatented claims hereafter located the United States shall have the right to dispose of the timber and other nonmineral surface resources, provided that such disposal shall not endanger or materially interfere with mining operations; and it established a procedure whereby the rights to the use of timber and other surface resources on existing, inactive mining claims may be canceled or waived.

1955. Act of August 1 (69 Stat. 434) repealed the Timber and Stone Act of June 3, 1878, as amended.

1956. Joint Resolution of March 29 (70 Stat. 57) declared the General Grant Tree ("the Nation's Christmas Tree") in Kings Canyon National Park a national shrine in memory of the men and women of the Armed Forces, and directed the Secretary of the Interior to make appropriate provision for its "perpetual care and maintenance."

1956. Soil Bank Act of May 28 (70 Stat. 188) provided for management as a "conservation reserve" of certain lands retired from agricultural production.

1956. Act of July 9 (70 Stat. 498) modified and extended the Water Pollution Control Act of 1948.

1956. Act of July 26 (70 Stat. 656) authorized the exchange of national-forest lands for military lands within or adjacent to national forests. (Lands within the Los Padres National Forest and the Hunter Liggett Military Reservation were exchanged under this act in 1957.)

State

1849. First Constitution, ratified by the people on November 13, provided in Article IX, Section 2, that the proceeds from all lands granted to the state by the United States for the support of schools and from the 500,000-acre grant, and also such per cent as may be granted by Congress on the sale of lands in the state, shall constitute a permanent fund, the interest on which shall be inviolably appropriated for the support of the common schools of the state. Article IX, Section 4, provided that the legislature shall take measures for the protection, improvement, or other disposition of such lands as have been, or may hereafter be, granted by the United States, or any person or persons, to the state for the use of a university.

1850. Act of April 16 (Ch. 99 p. 229) provided a penalty for willfully and intentionally, or negligently and carelessly, setting fire to any woods, prairies, or other grounds in the state.

1851. Act of May 1 (Ch. 6, p. 153) provided for the sale and redemption of tax-delinquent lands. It also exempted from taxation "the real and personal property of the United States, and of this state."

1852. Act of May 3 (Ch. 4, p. 41) provided for the sale of lands included in the 500,000-acre grant to the state at $2.00 per acre in amounts of not more than 640 acres to any one purchaser. Purchasers were authorized to select any vacant or unappropriated lands, and were required to swear that they wanted the land "for the purpose of making a permanent settlement thereon." Receipts were placed in a general fund, the interest on which was to be used for the support of schools.

1855. Act of April 28 (Ch. 151, p. 189) provided for the sale at $1.00 per acre of swamp and overflowed land granted to the state. Original purchasers were limited to 320 acres, and actual settlers had a prior right to purchase for a period of 6 months.

1855. Act of May 7 (Ch. 213, p. 281) authorized the Surveyor General (instead of the purchaser) to select lands in the 500,000-acre grant, in the 10 sections granted to aid in the erection of public buildings, and in lieu of occupied school sections.

1858. Act of April 10 (Ch. 176, p. 127) established the State Land Office, with responsibility for maintaining all records pertaining to state lands.

1858. Act of April 21 (Ch. 235, p. 198) repealed the act of April 28, 1855 (Ch. 151), relating to the sale of swamp and overflowed lands, and reenacted it in modified form. The price was continued at $1.00 per acre, but actual settlers were given a prior right to purchase for a period of one year. The act established a Swamp Land Fund to be used for reclamation of the lands.

1858. Act of April 23 (Ch. 281, p. 248) repealed the act of May 3, 1852 (Ch. 4), and reenacted it in modified form. The new act provided for the location of the land included in the 500,000-acre grant and in the 72 sections granted for a seminary of learning, and for their sale at $1.25 per acre, with a limitation of 320 acres per person.

1858. Act of April 26 (Ch. 335, p. 318) authorized county boards of supervisors to sell school sections 16 and 36 at auction to the highest bidder at not less than $2.00 per acre in tracts not exceeding 320 acres. Actual settlers already on the land could buy at $2.50 per acre. Receipts were set apart as a permanent school fund, interest on which was to be used for the support of common schools in the township concerned.

1859. Act of February 21 (Ch. 48, p. 83) amended the act of April 23, 1858 (Ch. 281), in various ways, including the provision that the 10 sections granted to aid in the construction of public buildings should be sold in the same manner and at the same price ($1.25 per acre) as the "school lands" (500,000-acre grant) covered by that act.

1859. Act of April 18 (Ch. 314, p. 340) amended the act of April 28, 1855 (Ch. 151), by raising to 640 acres the area that could be purchased by one person.

1861. Act of April 22 (Ch. 218 p. 218) repealed the act of April 26, 1858 (Ch. 335), and provided that land in school sections 16 and 36 should be sold in the same manner and at the same price as land in the 500,000-acre and "seminary of learning" grants. (This removed sale from the county supervisors.) All receipts were to be paid into the State School Fund.

1861. Act of May 13 (Ch. 352, p. 355) established a board of five swamp land commissioners to handle the reclamation of swamp, overflowed, salt marsh, and tide lands belonging to the state.

1862. Act of May 14 (Ch. 432, p. 552) granted to the United States all state lands within Indian reservations.

1863. Act of April 27 (Ch. 347, p. 591) revised much of the detailed legislation relating to state lands but provided that swamp land should continue to be sold at $1.00 per acre and other grant land at $1.25 per acre.

1863. Act of April 27 (Ch. 467, p. 739) provided penalties for cutting or removing timber from state lands for sale. Fines were payable to the School Fund or the Swamp Land Fund.

1864. Act of March 2 (Ch. 147, p. 136) made it a misdemeanor to cut or girdle any tree on state or federal land except for lumber, firewood, tanning, agriculture, or mining. The act did not apply to the clearing of mineral land for the purpose of working the same or to the cutting of timber for lumbering purposes.

1864. Act of April 4 (Ch. 458, p. 508) appointed J. D. Whitney as State Geologist and prescribed the duties of the office.

1866. Act of April 2 (Ch. 519, p. 674) established the Agricultural Land Board to select the 150,000 acres granted for the establishment of The Agricultural, Mining, and Mechanical Arts College, and to arrange for their withdrawal from private entry.

1866. Act of April 2 (Ch. 570, p. 799) granted the swamp and overflowed lands belonging to the state to the counties in which they were located "to hold in trust for the purpose of constructing the necessary levees and drains to reclaim the same." The State Board of Swamp Land Commissioners was abolished and its duties were transfered to the county supervisors.

1868. Act of March 28 (Ch. 415, p. 507) codified and revised the legislation relating to state lands but made no major changes in its main provisions. The Board of Directors of The Agricultural, Mining, and Mechanical Arts College, or its successor, was authorized to select and dispose of the 150,000-acre grant at such price and in such manner as it deemed in the best interest of the college.

1868. Act of March 30 (Ch. 543, p. 716) provided in detail for the disposal of salt marsh and tide lands belonging to the state. Sale was to be at public auction, with a preference right to actual settlers to purchase at the appraised value.

1872. Act of February 13 (Ch. 102, p. 96) made it a misdemeanor to set fire, willfully or accidentally, to any wooded country or forest belonging to the state or to the United States.

1872. Penal Code, adopted February 14, provided in Section 384 that "every person who willfully or negligently sets on fire, or causes or procures to be set on fire, any woods, prairies, grasses, or grain, on any lands, is guilty of a misdemeanor." Sections 626-637 dealt with violation of the laws for the preservation of game and fish.

1874. Act of March 13 (Ch. 250, p. 347) forbade the willful cutting down, stripping of its bark, or destruction by fire of any tree over 16 feet in diameter in the groves of big trees in the counties of Fresno, Tulare, and Kern.

1874. Act of March 28 (Ch. 531, p. 767) provided for the sale of mineral lands in Sections 16 and 36 at $2.50 per acre in tracts not exceeding 40 acres in size. Persons with bona fide mining claims and others in actual possession of lands were made preferred purchasers.

1880. Act of April 16 (Ch. 105, p. 115) created a State Mining Bureau headed by a State Geologist appointed by the Governor, and established a Mining Bureau Fund.

1880. Act of April 23 (Ch. 117, p. 123) created a Board of Drainage Commissioners consisting of the Governor, Surveyor General, and State Engineer, and authorized the establishment of drainage districts to promote drainage activities, including the control of debris from mining and other operations, under the direction of the State Engineer.

1885. Act of March 3 (Ch. 11, p. 10) created a State Board of Forestry consisting of three members appointed by the Governor for four-year terms. The board was given comprehensive duties and was instructed "to act with a special view to the continuance of water sources that may be affected in any measure by the destruction of forests near such sources; to do any and all things in their power to encourage preservation and planting of forests, and the consequent maintenance of the water sources of the state."

1885. Act of March 21 (Ch. 156, p. 217) created a Board of Trustees of the State Mining Bureau consisting of five members appointed by the Governor.

1893. Act of March 23 (Ch. 173, p. 203) repealed the acts of April 16, 1880 (Ch. 105), and March 21, 1885 (Ch. 156), relating to the State Mining Bureau, but reenacted their basic provisions in modified form. The duty of the State Mineralogist was "to make, facilitate, and encourage special studies of the mineral resources and mineral industries of the state."

1893. Act of March 23 (Ch. 187, p. 229) abolished the State Board of Forestry, effective July 1, 1893, by repealing the act of March 3, 1885 (Ch. 11). "Experimental stations" of the Board were transferred to the University of California.

1893. Act of March 24 (Ch. 223, p. 337) authorized hydraulic mining wherever and whenever it "can be carried on without material injury to navigable streams, or to the lands adjacent thereto."

1893. Act of March 24 (Ch. 228, p. 339) authorized the Governor to appoint a competent civil engineer for a period of four years, to be known as the Debris Commissioner, to represent the state in consultation with the U. S. Board of Engineers, and appropriated $250,000 for construction of works to restrain and impound mining debris, subject to matching by the United States.

1901. Act of March 16 (Ch. 162, p. 517) created the California State Redwood Park Commission, consisting of the Governor and four appointees, for the purpose of purchasing and managing redwood lands at Big Basin, Santa Cruz County, as a state park. It also appropriated $250,000 for land purchase in yearly allotments of $50,000 over a 5-year period.

1902. Section 25½ of Article IV of the Constitution, adopted November

4, authorized the legislature to divide the state into fish and game districts and to enact laws for the protection of fish and game therein.

1903. Act of March 24 (Ch. 275, p. 399) required owners to properly case any oil or gas well, and to properly abandon any such well by withdrawing casing and filling well.

1905. Act of March 3 (Ch. 60, p. 54) receded the Yosemite Valley and the Mariposa Big Tree Grove to the United States "to be held for all times by the United States of America for public use, resort and recreation, and imposing on the United States of America the cost of maintaining the same as a national park."

1905. Act of March 18 (Ch. 264, p. 235) created a State Board of Forestry consisting of the Governor, Secretary of State, Attorney General, and State Forester to "supervise all matters of state forest policy and management." It also created the position of State Forester, to be held by a "technically trained forester" appointed by the Governor to "execute all matters pertaining to forestry within the jurisdiction of the state," including fire control and cooperation with counties, towns, corporations, and individuals in forestry matters; gave the State Board of Forestry supervision over the California Redwood Park; reenacted in revised form existing legislation relating to forest-fire control; created a forestry fund consisting of fines received as a result of violation of the act; and authorized county boards of supervisors to appropriate money for forest protection, improvement, and management.

1905. Act of March 20 (Ch. 337, p. 394) authorized counties to appropriate funds for the preservation, "reforestration," and protection from fire of forests upon public lands.

1907. Act of March 21 (Ch. 433, p. 788) authorized the establishment of state game preserves by providing for the transfer to the state by owners of patented lands of the right to preserve and protect the wild game thereon.

1907. Act of March 23 (Ch. 536, p. 996) revised and greatly expanded existing legislation relating to the entire subject of setting fire to woods.

1909. Act of March 13 (Ch. 205, p. 313) provided for the location of lode claims and placer claims. It did not affect any mining district or the rules and regulations thereof.

1909. Act of March 15 (Ch. 256, p. 392) united the fish commission fund and the game preservation fund into the "fish and game preservation fund."

1909. Act of March 25 (Ch. 444, p. 774) withheld from sale the shore and the bed of the ocean or of any navigable channel, stream, bay, or inlet between ordinary high and low water mark, over which the ordinary tide ebbs and flows.

1909. Act of April 28 (Ch. 729, p. 1129) authorized the board of supervisors, in any county in which a planning commission has been created, to appoint a board of forestry consisting of nine members of the planning commission, with authority to employ a county forester and a deputy county forester.

1911. Act of April 14 (Ch. 454, p. 904) provided that minerals contained in the waters of any lake or stream should not be extracted except on lease by the state.

1911. Act of April 27 (Ch. 612, p. 1154) withdraw from selection and sale all lands embraced within the original meander lines of streams and lakes belonging to the state the waters of which contain minerals in commercial quantities. Provision was made for leasing the right to extract minerals from such lands and waters.

1913. Water Commission Act of June 13 (Ch. 586, p. 1013), approved by referendum vote November 3, 1914, created a State Water Commission consisting of the Governor, the State Engineer, and three members appointed by the Governor. The commission was authorized to license the use and methods of use of the state's water, and to make and enforce regulations pertaining to the same throughout California.

1913. Act of June 16 (Ch. 679, p. 1327) repealed the act of March 23, 1893 (Ch. 173), relating to the State Mining Bureau, and reenacted most of its basic provisions in modified form except that the Board of Trustees of the Bureau was abolished.

1915. Act of May 19 (Ch. 389, p. 605) provided for the sale at public auction of certain school lands and unsold portions of the 500,000-acre grant. The Surveyor General was directed to withhold from sale lands containing growth valuable for forest-cover protection to watersheds or for reservoir sites.

1915. Act of May 19 (Ch. 395, p. 634) provided for the sale to actual settlers of certain school lands and unsold portions of the 500,000-acre grant which are suitable for cultivation, in tracts not exceeding 320 acres to any one person. An act of May 6, 1919 (Ch. 208, p. 308) defined "actual settlers" as "persons who have resided in good faith on the land for a period of not less than one year, to the exclusion of any other residence."

1915. Act of May 21 (Ch. 428, p. 708) authorized the creation of city planning commissions.

1915. Act of June 10 (Ch. 718, p. 1404) esablished a Department of Petroleum and Gas in the State Mining Bureau, under the general supervision of the State Mineralogist, who was instructed to appoint a State Oil and Gas Supervisor, with a term of four years. It also created an "oil protection fund" consisting of funds received by the state under the act, and established a State Board of Review, Correction, and Equalization to "have all the powers and perform such duties as shall devolve upon the county board of equalization under the provisions of Section 3672 of the Political Code." The purpose of the act was stated to be "protection of the natural resources of petroleum and gas from waste and destruction through improper operations in production."

1917. Act of May 15 (Ch. 475, p. 563) authorized a state nursery for the growing of stock for reforestation of public lands, the planting of trees along public streets and highways, and the beautifying of parks and school grounds. No funds were appropriated for the purpose.

1917. Act of May 17 (Ch. 493, p. 576) authorized the leasing of school-land sections 16 and 36 or lands selected in lieu thereof.

1917. Land Settlement Act of June 1 (Ch. 755, p. 1566) sought "to improve the general economic and social conditions of agricultural settlers within the state and of the people of the state generally." It created a State Land Settlement Board of five members appointed by the Governor with four-year staggered terms, with authority to buy, develop, lease, and sell lands "susceptible of intensive culture and suitable for colonization in an area of not more than ten thousand acres."

1917. Act of June 1 (Ch. 759, p. 1586) made numerous amendments in the oil and gas conservation act of June 10, 1915 (Ch. 718), including replacement of the former boards of arbitration by district oil and gas commissioners for each of the five districts into which the state was divided, with authority to pass on appeals from any order of the State Oil and Gas Supervisor. It also abolished the "oil protection fund" and created the "petroleum and gas fund." The act declared that the people of California have " a primary and supreme interest" in the deposits of petroleum and gas within the state.

1919. Act of May 2 (Ch. 176, p. 262) provided in detail for the prevention and suppression of forest fires. Among other things, it authorized the State Board of Forestry to divide the state into fire districts; to cooperate with other agencies and individuals; and to make such other rules and regulations as may be necessary for the organization and operation of the fire protective system.

1919. Act of May 25 (Ch. 544, p. 1191) amended that part of the act of March 18, 1905 (Ch. 264), creating a State Board of Forestry, to provide for a new type of board consisting of four non-salaried persons to be appointed by the Governor plus the State Forester. Appointees were to be persons familiar with the timber industry, the livestock industry, and the grain and hay industry, and one "at large."

1921. Act of May 25 (Ch. 303, p. 404) reserved from sale except upon a rental and royalty basis all coal, oil, shale, gas, phosphate, sodium, and other mineral deposits on lands belonging to the state. All subsequent sales of land were subject to a payment to the state of one-sixteenth of the receipts from coal, oil, gas, and other mineral deposits. Specific provision was made for the prospecting and leasing of mineral lands, including authorization of the Surveyor General to reserve to the state the right to sell, lease, or otherwise dispose of the surface in lands covered by mineral leases so far as the use of the surface is not necessary in extracting mineral deposits. The Surveyor General was also authorized to classify land for its various values and uses, and to call upon other agencies of the state to make such classification.

1921. Act of June 3 (Ch. 871, p. 1657) appropriated $300,000 for the purchase of redwood state parks in Humboldt and Mendocino Counties. The land was to be acquired and managed by the State Board of Forestry.

1923. Act of May 2 (Ch. 82, p. 156) provided for the control of insect pests on timberland and authorized the State Forester, with the approval of the State Board of Forestry, to declare zones of infestation within which the State Forester may take steps to abate the nuisance if the owner fails to do so.

1923. Act of May 23 (Ch. 191, p. 431) authorized county boards of supervisors to hold public hearings and elections for the purpose of forming fire protection districts in any unincorporated area of the county "not included in any other fire protection district or timber land patrolled by the state board of forestry, or in accordance with the rules and regulations of said state board of forestry." The board of supervisors was authorized to levy an annual tax upon the taxable real property in each district sufficient to defray the costs of administration.

1923. Act of May 26 (Ch. 229, p. 465) authorized the exchange of state lands within a national forest which are more valuable for timber than for any other purpose for timberlands of the United States of equal value in one or more compact tracts situated in California.

1923. Act of May 29 (Ch. 249, p. 495) instructed the State Board of Forestry to make a survey of forest lands suitable for state parks, but appropriated no funds for the purpose.

1923. Act of June 6 (Ch. 313, p. 656) required owners of forest lands other than redwood to provide a fire patrol therefor during the season of the year when there is danger of forest fires. It authorized the State Board of Forestry to prescribe the necessary rules and regulations to carry out the purposes of the act, and to provide such patrol at the cost of the landowner, at not to exceed 3 cents per acre, should he fail to do so.

1926. An amendment to Section 12 3/4 of Article XIII of the Constitution, adopted November 2, provided that "all immature forest trees which have been planted on lands not previously bearing merchantable timber, or planted or of natural growth, upon lands from which the merchantable original growth timber stand to the extent of seventy per cent of all trees over sixteen inches in diameter has been removed, shall be exempt from taxation. . .*provided,* that forest trees or timber shall be considered mature for the purposes of this act at such time, after forty years from the planting or removal of the original timber as above provided, as a board consisting of a representative from the State Board of Forestry, a representative from the State Board of Equalization, and the county assessor of the county in which the timber is located, shall by a majority thereof so determine."

1927. Act of April 5 (Ch. 72, p. 127) authorized the State Board of Forestry to accept gifts of forest or brush-covered lands suitable for forestry purposes or for the conservation of water or watershed protection.

1927. Act of April 13 (Ch. 128, p. 237) created the Department of Natural Resources with four divisions—Mines and Mining, Forestry, Parks, and Fish and Game. It reconstituted the State Board of Forestry to consist of seven members appointed by the Governor and to include persons familiar with the pine timber industry, the redwood industry, the livestock industry, general agriculture, and problems of water conservation. The act also created a State Park Commission of five members and a State Fish and Game Commission of three members.

1927. Act of May 16 (Ch. 544, p. 915) authorized the exchange of state lands within a national park which are more valuable for timber or recreational uses than for any other purpose for timberlands or other public lands of the United States in one or more compact tracts in California.

1927. Act of May 23 (Ch. 706, p. 1229) provided that any city or portion thereof, or any portion of the unincorporated area of any county not included in any other park, recreation, and parkway district may acquire all lands necessary to securing and maintain an adequate system of parks, recreation grounds, and parkways.

1927. Act of May 25 (Ch. 751, p. 1420) authorized the Director of Natural Resources (1) to close to trout fishing any stream or lake which has been stocked by the Fish and Game Commission, and (2) to close to camping any area in any state park or forest area when necessary in the interest of peace or safety.

1927. Act of May 25 (Ch. 763, p. 1477) established and defined the state park system and placed its control in the Department of Natural Resources through the State Park Commission.

1927. Act of May 25 (Ch. 764, p. 1479) authorized the State Park Commission to make a survey of sites suitable for state parks and appropriated $25,000 for the purpose.

1927. Act of May 25 (Ch. 765, p. 1480) provided for the issuance and sale of $6,000,000 in bonds to finance the purchase of park sites, created a State Park Finance Board, and appropriated $10,000 to handle the bond sales.

1927. Act of May 27 (Ch. 798, p. 1568) provided in detail for the issuance of hunting and fishing licenses. It also directed that all moneys collected from the sale of licenses and from fines should be credited to the fish and game preservation fund, and that for a period of five years not less than one-third of the receipts from the sale of hunting licenses should be used for the purchase, lease, management, and administration of game refuges and public shooting grounds; and created a game refuge and public shooting grounds advisory committee.

1927. Act of June 2 (Ch. 874, p. 1899) repealed the act of May 21, 1915 (Ch. 428), as amended, and authorized cities, counties, and cities and counties to appoint planning commissions and to establish official master plans. It also authorized the appointment of regional planning commissions and prescribed their powers and duties.

1928. Constitutional amendment ratified by the people on November 6 added to Article XIV a new section (Section 3) declaring that the right to the use of water in or from any navigable stream or water course in the state "shall be limited to such water as shall be reasonably required for the beneficial use to be served," and providing that riparian rights attach to only so much of the streamflow as the riparian owner can beneficially use.

1929. Act of April 16 (Ch. 115, p. 200) authorized the State Board of Forestry, under certain conditions, to designate "hazardous fire areas," and made it unlawful to smoke or to build a campfire therein, except at established camp sites. The act also made it unlawful to smoke or build a campfire on national-forest land except as authorized by the Secretary of Agriculture.

1929. Act of May 18 (Ch. 307, p. 616) amended the Political Code to establish four divisions in the Department of Natural Resources—Forestry, Parks, Fish and Game, and Mines. The chief of the Division of Mines must be a trained mining engineer appointed by the Director upon nomination of the State Mining Board, which was to establish the general policies of the Division.

1929. Act of May 28 (Ch. 527, p. 909) accepted the provisions and benefits of the federal Migratory Bird Conservation Act of February 18, 1929, and consented to acquisition by the United States of such areas as are necessary for migratory bird refuges in carrying out the provisions of the act.

1929. Act of May 28 (Ch. 535, p. 923) amended and expanded the act of June 10, 1915 (Ch. 718), establishing the Department of Petroleum and Gas in the State Mining Bureau. The division of the Department of Natural Resources now or hereafter created for the supervision of petroleum and gas was to be in charge of a chief to be known as "State Oil and Gas Supervisor."

1929. Act of May 29 (Ch. 568, p. 969) repealed the act of April 5, 1927 (Ch. 72), and authorized the Director of Natural Resources, subject to approval by the State Board of Forestry, to accept gifts of land suitable for forestry purposes or for purposes of reforestation, and also to accept contributions for the purchase, care, or maintenance of such lands.

1929. Act of May 31 (Ch. 588, p. 992) authorized any county to purchase, lease, or obtain by gifts lands located in that county or in any other counties for park and boulevard purposes.

1929. Act of June 1 (Ch. 629, p. 1042) authorized county supervisors to give land to the United States for national-park purposes and to exercise the right of eminent domain in acquiring such land.

1929. Planning Act of June 17 (Ch. 838, p. 1805) repealed previous legislation on this subject and enacted new legislation authorizing the appointment of city, county, and regional planning commissions, prescribing their powers and duties, and providing for the establishment of official master plans.

1931. Act of June 4 (Ch. 595, p. 1284) amended the act of May 25, 1927 (Ch. 763), by defining more precisely the areas constituting the state park system.

1931. Act of June 15 (Ch. 952, p. 1956) authorized the Division of Forestry to purchase land for lookout stations and administrative purposes.

1931. Act of June 15 (Ch. 966, p. 1979) authorized any county or city to assist the state in acquiring lands for recreational purposes.

1931. Act of June 19 (Ch. 1058, p. 2210) authorized boards of county supervisors, on petition of at least

15 per cent of the electors, to establish public recreation districts to be managed by five trustees (increased to seven in 1939) appointed by the board.

1931. Act of June 19 (Ch. 1208, p. 2521) provided for the organization, administration, and dissolution of resort districts.

1933. Act of April 11 (Ch. 73, p. 394) established the Fish and Game Code.

1933. Act of April 26 (Ch. 176, p. 622) made it a misdemeanor to graze livestock on any unreserved or unappropriated public lands of the United States when such grazing will interfere with the customary use of the land by any person in accordance with the customs of the graziers of the region involved.

1933. Act of June 10 (Ch. 821, p. 2174) authorized the formation of limited-dividend corporations for the protection and development of forests and other renewable natural resources. The cutting of timber or other work on forest lands must be preceded by approval of the State Board of Forestry, which may establish reasonable rules and regulations for the protection and preservation of forests and forest lands.

1933. Act of August 7 (Ch. 1043, p. 2664) provided "for the incorporation, government, and management of regional park districts, including therein city and county territory, for the purpose of acquiring, improving, and maintaining parks, playgrounds, beaches, parkways, scenic drives, boulevards, and other facilities for public recreation." The districts are administered by a board of five directors, chosen by the electors, with authority to acquire, lease, and manage land within or without the district for purposes of public recreation.

1935. Act of June 14 (Ch. 331, p. 1153) created, as a division of the State Department of Finance, a State Planning Board consisting of the Director of Finance, the Director of Public Works, the Director of Natural Resources, and five citizens appointed by the Governor. The board was authorized to employ a director of planning and to cooperate with any persons or organizations in devising means to develop the natural and economic resources of the state.

1935. Act of July 15 (Ch. 541, p. 1615) authorized the Director of Natural Resources (1) to accept gifts of forest lands from the United States Government or any private person, firm, or corporation, and (2) to exchange any lands so acquired for lands of the United States Government within California.

1937. Act of May 15 (Ch. 309, p. 684) repealed the act of July 15, 1935 (Ch. 541), regarding state forests but reenacted most of its basic provisions. It also authorized the Director of Natural Resources to enter into agreements with the federal government or others for the acquisition of lands desirable for state forests. The act was declared to be an urgency measure to enable the state to take advantage of the federal Fulmer Act of August 29. 1935.

1937. Act of June 19 (Ch. 460, p. 1402) provided for the levying and collection of fees from developers of oil and natural gas wells in order to support the division of the Department of Natural Resources charged with the supervision of petroleum and gas.

1937. Act of June 22 (Ch. 523, p. 1532) authorized the State Park Commission to lease lands for park and recreational purposes for periods of from two to twenty years, with option to purchase.

1937. Planning Act of July 1 (Ch. 665, p. 1817) made numerous changes in the Planning Act of June 17, 1929 (Ch. 838). One amendment directed the State Planning Board to divide the state into regional planning districts, each with a regional planning commission appointed by the Governor from nominees selected by the boards of county supervisors.

1938, Extra Session. State Lands Act of March 24 (Ch. 5, p. 23) revised and codified existing legislation relating to state lands. It established a State Lands Commission in the Department of Finance consisting of the Controller, the Lieutenant Governor, and the Director of Finance, and vested it with all of the powers formerly exercised by the Surveyor General, the Register of the State Land Office, the State Land Office, and the Division of State Lands in the Department of Finance. The act authorized the commission to make gas and oil leases on tide, submerged, and other lands, including the beds of navigable rivers and lakes be longing to the state, and provided for the prospecting and leasing of lands containing minerals other than oil or gas. All funds received from oil, gas, and mineral leases of state lands, except school lands, were to be deposited in the State Lands Act Fund. After making certain payments from this fund, 70 per cent of the balance was to be transferred to the General Fund and 30 per cent to the State Park Maintenance and Acquisition Fund created by the act.

1938, Extra Session. Act of March 29 (Ch. 7, p. 48) created a State Soil Conservation Committee, provided for the organization, management, and dissolution of soil conservation districts, and authorized the State Soil Conservation Committee to cooperate with other public agencies, individuals, and corporations. District directors were authorized to develop soil and water conservation plans, to establish standards of cropping and tillage operations and range practices, to assist private landowners or land occupants, and to acquire all lands and property necessary to carry out the plans and works of the district.

1939. Act of April 26 (Ch. 93, p. 1067) established the Public Resources Code by gathering and amending the parts of other codes having a close relationship to natural resources, except water control and use.

1939. Act of May 29 (Ch. 296, p. 1567) assented to the provisions of the federal Pittman-Robertson Act of September 2, 1937, providing federal aid in wildlife restoration projects.

1939. Act of May 29 (Ch. 312, p. 1584) made numerous amendments in the Soil Conservation Act of March 29, 1938 (Ch. 7), including the granting of authority to the directors of any soil conservation district "to formulate regulations governing the use of lands within the district in the interest of conserving soil and soil resources and preventing and controlling soil erosion by prohibiting cultural practices, methods of planting, or of land use that promote unreasonable damage."

1939. Act of June 6 (Ch. 426, p. 1759) provided that any portion of the unincorporated area of any county not included in any other park, recreation, and parkway district, and lying entirely outside any national forest, may be organized by the voters into a park, recreation, and parkway district. Each district is governed by a board of three trustees (increased to five in 1953) elected by the voters, with power to acquire real property and buildings, and to make rules and regulations for the administration of the district.

1939. Act of June 23 (Ch. 663, p. 2122) provided that thereafter swamp and overflowed lands belonging to the state should be sold by the State Lands Commission under rules and regulations prescribed by it and at a price fixed by it.

1939. Act of June 7 (Ch. 479, p. 1827) amended the forest nursery act of May 15, 1917 (Ch. 475), to permit the production and sale of planting stock for use on private lands for "soil erosion control, watershed protection, farm windbreaks, the production of forest products and farm woodlots."

1939. Oil and Gas Control Act of July 22 (Ch. 811, p. 2368) declared it to be the policy of the state "to conserve the oil and gas resources of the state, to regulate and stabilize the production and distribution of petroleum oil and natural gas and the products thereof, to prevent waste thereof and secure the benefits of said natural resources to the people of this and future generations," and enacted provisions for the achievement of these objectives. The act created an Oil Conservation Commission consisting of the Director of Natural Resources, the Director of Public Works, and the Director of Finance.

1939. Act of July 25 (Ch. 1113, p. 3058) increased the number of oil and gas districts from five to six.

1940, Extra Session. Act of February 28 (Ch. 21, p. 45) repealed the Soil Conservation Act of March 29, 1938 (Ch. 7), as amended, and reenacted it in amended form as Division 9 of the Public Resources Code. The name of the State Soil Conservation Committee was changed to State Soil Conservation Commission. Lands included in a district may be publicly or privately owned.

1940. An amendment to Section 25½ of Article IV of the Constitution, adopted November 5, provided for a Fish and Game Commission of five members with six year, staggered terms appointed by the Governor subject to confirmation by the Senate. It also authorized the legislature to delegate to the commission such powers relating to the protection, propagation, and preservation of fish and game as the legislature sees fit.

1940. Section 25 of Article I of the Constitution, adopted November 8, provided that "the people shall have the right to fish upon and from the public lands of the state and in the waters thereof. . .and no land owned by the state shall ever be sold or transferred without reserving in the people the absolute right to fish thereupon," provided the legislature may control the season when and conditions under which fish may be taken.

1941. Act of June 2 (Ch. 550, p. 1915) changed the name of the Division of Parks to Division of Beaches and Parks.

1941. Act of June 6 (Ch. 619, p. 2076) directed that one-third of the money deposited in the State Park Maintenance and Acquisition Fund be expended only for the acquisition, improvement, and maintenance of state beaches and the remainder for the acquisition, improvement, and maintenance of state parks and monuments. It also increased from 30 per cent to 70 per cent the amount of net receipts from mineral leases to be transferred from the State Lands Act Fund to the State Park Maintenance and Acquisition Fund.

1941. Act of July 15 (Ch. 1185, p. 2943) approved and adopted the coordinated plan for the conservation, development, and utilization of the water resources of the state as set forth in the report prepared in pursuance of Chapter 822 of the Statutes of 1929.

1941. Act of July 16 (Ch. 1215, p. 3023) provided for the control of stream pollution by placer mining, by operators not holding a permit from the California Debris Commission, in waters tributary to the Sacramento and San Joaquin Rivers.

1941. Act of July 19 (Ch. 1227, p. 3086) repealed the provision of the Public Resources Code relating to private fire patrols of forest lands (1923 Stat., Ch. 313) and appropriated $100,000 to enable the Division of Forestry to carry out the additional duties and functions imposed on it by this action.

1941. Act of July 19 (Ch. 1241, p. 3119) provided that the State Lands Commission may withdraw from sale, and also restore to sale, any public lands belonging to the state.

1942. Section 25 5/8 of Article IV

of the Constitution, adopted November 3, provided that all money collected under legislation relating to the protection of fish, game, mollusks, or crustaceans and all fines imposed for the violation of such legislation shall be used exclusively for the protection, conservation, propagation, and preservation of fish, game, mollusks, or crustaceans and for the administration and enforcement of laws relating thereto.

1943. Act of April 21 (Ch. 172, p. 1067) forbade the cutting for conversion into lumber of any sound, live coniferous tree less than 18 inches in diameter at 6 inches above the ground, in that part of California lying north of the 6th Parallel, without a permit from the State Forester.

1943. Act of May 13 (Ch. 368, p. 1604) established the Water Code.

1943. Act of May 20 (Ch. 641, p. 2278) provided that no state lands which front upon or are near to any lake, convenient access to which is not provided by public roads or otherwise, shall ever be sold, leased, or rented without reserving to the people of the state an easement across the lands.

1943. Act of June 1 (Ch. 967, p. 3854) created the State Beach Fund and provided that 23 1/3 per cent of the receipts from oil, gas, and mineral leases should be transferred to the State Beach Fund and 46 2/3 per cent to the State Park Fund.

1943. Act of June 1 (Ch. 969, p. 2856) abolished the State Park Maintenance and Acquisition Fund and created the State Park Fund.

1943. Act of June 1 (Ch. 970, p. 2857) made the State Park Commission responsible for supervising (1) state acquisition and management "of ocean beaches for public recreational purposes and control and correction of beach and cliff erosion," and (2) the expenditure of state funds for the development and protection of public beaches owned by counties and municipalities. Such expenditures must be matched by the county or municipality and must be in accordance with master plans adopted by the county. The commission was also authorized to cooperate with other public agencies.

1943. Act of June 1 (Ch. 980, p. 2893) authorized the State Lands Commission to arrange for land exchanges with the United States under Section 8 of the Taylor Grazing Act of 1934.

1943. Act of June 8 (Ch. 1086, p. 3025) created a committee to study the forest situation and appropriated $15,000 for its use. The committee consisted of two members each from the Senate and the Assembly, the Chairman of the State Board of Forestry, and the Director of Natural Resources.

1945. Act of February 10 (Ch. 25, p. 336) amended the insect-control act of May 2, 1923 (Ch. 82), with reference to the declaration of zones of infestation and the responsibilities of owners therein. It also authorized the State Forester to undertake control measures within such zones and to enter into cooperative agreements with private timberland owners, the Federal Government, and other public and private agencies, with the proviso that the State Board of Forestry shall set the ratio of state to private cooperation.

1945. Act of April 23 (Ch. 85, p. 394) provided "for forest practices which will promote maximum sustained productivity of the forest lands of California" by authorizing district forest practice committees to prepare forest practice rules which, after approval by two-thirds of the private ownership in the district and by the State Board of Forestry, have the force of law. Management plans submitted by the owners may be accepted by the committees and by the board as an alternate for the forest practice rules.

1945. Act of April 27 (Ch. 139, p. 625) provided that in oil well drilling under a parcel of land containing one or more acres, where the surface thereof is not available for drilling work, no more than one well shall be drilled or produced per acre, and no operator shall maintain or construct a derrick within 150 feet of any derrick then standing.

1945. Act of May 10 (Ch. 316, p. 773) provided for appointment by the Governor, subject to confirmation by the Senate, for four-year, staggered terms of a State Board of Forestry consisting of seven members representing the pine producing industry, the redwood producing industry, forest land ownership, the range livestock industry, agriculture, the beneficial use of water, and the general public.

1945. Act of May 10 (Ch. 317, p. 774) provided in detail for the acquisition, administration, and management of state forests. Purchases must be approved by a State Forest Purchase Committee composed of the Governor, the Director of Finance, the Director of Natural Resources, and the Chairman of the State Board of Forestry. Counties receive payments on lands acquired for state forest purposes equivalent to taxes levied by the county on similar lands similarly situated. Hunting, fishing, recreation, camping, grazing, and mining are permitted under rules and regulations established by the State Board of Forestry. Water facilities for power and irrigation may be developed as provided by law.

1945. Act of June 8 (Ch. 777, p. 1461) made many important revisions in the sections of the Public Resources Code relating to the prevention and suppression of forest fires.

1945. Act of June 15 (Ch. 904, p. 1687) directed the State Board of Forestry to "classify the lands of the state. . .for the purpose of determining areas thereof in which the financial responsibility of preventing and suppressing fires shall be primarily the responsibility of the state. The prevention and suppression of fires in all areas not so classified is primarily the responsibility of local or federal agencies, as the case may be. . .The primary responsibility of the state of preventing and suppressing forest fires is not confined or limited to Clarke-McNary lands."

1945. Senate Resolution 151 of June 15 (Sen. Jour., p. 3943) created the Senate Forestry Study Committee of five members, vested it with all the rights and powers of the committee created by the act of June 8, 1943 (Ch. 1086), and directed it to continue the study of the forest situation, including range lands and watersheds.

1945. Act of June 25 (Ch. 1018, p. 1964) authorized the Division of Forestry to enter into contracts or cooperative agreements with individuals, corporations, groups, or governmental agencies "owning or controlling brush-covered land within the area the fire protection of which is primarily state responsibility for the purpose of engaging in controlled land clearance and revegetation." The Division of Forestry was also authorized to engage in experimental land clearance and revegetation.

1945. Act of July 7 (Ch. 1109, p. 2118) authorized the Division of Forestry to issue permits for controlled burning of brush by owners of brush-covered land within the area the fire protection of which is primarily state responsibility, with suitable precautions to prevent spread of fire to other lands.

1945. Act of July 7 (Ch. 1121, p. 2130) provided that when income is derived directly from public shooting grounds the Fish and Game Commission shall reimburse the county in which such property is located the amount equal to the county taxes levied upon such property at the time it was transferred to the state.

1945. Act of July 9 (Ch. 1187, p. 2239) added to the purposes for which soil conservation districts may be formed the conserving and supplying of water for district lands, revised the membership of the State Soil Conservation Commission, provided for formation of an association of soil conservation districts, and excluded mineral rights from the assessed valuation upon which regular assessments are based.

1945. Act of July 10 (Ch. 1266, p. 2383) provided that the State Board of Forestry "shall classify all lands within the area of the state in which the financial responsibility of preventing and suppressing fires is primarily the responsibility of the state into types of land based on cover, beneficial use of water from watersheds, and probable damage from erosion, and fire risks and hazards, and shall determine the intensity of protection to be given to each such type of land. A plan for adequate state-wide protection of such areas shall be prepared by the State Board of Forestry in which all land in the same type shall be assigned the same intensity of protection." The act also authorized counties, under contract with the state, to assume the responsibility for fire control on lands in which the financial responsibility of preventing and suppressing fires is primarily the responsibility of the state, and to receive an appropriate allocation of Clarke-McNary funds.

1945. Act of July 17 (Ch. 1405, p. 2657) appropriated $40,000 for surveys and appraisals of forest lands by the Division of Forestry.

1945. Act of July 17 (Ch. 1420, p. 2672) authorized the Division of Forestry to engage in experimental controlled land clearance and revegetation of lands principally useful for range or forage purposes the fire protection of which is primarily state responsibility, and to conduct research to determine the effects and value of the methods used.

1945. Act of July 17 (Ch. 1422, p. 2676) appropriated $15,000,000 for the survey and acquisition of lands suitable for inclusion in the state system of beaches and parks. Two-thirds of this amount must be used for the purchase of ocean beaches and one-third for parks, and no funds shall be expended for acquisition (except for federal lands) unless the state money is matched from private or other sources.

1945. Act of July 17 (Ch. 1464, p. 2743) directed the State Lands Commission to sell the Latour Forest to the Division of Forestry and appropriated $100,000 to finance the purchase.

1945. Riding and Hiking Trails Law of July 17 (Ch. 1469, p. 2746) authorized the State Park Commission to develop a state trails system with the assistance of a Riding and Hiking Trails Advisory Committee of six members appointed by the Commission.

1945. Act of July 17 (Ch. 1483, p. 2757) made the first appropriation ($17,500 for the biennium) for the administration of the soil conservation activities of the state.

1945. Act of July 18 (Ch. 1496, p. 2774) authorized the purchase of the Mountain Home Forest Tract of 4,590 acres in Tulare County and appropriated $600,000 for the purpose. The tract is to be managed as a multiple-use forest and is not to be reduced below 4,000 acres.

1946, Extra Session. Act of March 14 (Ch. 146, p. 192) appropriated $2,000,000 to the Department of Natural Resources for the acquisition of land for state forests, for expenditure without regard to fiscal year.

1947. Act of May 13 (Ch. 227, p. 796) provided that the State Lands Commission may make authorized grants of land to the United States, by exchange or otherwise, with or without the reservation of minerals. It also specified lands, including those acquired for public use, over which the jurisdiction of the commission does not extend. Any state agency selling any of the excepted lands, with the exception of tax-deeded lands, may with the approval of the State Lands Commission reserve any of the mineral deposits.

1947. Act of May 29 (Ch. 441, p. 1341) provided that when property is deeded to the state for park or beach purposes, oil and mineral rights may be reserved by the grantor, provided that any extraction of oil and minerals shall not disturb the surface of the property or any improvements thereon.

1947. Act of June 4 (Ch. 539, p. 1530) authorized the State Park Commission to lease any interest in real property which it deems necessary for the development of the state park system.

1947. Act of June 10 (Ch. 647, p. 1684) authorized the Director of Natural Resources, whenever necessary in the interest of public safety or peace and with the consent of the owner, to close to entry any lands designated as a hazardous fire area.

1947. Conservation and Planning Act of June 18 (Ch. 807, p. 1909) repealed the Planning Act of June 17, 1929 (Ch. 838), as amended, and reenacted in considerably modified form its major provisions concerning city, county, and regional planning commissions. The act replaced the State Planning Board by a State Planning and Conservation Board, which "is the State Reconstruction and Reemployment Commission, any state board or commission which succeeds to the powers of said commission in relation to planning." The board was directed to encourage the extension and correlation of state activities by agencies of the state government and to participate in interstate and national planning efforts. Each planning commission (city, county, and regional) was directed to prepare and adopt a comprehensive, long-term, master plan, which may include a conservation plan, a land-use plan, and a recreation plan.

1947. Act of June 20 (Ch. 887, p. 2082) provided that no grazing or recreational lease of state lands by the State Lands Commission shall be for a period longer than ten years. It also amended Section 7301 of the Public Resources Code to provide that school sections 16 and 36, the 500,000-acre grant, and lands received in lieu of sections 16 and 36, "which are not suitable for cultivation may be sold by the commission under rules and regulations prescribed by it and at a price fixed by it."

1947. Act of July 8 (Ch. 1193, p. 2681) authorized two or more municipalities, and any parcel or parcels of city or county territory, to organize regional shoreline parks and recreational districts. The government of the district is vested in a board of five directors, elected by the voters, with power to acquire and lease land, and to develop and manage a system of parks for public recreation.

1947. Act of July 8 (Ch. 1239, p. 2745) created the Recreation Commission of seven members appointed by the Governor for four-year, staggered terms for study of the whole problem of recreation as it affects the people of the state. "The Commission shall aid and encourage, but not conduct, public recreation activities."

1947. Wildlife Conservation Act of July 10 (Ch. 1325, p. 2881) established "a single and coordinated program for the acquisition of land and facilities suitable for recreational purposes and adaptable for conservation, propagation and utilization of the fish and game resources of the state." It also created a Wildlife Conservation Board consisting of the President of the Fish and Game Commission, the Director of the Department of Fish and Game, and the Director of Finance, plus three members each from the Senate and the Assembly who meet with the Board and participate in its activities so far as such participation is not incompatible with their legislative positions.

The duties of the Board as stated in later legislation (1951) are to identify and acquire areas that "are most essential and suitable for wildlife production and preservation, and that will provide suitable recreation."

1947. Act of July 10 (Ch. 1327, p. 2883) established the Wildlife Restoration Fund to carry out the purposes of the Wildlife Conservation Act.

1947. Act of July 18 (Ch. 1559, p. 3200) provided for the spacing of oil wells and the behavior of participants in community oil and gas leases.

1949. Act of May 6 (Ch. 143, p. 371) authorized the Governor to appoint a Historical Landmarks Advisory Committee of seven members.

1949. Act of May 27 (Ch. 433, p. 778) authorized the State Lands Commission to exchange lands with other agencies or individuals on an equal-value basis for the improvement of navigation, aid in reclamation, or flood-control protection.

1949. Act of June 29 (Ch. 779, p. 1504) amended several provisions of the act of July 7, 1945 (Ch. 1109), relating to the burning of brush-covered lands. It also instructed the Division of Forestry to advise applicants for controlled-burning permits as to the precautions to be taken, and to provide stand-by fire protection to such extent as personnel and equipment are available.

1949. Act of July 2 (Ch. 811, p. 1554) authorized the State Forester to enter into agreements with governmental agencies, corporations, or individuals for the reforestation of burned, logged, or denuded lands.

1949. Act of July 20 (Ch. 1031, p. 1892), among other amendments to Division 9 (Soil Conservation) of the Public Resources Code, repealed the authority of the directors of soil conservation districts to enact land-use regulations. It also placed the Soil Conservation Commission in the Department of Natural Resources.

1949. Act of July 21 (Ch. 1081, p. 1982) created a State Mining Board of five members with four-year staggered terms, appointed by the Governor with the advice and consent of the Senate, "to represent the state interest in the development, utilization, and conservation of the mineral resources of the state."

1949. Act of July 25 (Ch. 1177, p. 2098) authorized the State Park Commission to enter into contracts for the operation of concessions within the state park system.

1949. Act of July 27 (Ch. 1332, p. 2328) authorized the Director of Natural Resources to close any state park to camping, hunting, trapping, or the use of firearms.

1949. Dickey Water Pollution Control Act of July 28 (Ch. 1549, p. 2782) created a State Water Pollution Control Board consisting of the Director of Public Health, the State Engineer, the Director of Natural Resources, the Director of Agriculture, and nine members appointed by the Governor for four-year, staggered terms. The Director of Fish and Game was added to the board in 1953. The act also divided the state into nine regions, for each of which the Governor was authorized to appoint a Regional Water Pollution Control Board, with authority to encourage and to require the correction of pollution.

1951. Act of May 5 (Ch. 334, p. 675) repealed the Conservation and Planning Act of June 18, 1947 (Ch. 807), and incorporated its provisions, with minor amendments, in Title 7 of the Government Code.

1951. Act of May 17 (Ch. 537, p. 1691) authorized the State Lands Commission to lease lands under its jurisdiction for such purposes as it deems advisable, "including but not limited to grazing leases, leases for commercial or industrial purposes, and leases for campsites."

1951. Charles Brown Fish and

Game Reorganization Act of May 29 (Ch. 715, p. 1979) created the Department of Fish and Game, to which was transferred the Division of Fish and Game in the Department of Natural Resources, and prescribed the duties, powers, and jurisdiction of the department and of the Fish and Game Commission.

1951. Act of May 30 (Ch. 720, p. 1985) made some minor amendments in the Forest Practice Act of April 23, 1945 (Ch. 85). It also authorized the Forest Practice Committees and the State Board of Forestry, in addition to approving specific management plans, to approve plans of procedure submitted by timberland owners as an alternate to any requirement of the forest practice rules.

1951. Act of June 22 (Ch. 1173, p. 2983) assented to the provisions of the federal Dingell-Johnson Act of August 9, 1950, providing federal aid in fish restoration and management projects.

1951. Act of July 6 (Ch. 1339, p. 3227) authorized the Governor, through the Director of Natural Resources, to close to hunting and fishing and to entry by the general public any area in which the State Forester shows the unrestricted use of any grass, grain, brush, or forest-covered land to be a menace to life or property because of the fire danger or because of their inaccessibility.

1951. Act of July 12 (Ch. 1505, p. 3488) authorized the Department of Fish and Game to obtain rights of way over private lands in order to furnish access to lands or waters open to public hunting, but did not authorize the use of eminent domain proceedings.

1951. Act of July 20 (Ch. 1652, p. 3744) declared it to be the policy of the state to acquire any Sequoia gigantea grove found by the State Park Commission or the State Forester to be suitably situated and of a size and character to justify its preservation.

1953. County Service Area Act of May 23 (Ch. 858, p. 2189) permitted unincorporated areas to extend governmental services to zones established by special elections. Services may consist of police, fire protection, recreation, and any other service authorized by law to be conducted by county government. Services may be contracted to be performed by other agencies, including the Division of Forestry.

1953. Act of June 13 (Ch. 1131, p. 2628) authorized the State Forester to demonstrate methods of developing, using, and protecting the forest and wildland resources of the state, and to that end to enter into cooperative agreements with other governmental agencies, persons, firms, or corporations.

1953. Act of June 13 (Ch. 1135, p. 2632) amended the provisions of the Public Resources Code relating to insect control (based on the act of May 2, 1923, Ch. 82) by including diseases.

1953. Act of June 17 (Ch. 1188, p. 2704) authorized the State Forester to engage in surveys of soils, vegetation, and forest products on the forest, range, and watershed lands of the state, and to that end to enter into cooperative agreements with other governmental agencies, persons, firms, and corporations.

1953. Act of June 25 (Ch. 1339, p. 2899) authorized the State Forester to maintain state nurseries for the growing of stock for reforestation of public and private lands, the planting of trees along public streets and highways, and the beautifying of parks and school grounds. All material is to be sold at a price established by the State Forester and approved by the State Board of Forestry.

1955. Act of April 1 (Ch. 71, p. 508): (1) authorized the State Park Commission or the State Forester to acquire any land containing trees of the species Sequoia gigantea when necessary to the preservation of the trees and to the public welfare; (2) authorized the State Lands Commission to refuse to grant permits for the erection on tidelands or submerged lands of any structure that might interfere with the recreational use of such lands; and (3) authorized the State Forester to enter into agreements with federal agencies to investigate the effect of forest cover in the conservation of water and the prevention of erosion on watershed areas.

1955. Act of April 26 (Ch. 258, p. 720) approved of the maximum production regulations in oil pools established by the Conservation Committee of California Oil Producers.

1955. Act of June 3 (Ch. 925, p. 1553) established a permissible density of oil wells per acre within the same zone or pool.

1955. Act of June 17 (Ch. 1026, p. 1936) repealed the act of April 21, 1943 (Ch. 172) forbidding the cutting of certain trees without a permit from the State Forester.

1955. Act of July 6 (Ch. 1680, p. 3018) repealed and reenacted the soil conservation provisions of the Public Resources Code. Major changes were designation of a Division of Soil Conservation in the Department of Natural Resources; changing the Soil Conservation Commission to a policy-making body; and making provision to facilitate cooperation with the federal government in allied programs.

1955. Greenbelt Law of July 6 (Ch. 1712, p. 3147) provided that any territory which is by consent of the owners zoned and restricted for agricultural uses exclusively pursuant to a master plan for land use in any county, shall not, while it is so zoned, be annexed to a city without the consent of the owners.

1955. Act of July 6 (Ch. 1724, p. 3165) made numerous amendments in existing legislation relating to oil, gas, and mineral leases of state lands. It prohibited the lease for the production of oil and gas from state-owned tide and submerged lands in certain areas in Los Angeles County, Santa Barbara County, and San Luis Obispo County.

1955. Watershed Protection and Flood Prevention Law of July 9 (Ch. 1886, p. 3484) provided for state financial assistance to local organizations carrying out the provisions of the federal Watershed Protection and Flood Prevention Act of August 4, 1954 (68 Stat. 666).

1956. Act of April 25 (Ch. 52, p. 421) created a Department of Water Resources, an Advisory State Water Board, and a State Water Rights Board. Practically all regulatory powers previously vested in the Department of Public Works in respect to water acquisition and use were transferred to the Department of Water Resources.

1957. Act of June 8 (Ch. 947, p. 2170) created a Soil Conservation Advisory Board to advise and assist the Soil Conservation Commission.

1957. Act of July 4 (Ch. 1648, p. 3018) amended the Forest Practice Act of April 23, 1945 (Ch. 85), by providing that every timber operator must obtain a permit to operate from the State Forester; that engaging in timber operations without a valid permit constitutes a misdemeanor; and that a permit may be suspended or revoked by the Director of Natural Resources for failure or refusal to comply with the forest practice rules or applicable forest management plan, for material misrepresentation or false statement, or for refusal to allow inspection by the State Forester.

1957. Act of July 4 (Ch. 1675, p. 3053) permitted the sale of certain state lands with reservation by the state of oil and other mineral deposits therein—a modification of the basic act of May 25, 1921 (Ch. 303).

1957. Act of July 8 (Ch. 2127, p. 3769) created the State Beach and Park Fund, which replaced the State Beach Fund, the State Park Fund, and the State Park Maintenance Fund.

1957. Act of July 8 (Ch. 2130, p. 3776) amended Section 4006.5 of the Public Resources Code relating to the revegetation and reforestation of burned, deforested, and denuded forest and watershed lands; established certain criteria for such rehabilitation; and authorized the Director of Natural Resources to "order the execution of surveys, work and contracts to fulfill the purposes of Section 4006.5, and [to] request the assistance of other state, local and federal government agencies therefor," whenever it is shown that impaired, burned, and denuded watershed lands may impose an imminent threat of disaster to the public health, safety, and welfare from flood and erosion.

1957. Act of July 8 (Ch. 2165, p. 3819) repealed those provisions of the Public Resources Code authorizing the establishment of three similar types of special recreation and park districts, and replaced them by authorizing establishment of a single type of recreation and park districts. No substantial authority was added to the powers already embodied in existing legislation.

1957. Act of July 10 (Ch. 2313, p. 4028) appropriated $9,500 to enable the State Forester to "undertake experiments and studies pertinent to determining costs and feasible methods of reforestation by planting, seeding, release of natural seedlings from competing brush, or other procedure deemed promising of the desired results, and involving also brush removal and control, soil preparation and control of rodents or other destructive organisms."

1957. Act of July 10 (Ch. 2412, p. 4167) established as state policy the multiple use of all public waters, with emphasis on recreation, to the extent that such use is consistent with public health and safety.

1957. Public Outdoor Recreation Plan Act of July 15 (Ch. 2318, p. 4034) created a Committee for the Development of the California Public Outdoor Recreation Plan consisting of the Director of Natural Resources, the Director of Fish and Game, the Director of Water Resources, the Director of Recreation, the Director of Finance, the Director of Education, the Chief of the Division of Beaches and Parks, and the Executive Officer of the State Lands Commission to develop and recommend to the legislature a California Public Outdoor Recreation Plan. The act appropriated $50,000 to enable the committee to initiate a three-year study leading to preparation of the plan, and authorized the committee to appoint a technical consultant group and an advisory council.

1957. Act of July 15 (Ch. 2405, p. 4153) provided that $100,000 shall be transferred annually, commencing with the fiscal year 1958 - 1959, from the State Lands Act Fund to the Division of Forestry "for basic research, field studies and operations with respect to the activities under its jurisdiction."

1957. Act of July 15 (Ch. 2406, p. 4154) appropriated $100,000 for use by the Soil Conservation Commission in making grants to districts for soil conservation work.

APPENDIX II

ANNOTATED BIBLIOGRAPHY

ADAMS, FRANK: "The Historical Background of California Agriculture", reprinted from Calif. Agriculture, Univ. of Calif. Press, Berkeley, 1946.

Pictures the development of agriculture in California from 1769 to 1870, with considerable attention to Spanish and Mexican land grants.

———, PAUL A. EWING, and MARTIN R. HUBERTY: "Hydrologic Aspects of Burning Brush and Woodland-Grass Ranges in California," Dept. of Nat. Res., Div. of Forestry, Sacramento, 1947.

Summarizes the results of previous studies, largely in the form of quotations from publications on the subject.

AMERICAN FORESTRY ASSOCIATION: "A Program for American Forestry," Washington, D. C., 1954.

Presents the Association's program in the fields of forest land ownership (including proposed national and state-by-state studies), forest land management, multiple-use policies, education and assistance to forest owners, and forest research and surveys.

BANCROFT, HUBERT HOWE: "History of California," 1542-1890, 7 vols., A. L. Bancroft and Company, San Francisco, 1884-1890.

All seven volumes contain much information on land grants, titles, ownership, and use. They comprise the most exhaustive history of all aspects of California's development brought together by any one author.

BARR, GEORGE W., et al.: "Recovering Rainfall," Parts I and II, Univ. of Arizona, Tucson, Ariz., 1956.

Part I describes the physical and economic characteristics of the Salt River watershed, and proposes a program of research and action to increase the yield of irrigation water by modification of the present vegetative cover. Part II presents reports by ten specialists on various aspects of the program.

BREWER, WILLIAM H.: "Up and Down California in 1860-1864," Univ. of Calif. Press, Berkeley, 1949.

The author's journal of his travels in California from 1860 to 1864. Contains a wealth of descriptive material but little on land ownership or management.

BROWER, DAVID R.: "Scenic Resources for the Future," Sierra Club Bul., Vol. 41, No. 10: 1-10, 1956.

Proposes a national Scenic Resources Review in which public and private agencies would combine "to find what scenic resources are still left, to make an estimate of the future need for them, and to devise ways of protecting them in time." Additional comments by the same author on our needs for scenic resources are given on pages 72-84 of this issue of the Bulletin.

BROWN, WM. S., and S. B. SHOW: "California Rural Land Use and Management — A History of the Use and Occupancy of Rural Lands in California," 13 chaps., Forest Service, Calif.

Region, San Francisco, 1957. Duplicated.

Contains a detailed history of the use of rural lands of all kinds in California up to 1944, with voluminous statistical data. Brings together under one cover a great deal of material culled from a wide variety of sources. There is an extensive bibliography and an index of 42 pages.

BURCHAM, LEVI T.: "California Range Land," State Printing Division, Documents Section, Sacramento 14, 1957.

Traces the history of the range livestock industry in California, with emphasis on the original and present character of the range resource, its deterioration, and recent efforts to increase its productivity through more intensive management based on research.

CALIFORNIA BLUE BOOK, 1954.[1]

Contains descriptions of the activities of the state departments and other state agencies, and an economic survey of California prepared by the Research Department of the California State Chamber of Commerce. The latter, published also as a separate, includes material on history, climate, resources, population, and industries, with detailed data by regions and counties.

CALIFORNIA CODES.

The codes, and particularly the Public Resources Code, contain the laws currently in force relating to natural resources, the conservation, utilization, and supervision thereof, and matters incidental thereto. There are annotated editions by Deering and by West.

CALIFORNIA COMMITTEE ON PLANNING FOR RECREATION, PARK AREAS AND FACILITIES: "Guide for Planning Recreation Parks in California – A Basis for Determining Local Recreation Space Standards," Sacramento, 1956.

"The guide is limited solely to the presentation of planning principles and a basis for determining space standards for recreation parks in urban centers of population," but much of the material will prove helpful in similar studies in rural areas.

CALIFORNIA DEPARTMENT OF AGRICULTURE, CROP AND LIVESTOCK REPORTING SERVICE, in Cooperation with U. S. Department of Agriculture: "California Livestock and Poultry: A Statistical Summary, 1867-1942," Spec. Pub. 192, 1943.

Discusses the economic position of the livestock and poultry interests of California and the physical factors affecting livestock production, and gives detailed information concerning the production of cattle, calves, milk cows, sheep and lambs, hogs, horses and mules, and poultry.

———, DIVISION OF LAND SETTLEMENT: "Final Report, June 30, 1931," 1931.

Contains a history of the state's land-settlement program authorized in 1917 and discontinued in 1931, with detailed information concerning the colonies established at Durham and Delhi.

CALIFORNIA DEPARTMENT OF NATURAL RESOURCES, DIVISION OF BEACHES AND PARKS, in Cooperation with the Planning Commissions and Boards of Supervisors of the Coastal Counties of California: "Preliminary Master Plan of Shoreline Development for the State of California and Status Report on County Master Plans of Acquisition," prepared by Edwin C. Kelton, Beach Erosion Engineer, 1946.

The first section of the plan sets forth the current legislation, certain basic data, the physical characteristics of the coast, the method of coordinating the plans of the several counties, the erosion problems, the present and contemplated use of the beaches, a summary of the acquisition programs of the county master plans, and a status report on the development

[1] All State of California publications are published by the State Printer, Sacramento.

plans. The second section establishes the state and county first-priority acquisition program to be executed from the $10,000,000 appropriated by the Legislature in 1945 and matched by an equal amount in land or money from sources other than the state.

———, ———: "Property Ownership Report, Jan. 1, 1957," 1957. Duplicated.

Gives a complete list of California state beaches and parks, with acreage, front footage, and date and method of acquisition of each, including the purchase price or gift evaluation.

———, ———: "California State Park System – Five Year Master Plan, July 1, 1956 to June 30, 1961," 1956.

Presents an itemized statement of the proposed acquisition program and development program for the next five years, with estimated areas and costs.

———, DIVISION OF FORESTRY "Forest and Fire Laws, 1953."

Contains a summary of all legislation relating to forests, forest lands, and forest fires, in force at the close of the legislative session of 1953.

———, ———, and other agencies: "Facts about the Forest and Brush Fire Problem in Southern California Watersheds," 1954.

A popular presentation in tables, maps, and charts of California's wealth and economic development, and of southern California's watershed fire problem.

———, ———: "Forests of California–Treasure Chest for the Needs of Men," 1955.

Discusses characteristics, uses, products, and management of the forests of California.

———, DIVISION OF MINES: "Annual Report of the State Mineralogist for the Fiscal Year 1956," prepared by Olaf P. Jenkins, 1956.

Discusses the mineral wealth of California and the current activities of the Division of Mines.

CALIFORNIA FORESTRY STUDY COMMITTEE: "The Forest Situation in California – Report to the Legislature," 1945.

Contains a detailed analysis and discussion of all aspects of the forest situation in California. One of the appendices calls attention to the great diversity of ownership, particularly in small scattered holdings, as a deterrent to effective forest managemet. The report served as the basis for the large number of important laws dealing with forestry enacted by the 1945 legislature. It is an historical document of major importance.

———: "The Forest Situation in California – Report to the Legislature, Vol. 2," 1947.

Covers more briefly many of the subjects included in the 1945 report of the committee, with information concerning progress during the two preceding years.

CALIFORNIA LEGISLATURE, ASSEMBLY INTERIM COMMITTEE ON AGRICULTURE: "Public Lands, Grazing and Forest Practices," First Progress Report, 1952.

Presents factual information (1) on the range improvement program of the Division of Forestry, and (2) on the range research program of the University of California. The report states that "several instances of duplication of research studies have already occurred" and that the committee "has aimed at correlating the activities of the many agencies involved to achieve the economy and efficiency of close cooperation."

———, ———: "Public Lands, Grazing and Forest Practices," Second Progress Report, 1953.

Considers the improvement and management of range lands in California and gives a transcript of a public hearing on the subject held on May 17, 1952. The subcommittee in charge of the study concludes that significant results are being obtained and that there is a healthy spirit of cooperation among the several state and federal agencies engaged in range improvement work.

———, ———: "Public Lands, Grazing and Forest Practices," Third Progress Report, undated, probably 1953.

Deals with the Division of Forestry and covers the subjects of forest practices; protection from fire, insects, and disease; forest regeneration; watershed management; timber taxation; range-improvement program; and training policies. The subcommittee "suggests that the California Legislature go forward in formulating a constructive and efficient program" for the division.

———, ———: "Division of Beaches and Parks," Final Report of the Subcommittee on Public Lands, Grazing and Forest Practices, 1955.

This report "limits its scope to the subject of concessions, acquisition, and the administrative staff. The investigation has revealed certain practices and procedures of administration which seem to require the immediate attention of the Legislature."

———, ASSEMBLY INTERIM COMMITTEE ON CONSERVATION, PLANNING AND PUBLIC WORKS: "Interim Report," 1952.

Discusses various aspects of the conservation of natural resources, state and local planning, and public works programs. Included are preliminary reports by the Subcommittee on Bay Area Regional Problems, the Subcommittee on Ground-Water Rights, and the Subcommittee on Pollution Problems, and also a report by the State Forester on a forest and range program for California.

———, ———: "Final Report," 1953.

Discusses the subjects of conservation of natural resources, public-works financing, and progress in planning, 1949-1952. The committee comments on the "haphazard development" of state activities in the field of natural resources and proposes a reorganization of natural resources administration.

———, ASSEMBLY INTERIM COMMITTEE ON GOVERNMENT ORGANIZATION: "A Department of Water Resources," 1956.

Reviews the current status of state administrative activities dealing with water resources and recommends the establishment of a Department of Water Resources and a State Water Rights Board. The report includes a complete transcript of committee hearings held from December 15, 1955, to January 6, 1956.

———, SENATE INTERIM COMMITTEE ON CALIFORNIA INDIAN AFFAIRS: "Progress Report," 1955.

Contains a full discussion of the problems presented by the Congressional proposal to free the Indians in California from federal supervision and control, and by the Act of August 15, 1953, transferring civil and criminal jurisdiction over the Indians in California to the state. The report includes a record of five hearings held by the committee in 1954. Several appendices give detailed information on existing reservations, with special reference to water supply and water rights.

———, ———: "Progress Report," 1957.

Reviews briefly the conclusions and recommendations contained in the 1955 report of the previous interim committee, and presents for the consideration of Congress a proposed bill "To provide for certain preliminary actions that need to be taken before Federal supervision over Indian affairs in California can be terminated." The committee believes that if its recommendations are carried out, "all distinctions between the affairs of the Indians and those of other Californians will have been removed." Considerable attention is paid to the difficulties that have developed in effectuating the provisions of the termination act for the Klamath tribe of Indians in Oregon.

———, SENATE INTERIM COMMITTEE ON GOVERNMENTAL ORGANIZATION: "Analysis of Proposals for Reorganization of California Water Resource Agencies," undated, probably 1954.

Analyzes the various proposals for reorganizing the water resource agencies of California and concludes that "consolidation of water resource agencies and functions in a Department of Water Resources would provide for responsible administration and coordination of essential functions." The three functions of watershed management, negotiation of interstate compacts, and control of water pollution "require coordination but do not necessitate consolidation with the water resource planning and operation functions."

———, SENATE INTERIM COMMITTEE ON PUBLIC LANDS: "Partial Report," 1951.

Presents the committee's preliminary "analysis of all facts relating to public lands and the state, federal, and local governmental relationships involved therein." The last of the committee's thirteen recommendations is that "continued study should be made of the public land problems in California."

———, ———: "Forestry Problems," 1953.

Discusses in considerable detail the development of forestry in California, fire protection, forest-practice regulation, service forestry, forest products industries, forest regeneration and insect control, forest and watershed research, forest taxation, and public land policies.

———, ———: "State Land Ownership," 1955.

Gives itemized lists by counties (1) of the area under each of the state departments, and (2) of the area of departmental lands (combined), tax-deeded lands, state (school) lands, and federal lands. The land management activities of each department are discussed, and there are separate chapters on in-lieu taxation, school-land administration, and lease of state land.

———, SENATE INTERIM COMMITTEE ON RECREATION, STATE BEACHES AND PARKS: "California's State Park Program," 1956.

Discusses at length the current status and major problems of the state park program. Chapter headings include origin and growth of the system; size; administration; the program at a crossroads; purpose of state parks; general policies; classification of and criteria for state parks; financing the program; the program in operation; priorities for action; and elements of a balanced program. There is a separate report by an independent consultant, Hubert O. Jenkins.

———, ———: "Recreation and State Parks," 1957.

Discusses and emphasizes the importance of recreation in the state park program. Among other recommendations, the committee proposes that a state-wide State Park Acquisition Advisory Committee be established for a two-year period, and that an interdepartmental coordinating committee be formed to confer on matters of recreation and natural-resources development.

CALIFORNIA RECREATION COMMISSION: "Recreation Policy—State of California," 1955.

Contains a digest of all state legislation relating to recreation in California; describes the activities of all of the state agencies concerned with recreational matters; and gives the statutory authorization for the provision of recreational services by cities, counties, school districts, and special districts.

CALIFORNIA STATE CHAMBER OF COMMERCE: "Public Lands Policy," San Francisco, 1931. Duplicated.

Recommends that the unreserved public domain be retained and placed under management by the federal government; that a scientific study and classification of these lands be made by a commission appointed by the President; that homesteading of unproductive areas in the unreserved public domain be discouraged by the federal government; and that the Stockraising Homestead Act of 1916 be repealed.

California Tax Research Bureau: "Summary Report Submitted to the People and the Legislature of California," San Francisco, 1932.
Devotes six pages to a "timber survey" and concludes that "there is a lack of information and machinery for efficient taxation of timber properties."

California Water Resources Board: "Water Resources of California," Bul. No. 1, 1951.
Presents in detail the water resources of the state by major hydrographic areas, with a brief history of water development in California.

———: "Water Utilization and Requirements of California," Bul. No. 2, 1955.
Volume 1 presents in detail the current utilization of and estimated requirements for water by the same hydrographic areas discussed in Bul. No. 1. Vol. 2 consists of appendices and plates and includes numerous colored maps.

———: "Preview of the California Water Plan," 1956.
Summarizes the California Water Plan, which envisions the construction and operation of 260 new major reservoirs in the state. If fully implemented, the plan would permit the expansion of the irrigated area from the present 7,300,000 acres to more than 19,000,000 acres, with an accompanying increase in urban and suburban areas from 1,000,000 to about 3,400,000 acres.

Caughey, John W.: "California," Prentice-Hall, Inc., New York, 1953.
A comprehensive and excellent political, economic, social, and intellectual history of California, with considerable material on land ownership.

Chamber of Commerce of the United States: "Proceedings of the Western Chambers' Conference on Federal Lands, San Francisco, Calif., Sept. 30, 1953." Washington 6, 1953.
Presents the views of some of the western chambers of commerce, and others, on the retention, acquisition, and administration of federal lands, with special reference to the national chamber's "Policy Declarations on Natural Resources."

———: "Policy Declarations on Natural Resources," Washington 6, 1957.
Contains the official policies of the chamber with respect to natural resources of all kinds except agricultural lands.

Clar, C. Raymond: "Forest Use in Spanish-Mexican California," Calif. Dept. of Nat. Res., Div. of Forestry, 1957. Duplicated.
Gives a brief but itemized history of the economic interest in the forest and the actions of government prior to American statehood.

———: "Brief History of the California Division of Forestry," Calif. Dept. of Nat. Res., Div. of Forestry, 1957. Duplicated.
Contains a detailed account of the development of the California Division of Forestry, with copious references to legislation, administrative action, and personnel.

Clawson, Marion: "Uncle Sam's Acres," Dodd, Mead & Company, New York, 1951.
Presents "a comprehensive, balanced picture of the federally owned lands and of the major federal water developments in the United States, in relatively simple terms, and primarily for the non-specialist reader."

———: "Federal Forest Land: How Much or How Intensively Managed?" Amer. Forests 63 (No. 9): 14-15 +, Sept., 1957.
Discusses the American Forestry Association's study of land ownership in California from the point of view that "the real problem of public forest

lands is not, how much, but how to get the best possible management."

———, and BURNELL HELD: "The Federal Lands: Their Use and Management," The Johns Hopkins Press, Baltimore, Md., 1957.

Seeks "to bring together accurate and full information on the management and use of the federal lands, and to present some suggestions of the problems and opportunities of the future." A wealth of statistical information, mostly on a national basis, is contained in numerous tables and figures.

CLELAND, ROBERT G.: "A History of California; The American Period," The Macmillan Company, New York, 1922.

A detailed history of the state, with some, but not extensive, discussion of land problems and of the livestock industry.

———: "The Cattle on a Thousand Hills," The Huntington Library, San Marino, Calif., 1941.

"This book is an economic and social history of the southern California of those half-forgotten, formative years. It is chiefly concerned with the impact of Anglo-Saxon customs and institutions upon the pastoral life of the Spanish-Californians, with the conversion of great grazing ranchos into farms and settlements, with the gradual displacement of frontier violence and instability by a more restrained, law-abiding society, and with the transformation of the so-called 'Cow Counties' of the post-Gold Rush era into the small beginnings of the southern California of our own time. . . .With the exception of the first two chapters, devoted to an account of the Spanish-Mexican land-grant system, the story is chiefly confined to the period which lay between the Gold Rush of 1849-51 and the completion of the Pacific Railroad, some two decades later."

———: "From Wilderness to Empire," Alfred A. Knopf, New York, 1944.

Presents the history of California from 1542 to 1900, with considerable material on land grants, missions, ranchos, and the livestock industry.

COMMONWEALTH CLUB OF CALIFORNIA, BUSINESS ECONOMICS SECTION: "Economic Problems of California's Rapid Growth," The Commonwealth Vol. 32, No. 3, 1956.

Presents in highly condensed form detailed information on the subjects of population, employment, agriculture, water, industry, utilities, transportation, social and political aspects, financing California's rapid growth, and forecasting. Recommends that the Section "make a study looking to a definite recommendation to the Commonwealth Club and to the public as to whether or not there should be established an over-all state-wide planning organization dedicated to coordinating the future development of California in such fields as economics, transportation, population, etc."

———, WATER PROBLEMS SECTION: "Water Reservations for Areas of Origin," The Commonwealth Vol. 33, No. 15, Part 2, 1957.

Presents the viewpoints of the areas of water origin and the areas of water deficiency, with special reference to ways and means of harmonizing their opposing views.

DANA, SAMUEL T.: "Forest and Range Policy—Its Development in the United States," McGraw-Hill Book Company, Inc., New York, 1956.

Many of the laws and policies discussed apply to California as well a to other parts of the country.

———: "Research Needs in Forest Recreation," Proc. Soc. Amer. Foresters, 1956: 33-38.

Discusses current needs for research in the rapidly growing field of forest recreation with respect to supply and demand, costs and returns, and management and administration.

———: "Problem Analysis — Research in Forest Recreation," U. S. Forest Service, Washington, D. C., 1957. Duplicated.

Analyzes the problems requiring research in the field of forest recreation, with special reference to the responsibility of the Forest Service.

DAVIDSON, R. D.: "Federal and State Rural Lands, 1950, With Special Reference to Grazing," U. S. D. A. Cir. No. 909, 1952.

Contains detailed figures concerning federal and state ownership and use of rural lands by nation, regions, and states.

DECKER, KENNETH: "The Tourist Trade in California," Univ. of Calif., Bur. of Public Administration, Berkeley, 1955.

Discusses the economic characteristics of the tourist trade; the volume and trend of California's tourist trade; the importance of tourist expenditures to retail and service industries; and tourist promotion in California and other states.

DONALDSON, THOMAS: "The Public Domain: Its History, with Statistics," H. R. Misc. Doc. 45, 47th Cong., 2d Sess., Part 4, Govt. Printing Office, Washington, D. C., 1884.

Gives a complete history of the acquisition and disposal of the public domain to June 30, 1880, with addenda to December 1, 1883.

FRITZ, EMANUEL: "A Proposal for Reorganizing and Realigning Federal Forest, Forage, Park, and Game Lands," Jour. Forestry 44:278-281, 1946.

Proposes (1) creation of a new federal department to administer all federal forest, forage, park, and game lands; (2) realignment of present forest, grazing, and park land units on a functional basis; and (3) the setup of service offices for research, education, public relations, engineering, and the like as separate bureaus in the new department, or, in part, in the Department of Agriculture.

———: "Winning the Battle of Timber," Fortune 42:62-65+, 1950.

Calls attention to the progress being made by private owners in forest management, and states that "to do a creditable job of lumbering and forest management, annual output should be about 25 million board feet. This requires permanent operation on an estate of 40,000 to 100,000 acres, depending on the region. Such an enterprise can well afford integration, i.e., owning, operating, milling, and preparing a dry, planed product. . . .In many cases, if many small timber properties were to consolidate, they could afford better forest management and logging practices."

GARRISON, MYRTLE: "Romance and History of California Ranchos," Harr Wagner Publishing Company, San Francisco, 1935.

Gives the history of the Spanish and Mexican land grants and describes the ranchos resulting from many of them.

GORDON, SETH: "California's Fish and Game Program – Report to the Wildlife Conservation Board," Calif. Senate, undated, probably 1950.

Contains detailed information concerning the history and current status of wildlife administration and conservation in the state, with conclusions and recommendations.

GULICK, LUTHER HALSEY: "American Forest Policy: A Study of Government Administration and Economic Control," Duell, Sloan and Pearce, New York, 1951.

Attempts to answer the question: "In the area of forestry, how has the government sought to influence the economy, through what devices, with what results in administration and to the economy?"

HASEL, A. A., and ADON POLI: "A New Approach to Forest Ownership Surveys," Land Economics 25:1 - 10, 1949.

Discusses use of the line-sampling method for estimating acreage and number of owners by class of ownership, and points out the need for additional data to that provided by the line sample in estimating the number of owners in a class.

HIBBARD, BENJAMIN H.: "History of the Public Land Policies," The Macmillan Company, New York, 1924.

States and analyzes the policy of the United States in the disposal of its public lands.

HITTELL, JOHN S.: "The Resources of California," A. L. Bancroft and Company, San Francisco, 1879.

Published in seven editions (1863 - 1879), this book contains a detailed statement of the nature and characteristics of the resources, industry, trade, and society of California, with relatively little historical data. The author attributes the slow growth of the state (to 1879) to the unsettled condition of society, the insecurity of land titles, the great expense of bringing families from the eastern states, the uncertainty of crops in the drier valleys, and the scarcity of irrigation canals and of reclamation dikes, but concludes that the state "can and will support a population of twenty millions."

HUTCHINSON, WALLACE I.: "Water for Millions," U. S. D. A., Forest Service, Calif. Region, San Francisco, 1956.

A popular, well-illustrated presentation of the water needs of Southern California; the steps that have been taken to meet those needs; the role of forests in the protection of the water supply and the prevention of erosion; and prospects for future needs and supplies. Contains much detailed information concerning the reservoirs, canals, and aqueducts that have been built, and other steps that have been taken, to meet the water requirements of the region.

ISE, JOHN: "The United States Oil Policy," Yale Univ. Press, New Haven, Conn., 1926.

Contains detailed information concerning the exploitation of petroleum in the United States, together with a full discussion of federal and state legislation on the subject up to 1924. California receives considerable attention.

JOHNSON, CLINTON: "Fraudulent California Land Grants," published by the author, 1926.

Presents evidence to prove that "the titles to several million acres of California lands are affected by grants that were issued by Pío Pico and other Mexican governors contrary to the laws of Mexico and in violation of the treaty engagements between Mexico and the United States." Quotes from the 1886 report of the Commissioner of the General Land Office in support of his thesis, and urges action by the Executive Branch of the Government to remedy the situation.

LOOMIS, EDWARD W.: "A Study of Forest Taxation on Second Growth Timber and Lands in Humboldt County," 1954. Duplicated.

Concludes that the tax on second-growth timber should constitute a very minimum burden while the timber is growing and some method of taxing the volume should be applied upon harvesting the timber. Suggests consideration of the "deferred timber tax."

MAASS, ARTHUR: "Muddy Waters," Harvard Univ. Press, Cambridge, Mass., 1951.

Contains a discussion of the civil functions and responsibilities of the Army Corps of Engineers, with a detailed history of the Kings Canyon Project, California.

MADSEN, B. A., and R. MERTON LOVE: "Forage Crops in California," U. S. D. A. Yearbook 1948: 582-586, 1948.

Discusses cultivated forage crops in California, with special reference to perennial and annual irrigated pastures. Points out the trend "to use ranges primarily to produce feeders to be finished on pasture and concentrates."

MANNING, RAYMOND E.: "Taxes and Other In-Lieu Payments on Federal Property," Preliminary Report Prepared by Legislative Reference Service, Library of Congress, for House Committee on Interior and Insular

Affairs, Com. Print No. 23, 83d Cong., 2d Sess., 1954.

Presents detailed information on the economic picture, the legal picture, the picture by type of property, and proposals for changes in the law. Most of the material deals with the country as a whole, but there are illustrative examples of the situation in various states, including one for California (pp. 11-12).

McWILLIAMS, CAREY: "Factories in the Field," Little, Brown and Company, Boston, Mass., 1939.

Discusses the history of agriculture in California. "To understand why the valleys are made up of large federal empires; to know why it is that farming has been replaced by industrialized agriculture, the farm by the farm factory; to realize what is back of the terror and violence which breaks out periodically in the farm valleys, it is necessary to know something of the social history of California. . . .It is, in many respects, a melodramatic history, a story of theft, fraud, violence, and exploitation." There are chapters on "Land Monopolization," "Empires and Utopias," and "The Land Settlements: Delhi and Durham."

————: "Southern California Country," Duell, Sloan & Pearce, New York, 1946.

Presents a detailed description of the history, development, and characteristics of the region, with considerable emphasis on its uniqueness. Land ownership receives some attention in connection with the Indians, the missions, and the Mexican grants (both before and after 1848).

————: "California: The Great Exception," A. A. Wyn, New York, 1949.

Attempts to demonstrate that California is unique in its characteristics and history, and "to isolate the peculiar dynamics underlying California's remarkable expansion."

MORROW, WILLIAM W.: "Spanish and Mexican Private Land Grants," Bancroft-Whitney Company, San Francis, 1923.

A brief but pithy pamphlet summarizing the history of the acquisition of California as a result of the Mexican War, and of the action of the American Government on the Spanish and Mexican land grants.

NATIONAL EDUCATION ASSOCIATION OF THE UNITED STATES: "Status and Fiscal Significance of Federal Lands in the Eleven Western States," Report of Com. on Tax Education and School Finance, Natl. Educ. Assn., Washington, D. C., 1950.

Considers in detail for each of the eleven western states the following aspects of intergovernmental fiscal relations: "(a) an inventory of federally owned real estate by counties, whenever possible; (b) a determination of the amount of taxes that would be payable if federally owned real estate were subject to state and local taxation; (c) a summary of all revenues received by states and counties that might be regarded as the equivalent of payments in lieu of taxes; and (d) a brief analysis of the question of federal versus state and/or private ownership of the public lands." The discussion of California covers fourteen pages. The committee suggests a classification of federal real estate and payment standards which it believes would do much to lessen the present "impairment of the finances of state and local governments."

NELSON, DEWITT: "The Forest and Range Program for California," reprint from report of Assembly Interim Committee on Conservation, Planning and Public Works, 1952.

Contains a concise but comprehensive account of the state's major forest and range problems and the program of the Division of Forestry for meeting them. Attention is centered on progress since 1945.

PEFFER, E. LOUISE: "The Closing of the Public Domain—Disposal and Reservation Policies, 1900-1950," Stanford Univ. Press, Stanford, Calif., 1951.

Describes in detail "the steps by which the concept of the public domain has veered from one of land held in escrow pending transfer of title, toward one of reservations held in perpetuity in the interest of the collective owners, the people of the United States." A chapter deals with the origin, reception, and results of President Hoover's proposal to transfer surface rights of the unreserved public domain to the states.

PINE, W. D.: "Humboldt's Timber—A Present and Future Problem," Humboldt County Board of Supervisors, Eureka, Calif., 1952.

Discusses the history and results of lumbering in other parts of the country and stresses the importance of sound forest practice in Humboldt County as a major factor in its economic prosperity.

POLI, ADON: "Ownership and Use of Forest Land in Northwestern California," Land Economics 32:144-151, 1956.

Discusses the development of the land ownership pattern and the present situation in the northern coast-range pine subregion, the northern redwood-Douglas fir subregion, and the southern coast-range pine and redwood-Douglas fir subregion.

PUTER, S. A. D.: "Looters of the Public Domain," Portland Printing House, Portland, Ore., 1908.

A detailed and highly picturesque account of the fraudulent acquisition of public timberland on the Pacific Coast, written by the "king of the Oregon land fraud ring." Contains considerable information concerning land frauds in California.

RESOURCES FOR THE FUTURE: "Annual Report for the Year Ending September 30, 1956," Washington, D. C., 1956.

Discusses the activities of the corporation in the fields of water resources, energy and mineral resources, land use and management, regional studies, and resources and national growth.

ROBBINS, ROY M.: "Our Landed Heritage," Princeton Univ. Press, Princeton, N. J., 1942.

"This volume presents perhaps the first attempt to integrate American land history with the other forces that have shaped our civilization. . .[It] constitutes not only a study in history and in public administration, but also a study in American democracy." Contains considerable material relating specifically to California.

ROBINSON, IRENE: "Ranchos Become Cities," San Pasqual Press, Pasadena, Calif., 1939.

Gives a complete list of all Spanish and Mexican land grants in California to which title was confirmed by the United States, with much historical and descriptive material concerning many of them.

ROBINSON, WILLIAM W.: "Land in California," Univ. of Calif. Press, Berkeley and Los Angeles, 1948.

Contains quite a complete account of Spanish, Mexican, and American land grants in California and their subsequent history. Probably the best single book on the subject.

———, and WILLIAM H. NEWBRO, JR.: "A Map of the Missions, Presidios, Pueblos, and Some of the More Interesting Ranchos of Spanish California," Automobile Club of Southern California, published by Westways, 1956.

Lists and describes briefly 23 missions, 4 presidios, 4 pueblos, and 249 ranchos.

ROSE, JOHN KERR: "Survey of National Policies on Federal Land Ownership," Sen. Doc. No. 56, 85th Cong., 1st Sess., 1957.

Summarizes the national policy with respect to federal land ownership during four periods—prior to 1789, from 1789 to 1860, from 1860 to 1900, and from 1900 to 1956—with special reference to studies conducted by committees of Congress or commissions of the

Executive Branch of the Government.

ROWE, P. B., C. M. COUNTRYMAN, and H. C. STOREY: "Hydrologic Analysis Used to Determine Effects of Fire on Peak Discharge and Erosion Rates in Southern California Forests," Calif. For. and Range Exp. Sta., Berkeley, 1954. Duplicated.

Presents basic data on the effect of the destruction of vegetative cover on floods and erosion. No conclusions are drawn, but the tabular and graphic material indicate marked effect of fire on both peak discharge and erosion.

SAMPSON, A. W.: "Some Management Suggestions for the Brushlands of Southern California," School of Forestry, Univ. of Calif., Berkeley, 1957. Ms.

Discusses the factors influencing the management of brushlands and the prospects for increasing their production of forage through controlled burning, and urges increased research. The author concludes that "most proponents of control-burning know little about the complications of southern California brush problems and advocate it in a sense of desperate frustration because of ignorance of other control measures."

———, and L. T. BURCHAM: "Costs and Returns of Controlled Brush Burning for Range Improvement in Northern California," Dept. of Nat. Res., Div. of Forestry, 1954.

Gives detailed figures on the costs of controlled burning, with special reference to size of burn, and compares these costs with the cost of wildfire suppression. Forage yields and grazing capacities of burned areas are also discussed.

SCHOFIELD, W. R.: "Report on Timber Taxation in the State of California," submitted to California Tax Research Bureau, 1932. Duplicated.

Contains detailed information by counties on timber areas and assessed values. Concludes that current taxation of both merchantable timber and cut-over lands discourages the practice of forestry; that a minimum land tax plus a severance tax would be the ideal method of taxing timber but is impracticable in California; and that majority taxpayers have a minority voice in local administration and expenditure.

SHANTZ, H. L.: "The Use of Fire as a Tool in the Management of the Brush Ranges of California," Dept. of Nat. Res., Div. of Forestry, 1947.

Discusses, both for California and elsewhere, the effect of fire on vegetation; the effect of the removal of vegetative cover by fire on climate, soil, wildlife, and forage production; the effect of vegetative cover on soil erosion and runoff; controlled and light burning; and the need for and desirability of land-use planning. The author warns against the unintelligent and uncontrolled use of fire and concludes that the proper management of brushland will require intensive research.

SOCIAL SCIENCE RESEARCH COUNCIL: "A Survey of Research in Forest Land Ownership," report of a Special Committee on Research in Forest Economics, New York, 1939.

Reviews progress to date and suggests lines for further investigation. The subjects considered include status and trends in forest land ownership; origin of present ownership patterns; stability of various classes of forest land ownership; size of holdings; separate versus combined ownership of timberland and manufacturing plant; effect of public policies upon ownership; and social aspects of forest enterprise in relation to ownership.

SOUTHERN CALIFORNIA WATER COORDINATING CONFERENCE: "Statement of Principles for State-Wide Water Development," 404 South Bixel Street, Los Angeles 54, 1956.

Proposes basic principles to guide the development of the water resources of the state.

TALBOT, M. W., and A. W. SAMPSON: "The Range in California," U. S. D.

A. Yearbook 1948: 575-582, 1948.
Discusses the characteristics, importance, and management of the range provinces west of the Sierra Nevada divide: open grassland, grass-woodland, chaparral and brush, and timber-grass-brush (coniferous forest zone).

TREADWELL, EDWARD F.: "The Cattle King," The Macmillan Company, New York, 1931.
A dramatic biography of Henry Miller, with considerable information on how he built up his enormous estate of land and cattle in California.

U. S. COMMISSION ON INTERGOVERNMENTAL RELATIONS: "Natural Resources and Conservation," Report of Study Committee, 1955.[1]
Discusses intergovernmental policies and specific grants-in-aid in the field of natural resources.

———: "Payments in Lieu of Taxes and Shared Revenues," Report of Study Committee, 1955.
Contains a detailed statement of present contributions to local communities in the case of federal properties associated with shared revenues and those not so associated, together with recommended changes.

U. S. COMMISSION ON ORGANIZATION OF THE EXECUTIVE BRANCH OF THE GOVERNMENT: "Natural Resources," Report of Task Force, Appendix L, 1949.
Deals chiefly with matters of organization but has considerable material relating to federal land ownership and administration.

U. S. COMMITTEE ON CONSERVATION AND ADMINISTRATION OF THE PUBLIC DOMAIN: "Report," 1931.
States five general principles that should be followed in dealing with the public domain and makes twenty specific recommendations. These include the proposal to transfer to the states all the unreserved, unappropriated public domain within their boundaries, subject to the reservation to the United States of all mineral rights, and to create national ranges out of any such lands not accepted by the states within ten years.

U. S. CONGRESS, HOUSE COMMITTEE ON GOVERNMENT OPERATIONS: "Real and Personal Property Inventory Report (Civilian and Military) of the United States Government Located in the Continental United States, in the Territories, and Overseas as of June 30, 1955," House Report No. 1930, 84th Cong., 2d Sess., 1956.
Gives detailed information, compiled by the General Services Administration, on the number of federal installations and their cost by state and by agency; on the total area and the building area of federal land by state, agency, and predominant usage; and the federally owned buildings, structures, and facilities by state, agency, and predominant usage.

———, ———: "Real and Personal Property Inventory Report. . . . as of June 30, 1956," Com. Print, 84th Cong., 2d Sess., 1956.
Contains new material on the area and estimated value of public domain properties held by various federal agencies.

———, ———: "Federal Timber Sales Policies," Part I—Report of Subcommittee on Public Works and Resources, House Report No. 2960, and Part II—Supplementary Staff Report, Com. Print, 84th Cong., 2d Sess., 1956. (Issued also as Com. Prints of the Subcommittee on the Legislative Oversight Function of the Senate Committee on Interior and Insular Affairs.)
Part I contains the joint findings, conclusions, and recommendations of the House and Senate sub-committees with respect to "Overall Policy" and "Operations and Sales Management" for lands under the jurisdiction of the Forest Service, Bureau of Land Management, and Bureau of Indian Af-

[1] Most federal government publications are published by the Government Printing Office, Washington 25, D. C.

fairs. Part II is a detailed analysis of the matters studied by the subcommittees. Transcripts of joint hearings before the two subcommittees were also printed in two parts comprising 2,229 pages.

———, HOUSE COMMITTEE ON INTERIOR AND INSULAR AFFAIRS: "Withdrawal and Utilization of the Public Lands of the United States" (hearings before the committee), Serial 29 and Serial 34, 84th Cong., 2d Sess., 1956.

Contain transcripts of hearings before the committee from January to July, 1956, on proposed legislation to prohibit the withdrawal or reservation of more than 5,000 acres of public land for defense purposes without approval of Congress. Testimony deals chiefly with withdrawal, reservation, area, and use of land in existing defense installations.

———, ———: "Military Public Land Witdhrawals," House Report No. 215, 85th Cong., 1st Sess., 1957.

Contains a full discussion of proposed legislation to prohibit the withdrawal, reservation, or restriction of more than 5,000 acres of public land for defense purposes without the approval of Congress, together with a detailed analysis of developments responsible for the proposal.

———, ———: "Military Land Withdrawals" (hearings before the committee), Serial 1, 85th Cong., 1st Sess., 1957.

Contains a transcript of hearings before the committee in January and February, 1957, on proposed legislation to prohibit the withdrawal or reservation of more than 5,000 acres of public land for defense purposes without the approval of Congress. Much historical and statistical information concerning defense installations, both nationally and by states, is included. Considerable attention is paid to the use of defense installations for hunting and fishing.

———, SENATE COMMITTEE ON APPROPRIATIONS: "Inventory Report on Federal Real Property in the United States as of June 30, 1955" (prepared by General Services Administration), Sen. Doc. No. 100, 84th Cong., 2d Sess., 1956.

Closely resembles the report of the House Committee on Government Operations ("Real and Personal Property Inventory Report. . . .as of June 30, 1955") so far as federal real property in the United States is concerned, but does not cover personal property or overseas possessions.

———, ———: "Inventory Report on Real Property Owned by the United States throughout the World as of June 30, 1956" (prepared by General Services Administration), Sen. Doc. No. 25, 85th Cong., 1st Sess., 1957.

Contains a fairly detailed inventory of federal real property in the United States by state, agency, and predominant usage.

U. S. DEPARTMENT OF AGRICULTURE, AGRICULTURAL CONSERVATION PROGRAM SERVICE: "Agricultural Conservation Program, Summary 1955," 1956.

Summarizes by states accomplishments and assistance in 1955.

———, AGRICULTURAL RESEARCH SERVICE: "Major Uses of Land in the United States—Summary for 1954," Agric. Inf. Bul. No. 168, 1957.

Presents detailed information on major land uses, land capability, land ownership, and changes in land use both for the country as a whole and for individual states. Constitutes the latest and most comprehensive publication on the subject.

———, BUREAU OF AGRICULTURAL ECONOMICS: "Federal Rural Lands," 1947.

An excellent picture of the situation for the nation as a whole, with considerable material for individual states.

———, FOREST SERVICE: "A Reappraisal of the Forest Situation," Reports 1-6, 1945-1946.

Appraises the situation in the United States with respect to the timber resources, potential requirements for timber products, management status of forest lands, wood waste, forest protection, and forest cooperatives.

———, ———: "Appraisal of the Economic and Social Effect of the Proposed Roosevelt Redwood Forest," 1947. Duplicated.

Concludes that "creation of the proposed Forest would enable the maintenance of a steady level of industrial employment for present and future generations, and would prevent a slow decline of basic values and eventual collapse of the main industry of the area."

———, ———: "Forests and National Prosperity: A Reappraisal of the Forest Situation in the United States," 1948.

Recapitulates the forest situation as presented in the six parts of the Reappraisal Report, and presents the three-point program of the Forest Service as to the action needed.

———, ———: "Transcript of Proceedings in the Matter of the Establishment of the Woodleaf Cooperative Sustained Yield Unit and on the Proposed Cooperative Agreement Between the Soper-Wheeler Company and the United States, at a Public Hearing held at Quincy, California, March 8, 1948," 1948. Duplicated.

Contains full information concerning the proposed cooperative unit and public reaction thereto. Most of the testimony at the hearing was in opposition to the proposal.

———, ———: "Timber Resource Review," Preliminary Review Draft Subject to Revision, Chap. I-IX, 1955.

Presents the most complete analysis yet made of the forest situation in the United States. Chapter IX-A contains the basic statistics for the report, mostly by states and regions.

———, ———: "National Forest Areas," 1956 and earlier editions.

Gives figures by states of the gross and net area of individual national forests, purchase areas, and land utilization projects.

———, ———, California Forest and Range Experiment Station: "The Forest Problems of California," 1940. Duplicated.

Presents detailed statistics on forest ownership, with a discussion of the problems and practices of both public and private owners.

———, ———, ———:

"Forest Land Ownership in Northern Mendocino County, California," by Adon Poli and Donald T. Griffith, For. Sur. Release No. 5, 1948.

"Area and Ownership of Forest Land in Siskiyou County, California," by George F. Burks and Adon Poli, For. Sur. Rel. No. 8, 1950.

"Area and Ownership of Forest Land in Trinity County, California," by Harold L. Baker and Adon Poli, For. Sur. Rel. No. 9, 1951.

"Area and Ownership of Forest Land in Mendocino County, California," by Harold L. Baker and Adon Poli, For. Sur. Rel. No. 10, 1951.

"Area and Ownership of Forest Land in Lake County, California," by Harold L. Baker and Adon Poli, For. Sur. Rel. No. 11, 1952.

"Area and Ownership of Forest Land in Sonoma County, California," by Harold L. Baker and Adon Poli, For. Sur. Rel. No. 14, 1952.

"Area and Ownership of Forest Land in Humboldt County, California," by Harold L. Baker and Adon Poli, For. Sur. Rel. No. 16, 1952.

"Area and Ownership of Forest Land in Del Norte County, California," by Harold L. Baker and Adon Poli, For. Sur. Rel. No. 18, 1953.

"Area and Ownership of Forest Land in Santa Cruz County, California," by Harold L. Baker and

Adon Poli, For. Sur. Rel. No. 21, 1953.

"Area and Ownership of Forest Land in San Mateo County, California," by Harold L. Baker and Adon Poli, For. Sur. Rel. No. 22, 1954.

"Area and Ownership of Forest Land in Shasta County, California," by Harold L. Baker and Adon Poli, For. Sur. Rel. No. 24, 1954.

"Area and Ownership of Forest Land in Tehama County, California," by Harold L. Baker and Adon Poli, For. Sur. Rel. No. 26, 1955.

This series of publications contains detailed information, largely in tabular and graphic form, on areas, types, and ownerships of forest land in the counties concerned.

———, ———, ———:

"Production of Logs and Bolts for Plywood, Pulp, Container Veneer, Shingles, Cooperage, Poles, and Piling in California, 1950," by Richard H. May, For. Research Notes No. 79, 1951.

"Forest Statistics for the Coast Range Pine Subregion in California," For. Sur. Release No. 12, 1952.

"Lumber Production in California and Nevada, 1951," For. Sur. Release No. 17, 1952.

"Forest Statistics for the Redwood-Douglas-Fir Subregion in California," For. Sur. Release No. 19, 1953.

"Output of Forest Products in California, 1952," by Richard H. May, For. Sur. Release No. 23, 1954.

"A Century of Lumber Production in California and Nevada," by Richard H. May, For. Sur. Release No. 20, 1953.

"Production and Plant Receipts of Veneer Logs in California, 1956," by Richard H. May, For. Sur. Release No. 27, 1957.

These seven publications contain detailed information, largely in tabular and graphic form, concerning area, volume, growth, and drain in the two subregions, and concerning lumber production in the entire state.

———, ———, ———:

"Ownership and Use of Forest Land in the Coast Range Pine Subregion of California," by Adon Poli and Harold L. Baker, Tech. Paper No. 2, 1953.

"Ownership of Forest Land in the Redwood-Douglas-Fir Subregion of California," by Adon Poli and Harold L. Baker, Tech. Paper No. 7, 1954.

These two publications contain detailed data concerning both public and private ownership of forest land in the two subregions, with suggestions for improvement in the ownership pattern.

———, ———, ———: "Forest Statistics for California," For. Sur. Rel. No. 25, 1954.

Contains detailed data as of January 1, 1953, on forest area, timber volume, growth, mortality, annual cut, and output of timber products for the state as a whole and for subregions.

———, ———, California Region: "The Administration and Improvement of National Forest Grazing Lands (as of January 1, 1955)," San Francisco, undated, probably 1956. Duplicated.

Deals with the objectives and history of grazing use of the national forests of California, and with a twenty-year program of range improvements. Contains much detailed information and numerous calculations of costs and returns.

———, ———, ———: "Facts About the California Region," San Francisco, 1956.

A popular, illustrated presentation of some of the main facts concerning the national forests in California and their utilization.

———, Soil Conservation Service, Pacific Region: "Land Capability Classification Guide," 1952.

Describes and discusses the significance of the eight land capability classes recognized by the Soil Conservation Service.

U. S. DEPARTMENT OF THE ARMY, CORPS OF ENGINEERS: "The Corps of Engineers in California," San Francisco, 1950.

Describes and locates the navigation, flood-control, and debris-control projects completed, under way, and authorized in California.

U. S. DEPARTMENT OF COMMERCE, BUREAU OF THE CENSUS:

"Census of Agriculture, 1950—Counties and State Economic Areas, California," Vol. 1, Part 33.

"Census of Agriculture, 1954—Counties and State Economic Areas, California," Vol. 1, Part 33.

Both volumes contain detailed data on farm areas, ownership, labor, crops, livestock and poultry, irrigation, and land-use and conservation practices by counties.

———, ———, and U. S. DEPARTMENT OF AGRICULTURE, BUREAU OF AGRICULTURAL ECONOMICS: "Graphic Summary of Land Utilization in the United States—A Cooperative Report," 1947.

Contains many charts and maps showing land use by states as a part of the national picture, but there are no maps for individual states. Special attention is paid to cropland, woodland, and pasture land in farms.

U. S. DEPARTMENT OF THE INTERIOR: "Forest Conservation on Lands Administered by the Department of the Interior," 1940. Duplicated.

A comprehensive report in seven parts dealing with the disposal of the public domain and with the administration and optimum use of forest and range lands under the jurisdiction of the Department of the Interior. Most of the material deals with the national situation, but there is considerable information on individual states, including California.

———, BUREAU OF LAND MANAGEMENT: "Report of the Director, Statistical Appendix," 1947-1956.

Contains detailed statistical data, largely by states, concerning the current activities of the Bureau of Land Management, with some cumulative tables.

———, BUREAU OF RECLAMATION: "Central Valley Project, 1955 Annual Report."

Contains detailed statistical and financial data concerning the Central Valley Project, with a brief presentation of plans for the future.

———, ———: "The Growth and Contribution of Federal Reclamation to an Expanding National Economy," House Com. on Interior and Insular Affairs, Com. Print No. 27, 1955.

In addition to demonstrating the importance of federal reclamation, the report itemizes by projects the net area in cultivation, total gross crop values, and average value per acre; the kilowatt capacity of hydroelectric plants at reclamation projects; and the municipalities obtaining a water supply from reclamation projects.

———, ———: "California Water," Sacramento, 1956.

A brief, popular account of California's water problems and the answer.

———, NATIONAL PARK SERVICE: "State Parks—Areas, Acreages, and Accommodations," 1955.

Gives detailed information by states for each park area as of January 1, 1955.

———, ———: "State Park Statistics—1954," 1955.

Gives detailed information by states on number of park areas and acreages, expenditures, revenues from operations, attendance, and personnel.

———, ———: "Areas Administered by the National Park Service, December 31, 1956," 1957.

Contains a complete list of units administered by the National Park Service, with areas, dates of establishment, outstanding characteristics, and addresses.

———, PACIFIC SOUTHWEST FIELD COMMITTEE: "Natural Resources of Northwestern California—Preliminary Report," 1956. Duplicated.

Contains detailed information concerning the character, location, ownership, and management of the resources of northwestern California. There are numerous maps, charts, tables, and photographs.

———, OFFICE OF THE SECRETARY: "The Conservation of Natural Resources," Annual Report of the Secretary for 1956.

Contains the annual report of the Secretary and of the directors of the various bureaus and offices in the Department.

U. S. INTERDEPARTMENTAL COMMITTEE FOR THE STUDY OF JURISDICTION OVER FEDERAL AREAS WITHIN THE STATES: "Jurisdiction Over Federal Areas Within the States," Part I of the committee's report, 1956.

Discusses at length the several categories of federal jurisdiction over federal lands within the states. The committee concludes that with respect to the large bulk of federal lands a proprietorial status is adequate to protect the interests of the government, and recommends the retrocession to the states of unnecessary federal jurisdiction.

U. S. NATIONAL FOREST RESERVATION COMMISSION: "Annual Report for 1956," 1957.

Reports on the activities of the Commission during the fiscal year 1956, and summarizes purchases to June 30, 1956, by states, counties, and purchase units, with figures on area and price.

U. S. NATIONAL RESOURCES BOARD: "Forest Land Resources, Requirements, Problems, and Policy," Part VIII of the Supplementary Report of the Land Planning Committee, 1935.

Consists of a comprehensive report prepared by the Forest Service on the subjects indicated in the title, largely on the basis of "A National Plan for American Forestry" (Copeland Report). The report contains recommendations, by states, as to the area of forest land that should be in private ownership and in various forms of public ownership. A large increase in federal ownership in California is proposed, a sizeable decrease in state ownership, and a small increase in county and municipal ownership.

U. S. PUBLIC LANDS COMMISSION: "Report of the Public Lands Commission, with Appendix," Sen. Doc. No. 189, 58th Cong., 3d Sess., 1905.

Discusses the operation and results of the public land laws, and gives by states detailed information concerning the disposition of the public domain to June 30, 1904.

VAUX, HENRY J.: "Timber in Humboldt County," Calif. Agric. Exp. Sta. Bul. 748, Berkeley, 1955.

Presents and discusses the problem presented by the continuing depletion of old-growth timber in Humboldt County. It "spots trends and points out the opportunities and the dangers in the economic picture" of the county.

WEEKS, DAVID, A. E. WIESLANDER, and C. L. HILL: "The Utilization of El Dorado County Land," Calif. Agric. Exp. Sta. Bul. 572, 1934; and

———, ———, H. R. JOSEPHSON, and C. L. HILL: "Land Utilization in the Northern Sierra Nevada," Univ. of Calif., Giannini Foundation of Agric. Economics, 1943.

These two publications contain much detailed information concerning the characteristics and utilization of the land resources of all kinds in the regions covered.

WELLS, GEORGE and IRIS: "The Handbook of Wilderness Travel," Harper & Brothers, New York, 1956.

Contains a comprehensive guide to "wilderness areas" by states, with suggestions as to how to use them to best advantage. The section devoted specifically to California covers 23 pages.

WIESLANDER, A. E., and CLARK H. GLEASON: "Major Brushland Areas of the Coast Ranges and Sierra-Cascade Foothills in California," Calif. Forest and Range Exp. Sta. Misc. Paper No. 15, 1954.

Gives the area of the five brushland types in the Coast Ranges and Sierra-Cascade foothills, together with a map showing their distribution, and describes them briefly.

———, and R. EARL STORIE: "The Vegetation-Soil Survey in California and Its Use in the Management of Wild Lands for Yield of Timber, Forage, and Water," Jour. Forestry 50: 521-526, 1952.

Describes the character and uses of the vegetation-soil survey, which was initiated in 1946 in partial response to a recommendation of the California Forest Study Committee (1945) that: "As soon as possible the State should undertake a study of land classification to determine factually which lands should be dedicated to timber growing, which to livestock raising, and which are too poor or unsatisfactory for either pursuit."

WILLIAMS, ELLIS T.: "National Forest Contributions to Local Governments," Land Economics 31:204-214, 1955.

Compares 25 per cent fund payments to counties and contributions in kind with estimated taxes if the land were in private ownership, for 135 sample counties in the northern, southern, Rocky Mountain, and Pacific Coast regions.

WOHLETZ, LEONARD R., and EDWARD F. DOLDER: "Know California Land—A Land Capability Guide for Soil and Water Conservation in California," Calif. Dept. of Nat. Res. and U. S. Soil Conservation Service, 1952.

Discusses the characteristics of the land resources of California by land capability classes both for the state as a whole and for specific watersheds. Contains two excellent colored maps showing the location of the different land capability classes.

ZIERER, CLIFFORD M.: "Land Utilization in Western United States," Proc. of Fifth Pacific Science Cong., Canada, 1933, Vol. II:1341-1349, Univ. of Toronto Press, Toronto, 1934.

Discusses the federal land policy; predicts an increase in federal reservations; and recommends placing the unreserved public domain under administration. The rapid increase in the urban population of the Pacific Coast States is stressed.

——— (ed.): "California and the Southwest," John Wiley & Sons, Inc., New York, 1956.

Discusses at length the physical and cultural characteristics of the region. Chapter 18 on Forests, Forest Industries, and Forest Problems, by Emanuel Fritz, contains some material on effects of ownership patterns.

INDEX

Page numbers from 243 on refer to items in Appendix I, Chronological Summary of Federal and State Legislation. All references to agencies of the state government (including the Legislature) are listed under "California State Government," and all references to federal agencies (including Congress) under "United States Government." References to individual officials, such as Director of Natural Resources and Secretary of the Interior, are not listed separately, but are included under the unit with which the official is connected.

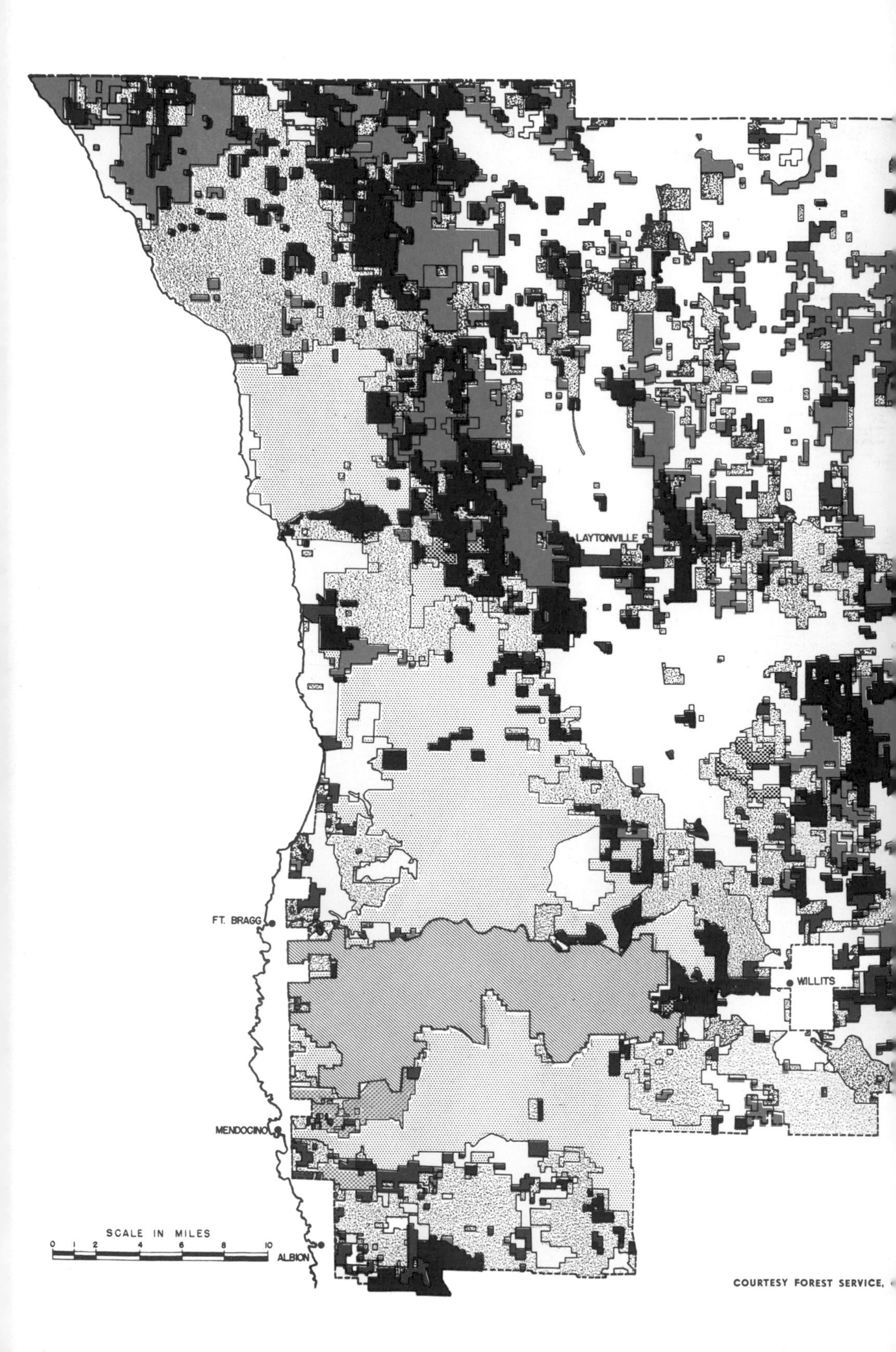

COURTESY FOREST SERVICE,